The Conscience of Psychiatry

The Reform Work of Peter R. Breggin, MD

The Conscience of Psychiatry

The Reform Work of Peter R. Breggin, MD

Edited by the
International Center
for the
Study of Psychiatry and Psychology

The Conscience of Psychiatry
The Reform Work of Peter R. Breggin, MD

A Lake Edge Press book

Edited by
The International Center for the Study
of Psychiatry and Psychology
www.icspp.org

Cover photograph and book design
by Ginger Ross Breggin

Printing History
Lake Edge Press / 2009

For information address:
Lake Edge Press
101 East State Street, No.112, Ithaca, New York 14850

ISBN: 978-0-9824560-0-2
1. Breggin, Peter R., MD 1936- 2. Biography
3. Psychiatry 4. Psychology

Contents

vii *Acknowledgements*

ix *Contributors*

xv *Forward by Dominick Riccio*

xxii *Introduction by Ginger Breggin*

1 *Chapter 1:* The Boy and the Man

53 *Chapter 2:* Reforming the "Snake Pits"

61 *Chapter 3:* Stopping the Resurgence of Psychosurgery

101 *Chapter 4:* Opposing Shock Treatment

109 *Chapter 5:* Winning the Medical License Attack

127 *Chapter 6:* Stopping the Federal Violence Initiative

141 *Chapter 7:* Exposing Drug Company Influence

189 *Chapter 8:* Testifying in Court

209 *Chapter 9:* Advocating for Children

273 *Chapter 10:* Working with Psychiatric Survivors

289 *Chapter 11:* World-Wide Influence

323 *Chapter 12:* Departed Friends and Colleagues

331 *Chapter 13:* The Journal Honors Peter Breggin

353 *Chapter 14:* Thanking the Breggins

385 *Chapter 15:* Empathic Therapy and Principled Living

Appendices

433 I. Books by Peter R. Breggin, MD

435 II. Selected Articles, Letters and Scientific Papers

440 III. Brief Biography of Peter R. Breggin, MD

442 IV. Glossary

Acknowledgements

The International Center for the Study of Psychiatry and Psychology (ICSPP) is grateful to those who helped create, design, compile and edit this book. Peter Breggin's wife, Ginger, compiled and edited more than fifty years of media excerpts and quotes about her husband's work starting with a lengthy article published in 1957 in the *Saturday Evening Post* that showcased the college volunteer program that he directed. Ginger also designed and produced this book.

ICSPP wants to thank all of the contributors who have been generous with their creativity and time in offering personal and unique perspectives of Peter Breggin, his work and his impact upon psychiatry, psychology, medicine and the social sciences. This project has been greatly enriched by every one of you.

ICSPP members Andrew Crosby and Al Galves edited and proofread this book and made many helpful suggestions. ICSPP member Nadine De Santo spent many hours editing the book and made invaluable contributions that improved its quality. Susan Close provided extensive proofreading and made important design suggestions at several stages of the manuscript. In keeping with the principles of ICSPP, all the work was volunteered. Their corrections and commentary were valuable and contributed to the quality of this book.

Douglas Holleley provided invaluable insight and guidance in the design and production of this book. His good humor, experience, and talent have immeasurably improved the final product.

Ginger wishes to thank Claire Lesemann and Emily Aguilar for their early assistance in compiling the 50 years of media excerpts that have become a backbone of this project.

Original Contributions

David Antonuccio, PhD
Bart P. Billings, PhD
Fred Bemak, EdD
Bart P. Billings, PhD
Pat Bracken, MD
Derek Braslow, JD
Thomas E. Bratter, PhD
Ginger Ross Breggin
Dorothy Cassidy, MEd
Pam Clay, JD
Sharon Collins, MD
Michael Corry, MD
Andrew Crosby, MA
Richard Curtis
Tom Cushman, PhD
Nadine De Santo, EdS
M. N. G. Dukes, MD
Scott Davis, MA
Karen R. Effrem, MD
Don Farber, JD
Alberto Fergusson, MD
Robert Foltz, PhD
Al Galves, PhD
Michael C. Gilbert, PsyD
William Glasser, MD
Ian Goddard
Jim Gottstein, JD
Robert Grimm, MD
Bob Jacobs, PhD, JD
Delores Jankovich, MSW
Bob Johnson, MD
Jay Joseph, PsyD
Bert Karon, PhD
Brian Kean, PhD
Diane Kern, MFT
Adina Lambert, MA
Bruce Levine, PhD
Terry Lynch, MD
Jeffrey Masson, PhD
Joanna Moncrieff, MD
Benno Müller–Hill, PhD
Craig Newnes, MSc
David W. Oaks
Kelly O'Meara
Candace Pert, PhD
Larry Plumlee, MD
Libby
Nora Porter, MD
Sharon Presley, PhD
Dominick Riccio, PhD
Betsy Root, MSW
Jean Ross
Lloyd Ross, PhD
Dorothy, Rowe, PhD
Richard E. Rubenstein, JD
Carole Saltz
T. J. Scheff, PhD
Stuart Shipko, MD
Milton Shore, PhD
Al Siebert, PhD
Doug Smith, MD
Ursula Springer, PhD
David Stein, PhD
Joseph Tarantolo, MD
Sami Timimi, MD
James A. Tucker, PhD
Michael Valentine, PhD
Clemmont E. Vontress, PhD
Toby Tyler Watson, PsyD
Rick Winking, MMHC

Earlier Commentaries

Jack Anderson
Louise Armstrong
Steven Baldwin, PhD
Fred A. Baughman, Jr., MD
Joy M. Carter, MD
Paula J. Caplan, PhD
U S Cong. Ronald Dellums
M. Stanton Evans
Rhoda L. Fisher, PhD
Leonard Roy Frank
Daniel Goleman, PhD
James S. Gordon, MD
Thomas Greening, PhD
Jay Haley
James Hillman, PhD
John Horgan
Arianna Huffington
David H. Jacobs, PhD
Leon Kamin, PhD
Jonathan Kozol
Kevin McCready, PhD
Robert S. Mendelsohn, MD
Kate Millet, PhD
Thomas J. Moore
Loren Mosher, MD
Richard H. Phillips, MD
Steven Rose, PhD
John Rosemond, PhD
Raymond C. Russ, PhD
Jay Salwen, MD
Richard Shulman, PhD
Robert Seidenberg, MD
Tony Stanton, MD
US Congressman Louis Stokes
US Senator Steve Symms
Lawrence Tirnauer, PhD
Rae Unzicker
Eileen Walkenstein, MD
Wolf Wolfensberger, PhD
Samuel F. Yette

SELECTED MEDIA

Associated Press
Baltimore Sun
Boston Globe
British Medical Journal
Chronicle of Higher Education
Clinical Psychiatry News
Contemporary Psychology
Detroit Free Press
Glamour
Good Housekeeping
Hippocrates
Houston Chronicle
Human Behavior
Indianapolis Star
Larry King Live
Los Angeles Times
New Scientist
Newsday
Newsweek
New York Times
Oprah
People
Philadelphia Inquirer
Psychology Today
Reason
San Francisco Chronicle
San Francisco Magazine
Saturday Evening Post
Science
Science News
SmartMoney
Time Magazine
Village Voice
Wall Street Journal
Washington Post
Washington Star

In Memorium

Steven Baldwin, PhD
Kevin McCready, PhD
Loren Mosher, MD
Victor D. Sanua, PhD
Al Siebert, PhD
Marvin Skolnick, MD
Lawrence Tirnauer, PhD
Rae Unzicker

With gratitude from the members of the
International Center
for the Study of
Psychiatry and Psychology

To Dominick Riccio

Whose wisdom, strength and hard work
Successfully guided our organization
Into its second generation

In questions of science,
the authority of a thousand
is not worth the humble reasoning
of a single individual.

GALILEO GALILEI

Forward

Dominick J. Riccio, PhD

The seeds of *The Conscience of Psychiatry* began to germinate when the International Center for the Study of Psychiatry and Psychology (ICSPP) asked for papers and commentaries in appreciation of the life and work of Peter Breggin on the 10th anniversary of our peer-reviewed journal, *Ethical Human Psychology and Psychiatry (EHPP).* Dr. Breggin, with his wife Ginger Breggin, had originated the idea for the journal and developed the concept with Dr. Ursula Springer of Springer Publishing Company.

In response to our request, we received a number of scientific papers that were published as a "Festschrift" or appreciation of his work in the journal (*EHPP* volume 9, number 3, 2007). In addition, we were flooded with personal and informal commentaries about Dr. Breggin that were more suitable for a book than for a scientific journal. These more personal communications illustrate and document Dr. Breggin's influence on the lives and careers of psychologists, psychiatrists, professors, educators, and researchers, as well as social activists and individuals exposed to psychiatric treatment. As a result, ICSPP decided to produce a book documenting Dr. Breggin's career through these dozens of testimonials.

When Ginger Breggin learned that the journal was planning an appreciation of her husband's work, she dug into the office files to document her husband's 50-year career through excerpts of media coverage going all the way back to the state hospital volunteer program that he directed as a Harvard undergraduate

(1954-1958). The result was too lengthy for the journal and instead provides the backbone of this book. *The Conscience of Psychiatry* combines Ginger's history of media coverage with other commentaries on Dr. Breggin's work over the years, and then adds 70 new contributions. These documents produce the first detailed biography of Dr. Breggin's work and influence.

Toxic Psychiatry was the single most significant, objective, and comprehensive critique of the biopsychiatric movement ever published. Peter Breggin said it all, and he said it with psychiatry's own dismal data.

Like the dozens of other professionals whose words you will read in this book, my own clinical work was deeply influenced by Peter's perspicacity. Although he is not a psychoanalyst, I first met Peter Breggin in 1993 at the APA's Psychoanalysis meeting (Division 39). He was delivering a talk on the side effects and lack of efficacy of psychotropic drugs as well as issues surrounding the biological theories of psychiatry. Upon hearing him I realized that he was saying the same things that I had been teaching psychoanalytic trainees in a drugs and therapy course, based upon my own experience and a few esoteric texts and references. The difference was that Dr. Breggin had fully analyzed and dissected most of the time-honored studies including the badly flawed twin studies that were reported in standard psychiatric and psychological texts. These poorly designed studies had been accepted and propounded for decades without ever being effectively challenged. In addition, he brilliantly reassessed the data and statistics of the biochemical theories and the efficacy and side effects of all psychotropic drugs and electroshock treatment in his groundbreaking book *Toxic Psychiatry.* In my opinion this was the single most significant, objective, and comprehensive critique of the biopsychiatric movement ever published. He said it all, and he said it with psychiatry's own dismal data.

It was then and there that I realized that my next direction in the practice of psychology was to help, in my own small way, to defend and inform the public about the growing brain-damaging movement called biopsychiatry. In a single lunch discussion with Peter, my whole attitude in the field of psychology had been changed. It was no longer enough to remain in my own psychoanalytic practice working with suffering souls. I felt personally compelled to follow Peter's lead and reach out to the millions of people being damaged worldwide by the economically motivated lies of biopsychiatry.

> From the first day that Peter stepped into a state hospital as a college student volunteer, he became a leader and humanitarian who worked with and fought for patients' rights and humane care.

Peter followed up *Toxic Psychiatry* year after year with timely and effective books that addressed each new poisonous initiative of biopsychiatry and its unholy alliance with the pharmaceutical companies. He has been a prolific author and constant defender of the often-neglected consumers of psychiatric services, especially children. He cogently spoke out against Ritalin and all the psychostimulants, against the lies of the selective serotonin reuptake inhibitor (SSRI) antidepressants, and the deadly effects of neuroleptics and atypical antipsychotic drugs. He exposed the damaging effects of psychosurgery and shock treatment and revealed the nefarious intention of the government and the National Institutes of Health in their war on inner-city children via the violence initiative. Peter has done it all.

> In recent years Peter entered the arena of law as an expert witness on behalf of the many who have been damaged by psychotropic drugs. Lawyers asked Peter to tell the same truths to the courts that he had been telling to the world for years.

From the first day that he stepped into a state hospital as a college student volunteer, he became a leader and humanitarian who worked with and fought for patients' rights and humane care. He and a group of concerned fellow students were able to work successfully with "back ward" patients who were literally deemed hopeless by all of the professionals. During college he and his classmates witnessed dozens of "hopeless" patients vastly improved and released from the hospital. Before Peter completed his college degree he was writing his first book, and taking a leadership role in the profession.

After finishing his psychiatric training, he then turned his attention to providing organization and leadership to the small minority of professionals who saw the same truths about psychiatry that Peter was experiencing. After going into private practice in 1968, Peter was appalled to learn in 1971 that lobotomy and other forms of psychosurgery were experiencing a resurgence and he began his reform career in earnest with a successful international campaign that stopped the return of this violent "treatment." Through the eyes of the media, this book documents his successful efforts to stop the widespread return of this barbaric "treatment."

Peter was a talented writer who realized that the most effective mode of organizing was by writing his many thought-provoking and well-researched books and by founding the International Center for the Study of Psychiatry and Psychology, Inc. (www.ICSPP.org). After Peter was joined by Ginger Ross Breggin, and she decided to become his partner in reform work, together they greatly expanded ICSPP, founded a peer-reviewed journal, issued a newsletter, developed an internet community for professionals to share their interests and concerns, and began to hold conferences that continue to bring together professionals and consumers from all spheres of life to share ideas, give mutual support, and mobilize programs and social activism.

I salute you and applaud you for your courage, resilience, and insight as a researcher, practitioner, and leader of the movement for humane, caring, and thoughtful treatment of the many human beings suffering with emotional conflicts.

In recent years Peter entered the arena of law as an expert witness on behalf of the many who have been damaged by psychotropic drugs. Lawyers asked Peter to tell the same truths to the courts that he had been telling to the world for years.

Finally, before moving to central New York in 2002, Peter

and Ginger decided to hand over management of ICSPP and its scientific journal to younger professionals. At that time, Dr. Breggin and the ICSPP board of directors selected me to direct the organization, an honor I have been privileged to fulfill. Now located in Ithaca, New York, Dr. Breggin continues with all his previous activities as a psychiatrist, medical-legal consultant, researcher and author—albeit with a little more time for enjoying nature and friends. He continues to present at the annual national meetings of our center (www.ICSPP.org) and to write for our scientific journal.

Dr. Peter Breggin, I salute you and applaud you for your courage, resilience, and insight as a researcher, practitioner, and leader of the movement for humane, caring, and thoughtful treatment of the many human beings suffering with emotional conflicts. Of course, it has often been difficult and even dangerous at times, but as this book demonstrates, your efforts have brought you rich rewards in terms of personal satisfaction, friendship and professional recognition from dedicated colleagues. I hope that *The Conscience of Psychiatry* will inspire others to stand up for the highest ethical standards in their professions.

Dominick J. Riccio, PhD

Dominick has been the International Executive Director of the International Center for the Study of Psychiatry and Psychology for almost a decade. He is a psychologist in private practice in New York City and was a supervisor and training analyst at various psychoanalytic institutes. He is past co-founder and Clinical Director of Encounter, Inc., a prototype drug rehabilitation program for teenagers, and Past President of the Association for Modern Psychoanalysis. He is also Founder and Executive Director of the Institute for the Treatment and Research of Psychosomatic Disorders. All the foregoing treatment programs provided treatment without the use of psychoactive drugs. He has been an active proponent of psychosocial solutions as opposed to biopsychiatric interventions and has lectured frequently at hospitals, colleges, professional conferences and other professional organizations. Dr. Riccio passes the baton to incoming International Executive Director for ICSPP, Toby Tyler Watson, PsyD, in 2009.

Introduction

Ginger Ross Breggin

For the past fifty years psychiatrist Peter R. Breggin, MD has worked to evolve his profession into a more humane, effective field. Because of the tremendous inertia, indeed, opposition that psychiatry has had to reform efforts, Peter has often taken his message to the broader culture through the media. At least in this manner he can warn, and try to empower, patients and their families against the myths and dangers of biopsychiatry.

Fifty years of media coverage of Peter Breggin's work has accumulated in our files. For this book I excerpted some of the most illuminating and interesting portions of various news coverage.

In reviewing five decades of press, I have found patterns in Peter's work. First came the formative years. Peter was just a teenager at Harvard when he began volunteering to work with patients in the local state mental hospital. Eventually he originated and coauthored a book about the college student volunteer program. This early work led to Peter's decision to go to medical school and to become a psychiatrist.

Just as significantly, this formative period provided Peter with the insight that was to inform his entire life of reform effort. He observed first hand as a volunteer college student that genuine human relationship brought about positive results and healing in the hospitalized mental patients fortunate enough to have contact with the student volunteers. Peter also observed that the biological 'treatments' consistently failed to produce real improvement in the hospitalized patients and instead made them more helpless and despairing.

After finishing his psychiatric training and two years at the National Institute of Mental Health (NIMH), Peter realized that biological psychiatry was taking over the profession. He planned to settle down to a quiet private practice that would allow time for him to write novels and occasional professional papers.

But in 1971 Peter learned that lobotomy and newer forms of psychosurgery were coming back in a second wave. He vowed to stop this abomination and ultimately succeeded. The psychosurgery campaign led Peter to face the brain damaging effects of other biological treatments in psychiatry—chief among them, electroshock, and soon after, psychiatric drugs. Peter's research documented the damage done by these intrusive interventions. Meanwhile, his private practice continued to affirm that the resources of human relationship provided better healing potential for persons in emotional crisis.

Peter continued his reform work. It is telling that the word 'science' lies within the word 'conscience.' Peter was moved to research, to write and to document the damaging effects of involuntary and biological psychiatric treatments in the 1970s and 1980s through extensive scientific scholarship. Springer Publishing Company—a premiere medical publisher—brought out his first medical books. He stayed in touch with like-minded colleagues through his non-profit organization The International Center for the Study of Psychiatry and Psychology (ICSPP, founded in 1972) and he offered confirmation and support to the growing psychiatric survivor network.

In 1987 Peter was invited onto the Oprah Winfrey Show along with Leonard Frank and Rae Unzicker, psychiatric survivors and national spokespeople for the reform movement in psychiatry. The show was so successful that the psychiatric establishment retaliated with an attack on Peter's medical license. During the attack, and following his complete exoneration, national media coverage established Peter's role as the leading reformer in the field of psychiatry. Book publishers became more aware of him and his work, and this resulted in Peter's first mass market book and bestseller, the 1991 classic *Toxic Psychiatry*.

The Decade of the Brain was launched by the U.S. Congress in 1990. This campaign on the part of the Psychopharmaceutical Complex was designed to market the concept of mental distress as a biological condition best addressed by drugs and other physical interventions.

Almost simultaneously the most powerful psychiatrist in the federal government announced plans for the Federal Violence Initiative, a massive interagency program aimed at finding biological and genetic causes of violence in inner-city children. This racist program planned to 'preventively' drug innumerable young children of poverty.

Millions of parents have been able to protect their children from psychiatric diagnosing and drugging, and millions of adults have become better informed about the ineffectiveness and hazards of bio-psychiatric treatments including drugs and electroshock.

The psychiatric diagnosis and drugging of millions of America's children became increasingly acceptable. Programs were developed to screen children in the schools to push them into taking psychiatric drugs. A larger and larger portion of the adult population became exposed to psychiatric drugs and even electroshock. Involuntary treatment was extended beyond hospital walls into the community with many people forced to take drugs even while remaining in their own homes.

Despite the enormous power of the drug companies, organized psychiatry and the entire Psychopharmaceutical Complex, the message of Peter and his colleagues still makes its way into the public forum. As a result, millions of parents have been able to protect their children from psychiatric diagnosing and drugging and millions of adults have become better informed about the ineffectiveness and hazards of bio-psychiatric treatments including drugs and electroshock. Peter Breggin and his many colleagues continue to work toward the day when ethical, rational and voluntary human services will fully replace the dangerous, irrational and abusive practices of biological psychiatry.

This book documents Peter Breggin's professional career through the eyes of the media, personal and professional commentaries on his work, and testimonials written to celebrate and honor Peter for more than 50 years of reform work on behalf of some of the worlds's most vulnerable and fragile human beings.

What a privilege it continues to be to witness and be part of my husband's reform efforts.

Ginger Ross Breggin

Since marrying Peter in 1984, Ginger has shared every aspect of his personal and professional life. She decided to set aside many of her unique talents, including writing and her award-winning photography, in order to support her husband's reform work. After winning the award for best social sciences paper of the year at American University, she also set aside her academic studies. Ginger's own reform efforts began at age eleven when she conducted a successful campaign to enforce the laws for the humane treatment of stray animals in her hometown, resulting in the building of a new animal shelter. An editorial in her local paper headlined, "Yes, Dogs, There is a Virginia," and radio commentator Paul Harvey drew national attention to her successful efforts. See her expanded biography in Chapter One.

Chapter One

The Boy and the Man

Who is Peter Breggin?

In his first year as an undergraduate at Harvard in 1954, eighteen-year-old Peter Breggin was studying American history and literature. He thought he was probably going to be a professor or perhaps an attorney. Then he was encouraged by a friend to volunteer at the local state mental hospital. While volunteering and then directing the Harvard-Radcliffe Mental Hospital Volunteer Program over the next four years, he made two discoveries: First, that the drug, electroshock and lobotomy treatments used by conventional psychiatry did more harm than good; and second, that caring relationships with college volunteers could help most patients improve enough to leave the hospital. Peter saw the humanity in the hospital patients and decided to become a psychiatrist to promote the ideal of truly healing human relationships in the field of mental health.

Early in his career as a psychiatrist, Dr. Breggin discovered in 1971 that lobotomy and new forms of psychosurgery were having a resurgence in a second wave, and he decided to attempt a campaign to stop this barbarous treatment from coming back. The campaign exceeded all expectations, almost completly shutting down psychosurgical projects in America and throughout the world.

The anti-psychosurgery campaign eventually grew to have international success and launched Dr. Breggin on a career of reform work in psychiatry that is unprecedented in the history of the profession. He has written many books and dozens of articles criticizing psychiatry's use of pseudo-medical diagnoses and biological treatments, including drugs and electroshock. His books continue to be widely read, including *Toxic Psychiatry* (1991), *Talking Back to Prozac* (with Ginger Breggin, 1994), *Brain-Disabling Treatments in Psychiatry* (2008) and *Medication Madness* (2008).

Dr. Breggin has been especially vigorous in opposing the mass diagnosing and drugging of America's children, including books like *Reclaiming Our Children* (2000), *Talking Back to Ritalin* (2001) and *the Ritalin Fact Book* (2002). Working with his wife Ginger Breggin, he opposed a racist federal program of potentially enormous size that was aimed at curbing inner city violence by diagnosing and drugging little children in large numbers. The Breggins wrote *The War Against Children of Color* (1998) documenting this chilling chapter in psychiatry and their successful efforts to stop the government program.

In 1972 Dr. Breggin founded the International Center for the Study of Psychiatry and Psychology (ICSPP), the only professional organization devoted to curbing biological psychiatry and promoting more caring psychological, social and educational approaches to helping children and adults in distress. When his wife Ginger later joined him, they built the organization in size and influence and then founded the peer-reviewed scientific journal, *Ethical Human Psychology and Psychiatry,* devoted to sponsoring the ideals of ICSPP.

When it became obvious that psychiatry had gone into an unholy partnership with the pharmaceutical industry, Dr. Breggin became active as a medical expert in the courts. In the early 1970s, he was the medical expert in a trial that stopped psychosurgery in the state mental hospitals of America. More recently he was the medical expert in the first and only malpractice trials won against a psychosurgeon and against a doctor who advocated electroshock. He was also the scientific expert in the combined Prozac suits against Eli Lilly in the 1990s, and since then has been involved in multiple product liability cases against drug companies, almost all of which have been settled satisfactorily for the injured patients or their survivors. He has also helped many people gain leniency in the courts when their criminal behavior has been driven by involuntary intoxication with psychiatric drugs.

Because of his reform efforts, Dr. Breggin has been called "the conscience of psychiatry." Dr. Breggin has appeared hundreds of times on radio and television, including network news shows, "Larry King Live," "Oprah," "60 Minutes," "20/20," "The O'Reilly Factor" and "Hannity and Colmes." His views have been covered in all of the major print media, including *Time, Newsweek,* the *New York Times,* the *Washington Post,* and *The Los Angeles Times.*

Due to his successful reform work, Dr. Breggin has been attacked by a range of interest groups that he calls the Psychopharmaceutical Complex, especially organized psychiatry and the pharmaceutical industry. Despite considerable media coverage and the publication of more than twenty books and dozens of scientific articles, the psychopharmaceutical complex has such a powerful influence in society that his work has not received its full measure of recognition. This has deprived the public of the full extent of Dr. Breggin's work and deprived young professionals of the personal example he has set by standing up for freedom, dignity and truth in the field of medicine and mental health.

The International Center for the Study of Psychology and Psychiatry (ICSPP) intends this book to remedy that situation by describing and documenting Dr. Breggin's accomplishments through hundreds of tributes and media descriptions of his personal and professional impact from 1954 to the present.

Peter Breggin: From Wunderkind to Ubermensch

by Richard Curtis

As Peter Breggin's literary agent, and a friend since high school, I feel utterly unqualified to appear in a collection of tributes to him by his distinguished professional colleagues. My only contribution to the world's scholarly canon is a Masters thesis on Henry James's *Innocents Abroad,* and scholars eager to mine it for insights may accompany me to a storage facility in the Bronx to view the only extant copy. For those who cannot make the pilgrimage I can furnish the abstract in four words: Americans good, Europeans bad.

I do however have a few observations about the young Peter Breggin that might shed some light on the man you celebrate here today. He and I were members of a brilliant high school class (Woodmere, Long Island '54) of which I was arguably the dullest of the lot. I did not grow up in the community but had transferred to it. The school's administrators offered my parents a choice: I could elect to be the oldest student in eighth grade or the youngest in ninth. My parents placed their deluded faith in me by choosing the latter, and I instantly found myself a pygmy among giants over whom Peter Breggin towered colossally. This is a dangerous confession to lay before psychiatrists, who will hasten to attribute an inferiority complex to me. But there was nothing complex about it; I was, simply, inferior to Peter Breggin.

An inveterate reader of Superman and Captain Marvel comic books, I was exposed to debates about Kant and Schopenhauer, Dostoyevsky and Hemingway, conducted by Peter and our classmates. These took place not only in classrooms but everywhere – in the gym, cafeteria, bowling alley, even cruising around the back roads of the Five Towns in our fathers' cars trying to pick up girls. The quality of the arguments was (at least it seemed then, and still seems now) worthy of Oxford and Cambridge. The exchanges were also raucous, personal, and frequently cruel (we were, after all, teenagers). I remember in particular being challenged by Peter and company to choose between Athenian democracy and Spartan oligarchy: if my grandmother proved to be a burden to our family, would it not be expedient, for the greater good of society, to leave her on a mountainside to die of exposure? I gaped dumbfounded at my inquisitors. "You want to put my grandma on a freezing mountainside? My grandma?"

Peter was not only an extraordinary intellectual—by junior year he was writing a novel—but also an athlete of no mean accomplishment. He played for the Woodmere football team and I particularly recall a game against Manhasset High School whose star, Jimmy Brown, went on to become one of the greatest running backs in National Football League history. And here was Brown wading the last ten yards of the field with Peter wrapped around his ankles and several teammates festooned from his shoulders, hips and arms. He scored anyway, but the image of Peter's bulldog grip on Jimmy Brown's legs is indelibly fixed in my mind's eye and serves as a metaphor for the person Peter was to become: fiercely single-minded, unshakably determined, and heroically courageous.

A joy ride with Peter and two or three members of his brain trust proved to be a transformative moment in my life.

I trudged resolutely through high school, achieving a well-deserved mediocrity and creating a niche for myself as a wag. But in the summer between graduation and commencement of college, a joy ride with Peter and two or three members of his brain trust proved to be a transformative moment in my life. As we cruised around town and they began quarreling about Newtonian cosmology, I made one wisecrack too many. They pulled the car over to the curb and gravely turned on me. "Can't you be serious?" "Don't you believe in anything?" "Doesn't it bother you that your life has no meaning?" I sat dumb, ashamed and bewildered. I not only had no answers, until that moment I did not even have any questions. But theirs had scored a direct hit on my conscience and changed me forever. I entered that car a clown, but left it a brooding seeker of truth.

That fall, my freshman year at Syracuse University, obsessed with catching up on all the knowledge I had avoided in my misspent youth, I performed the minimum of schoolwork and holed up in my dorm room exhaustively reading history, philosophy and world literature. I managed to make something of the rest of my undergraduate tenure and was eventually chosen to run the college's literary magazine. After graduation I went on to become a professional writer and novelist and went on to found a successful literary agency. It was in the latter capacity that I finally had an opportunity to pay Peter back for removing the scales of ignorance from my eyes.

By the mid-1980s, when he contacted me to represent him on the book that became *Toxic Psychiatry* (1991), his career was somewhere on the 15th page of a curriculum vitae that is now so lengthy and prodigious it makes my own look like that of an applicant for clerk in a hardware store. His courageous and controversial campaigns to stop abusive psychosurgical practices like lobotomy, his activist opposition to unethical and hazardous psychological experimentation on children, and his relentless criticism of business, government, and the medical profession have made him the conscience of psychiatry. Today his reforms are accepted as humane, reasonable, and practical. But to achieve them, Peter had to thrust his head into the lion's mouth, and not infrequently the beast closed its jaws.

Other contributors to this publication will elaborate in detail on my thumbnail sketch of his professional achievements. My purpose here is simply to set them in context: the young man I knew and idolized some fifty years ago was an intellectual prodigy who realized in adulthood all that had been predicted for him, thanks to which untold numbers of patients were spared the torments he combated unremittingly. That I was able to be of service to him and help him disseminate his message through his books has been an incredible privilege for me as well as an opportunity to repay him in modest measure for rescuing this young fool from the oblivion of an unexamined life.

Richard Curtis

Richard, president of Richard Curtis Associates, Inc., is a leading New York literary agent and a well-known author advocate. He is also the author of numerous works of fiction and nonfiction including several books about the publishing industry. His interest in emerging media and technology has enabled him to help authors anticipate trends in publishing and multimedia. He has lectured extensively and conducted panels and seminars devoted to raising consciousness in the author and agent community about the future of communications. He was the first president of the Independent Literary Agents Association and subsequently president of ILAA's successor organization, the Association of Authors' Representatives. His firm served for over a decade as agency for the Science Fiction Writers of America. He is married to author Leslie Tonner and has two children. He currently resides in Manhattan. His hobbies are sports, music and art.

Peter Breggin's Responsible Radicalism

by Richard E. Rubenstein, JD

We have become used to dividing reformers into two diametrically opposed types: the "radical" and the "responsible." In America the radical, who challenges existing institutional arrangements at their roots, is commonly thought of as a destroyer, not a builder. Bakunin's "the urge to destroy is also a creative urge" does not sell well in our current state of homeland insecurity. The responsible reformer, on the other hand, is one who can be counted on to leave the fundamental underpinnings of the status quo in place. As Adlai Stevenson once remarked, quoting the chair of a church committee seeking a "responsible" new minister, "We're looking for someone who's not too far to the right or too far to the left. You know, someone...mediocre."

Peter Breggin has been making hash of the radical/responsible dichotomy ever since I first met him, which was a long time ago.

One youthful incident remains especially vivid. Peter and I were sitting together on a bus that was transporting us high schoolers to a cultural event several hours' drive away. Somehow or other, as we motored along the highway, the subject of religion came up. (Peter was a skeptic; I wanted to believe.) "Richie, there is something that you need to read right now," he proclaimed, unearthing a small, tattered volume from his book bag. It was *The Age of Reason,* by the eighteenth-century American radical, Tom Paine. I spent the rest of that bus trip reading it. By the time we returned to our hometown on the Long Island's South Shore, I was an agnostic. (A Jewish agnostic, which is not an oxymoron, but that's another story.)

What does it take to produce a responsible radical – one who not only exposes and denounces an unjust, inhumane system, but works to replace it with ideas and practices that satisfy basic needs for autonomy and human development? I think that Peter's suburban upbringing in the expansive, optimistic decade following World War II may have had something to do with that. He and I were ambitious teenagers, successful at school, clucked over by our parents, but highly individualized, critical of the prevailing "Eisenhower consensus," and determined to transcend the limitations of our stuffily bourgeois community. (Peter sensed these limitations more acutely and understood them better than I did.)

> Somehow or other, as we motored along the highway, the subject of religion came up. "Richie, there is something that you need to read right now," he proclaimed, unearthing a small, tattered volume from his book bag. It was *The Age of Reason,* by the eighteenth-century American radical, Tom Paine.

In high school, we both encountered Eula Kielty, a semi-subversive Latin teacher who loved her students and hosted an Enlightenment-style salon for independent-minded Latinizers in her modest Rockville Center home. What didn't we talk about? Not even the Cold War was off limits, and Peter's penchant for questioning everything officially denominated sacred was prized for once rather than denigrated. Nature bless you, Mrs. Kielty! You are missed.

Thus fortified, we both attended Harvard College, and then went on to professional schools, he in medicine, and me in law. A bit later, we both discovered that the professions that had claimed our time and energies were rackets elaborately structured to serve well-entrenched, privileged interests, and that they would kill our dreams of service and self-development if we let them.

"Every profession tends to become a caste," said Max Weber. Caste membership turned out to be a curse…so we became – almost – Untouchables. Peter took up with Thomas Szasz and I with Leon Trotsky. Both of us wrote books and plotted against the Establishment, but he was considerably more successful in shaking the foundations of the psychiatric world than I was at smashing the Capitalist State. Peter was – is – a legendarily effective organizer, a man absolutely driven to embody his ideas in practice. This drive gave him a particular intensity that outsiders sometimes branded "fanatical". "Fanatic," as a modern Dr. Johnson might define it, is a derogatory term used by the disengaged to describe the committed. It describes the sort of willfulness and tenacity needed to overcome the customary inertia of institutions and to make change happen.

About twenty years ago in Washington, D.C., Peter and I had a joyous reunion. He had met and married Ginger, which would make anyone joyous. Peter had just published *Toxic Psychiatry (1991). The War Against Children of Color,* that excellent book on drugging kids in order to control them, was waiting in the wings. I had found my heart's desire, vocationally speaking, at the Institute for Conflict Analysis and Resolution, a department of George Mason University dedicated to resolving serious conflicts by restructuring the systems that generate them. I had followed Peter's career with interest and pride ever since the days of his great campaigns against shock treatment and lobotomy. At this point, he was looking for some new teaching experience; I was seeking someone extraordinary to teach the psychology of conflict; and voila! A new teacher of conflict studies was born. There are graduates of my institute who still remember Peter's angry, perceptive, compassionate lectures on the war of the old and complacent against the young and alienated.

His work on conflict resolution, *Beyond Conflict,* followed shortly afterwards, and then, of course, his career continued to exfoliate and evolve in new directions. Peter never paid much attention to the boundaries that demarcate fields of study and modes of thought. He saw academic boundaries, like other institutional conventions, as methods of instantiating current power disparities and as obstacles to serving people in need. Determined to put clients' interests (aka the public interest) ahead of all others, Peter made himself at home everywhere, to the discomfort of a legion of officious boundary-maintainers.

In this respect, as in respect of his chutzpah and straight-talking style, his ability to treat clients as self-determining equals, and his passion for praxis, Peter long served as a role model for me. He still does.

Richard E. Rubenstein, JD

Richard is University Professor of Conflict Resolution and Public Affairs at the Institute for Conflict Analysis and Resolution of George Mason University. After studying at Harvard College, Oxford University, and Harvard Law School, he taught political science and law, then came to George Mason, and served as director of the conflict resolution program there from 1988-91. He is the author of seven books, including When Jesus Became God *(1999),* Aristotle's Children *(2003), and* Thus Saith the Lord: The Revolutionary Moral Vision of Isaiah and Jeremiah *(2006). His forthcoming book is entitled* Why People Fight: Learning from History and from Each Other.

Before Anyone Else
by Candace Pert, PhD

Dr. Peter Breggin is one of the most amazing, wise and compassionate human beings I have ever known.

In the current landscape, even the media has accepted and is actively promoting the pharmaceutical fabrication of "chemical imbalance" as an explanation for all mood swings and behavioral deviations from the so-called "norm." Peter stands firm, working diligently to bring attention to correct the shoddy science behind the erroneous assumptions that have been used to justify the outrageous and dangerous epidemic use of untested combinations of powerful psychoactive drugs in children and adults. While the Goliath still stands, somehow Peter's David has managed to inspire, educate and organize an army of like-minded courageous pioneers who are committed to correcting this unspeakable situation, despite the odds.

> Peter is a warrior of course, but at his core he is fueled much more by love, kindness and genuine compassion than anger. Peter WANTS to help people, he LIVES to help people and that is the source of his power.

Peter Breggin started this movement by speaking out before anyone else understood the situation or had the courage. At this point, more and more people now understand the challenge we face and Peter's contributions in educating us.

I wanted to add a note of personal appreciation to Peter that might reveal more of the kind of guy he is. During a very hard personal time I was going through about 8 years ago, Peter and his terrific and supportive wife Ginger (who has played no small role in Peter's successes as he would be the first to admit) invited me and a friend to join them for the weekend at their lake side summer cottage. During quiet, private conversations and joyous boat rides with other guests, he put his full attention on my problem, and I got a glimpse of the real Peter. Peter is a warrior of course, but at his core he is fueled much more by love, kindness and genuine compassion than anger. Peter WANTS to help people, he LIVES to help people and that is the source of his power. Yes, of course, I am saying that Peter is a man of generosity and authenticity—his integrity is unmatched—this we all know. And he is a kind and caring man with a brilliant mind which he uses, along with his humor and the greatest dedication I have ever seen, to help others by changing the world. I wish he still lived in Bethesda. I miss spending time with this wonderful, inspiring man.

Candace Pert, PhD

Candace is an internationally recognized psychopharmacologist who is a former Research Professor at Georgetown University School of Medicine and Section Chief at the National Institute of Mental Health. She has a PhD in pharmacology from Johns Hopkins School of Medicine and has published more than 250 scientific articles. Candace's appearance in the film "What the Bleep Do we Know!?" and her best-selling book, Molecules of Emotion: The Science Behind Bodymind Medicine *(1997) have popularized her ground-breaking theories on consciousness, neuropeptides, and reality. She's currently developing Peptide T, a therapeutic for the treatment of HIV.*

All I Know about Peter Breggin

by Bertram P. Karon, PhD

I first heard Peter Breggin discuss the history and data on lobotomy at a meeting of the American Psychiatric Association in the early 1970s. I had been invited to give a paper at an early morning symposium. But I am addicted to the field, so I went to the rest of the meeting. Breggin's talk was scheduled to conflict with one of the featured speakers, but his topic interested me.

Dr. Breggin pointed out that, as presented by its advocates, lobotomy was very helpful, but a case-by-case review showed that this was not reflected in the original data. Patients were called cured who never left the hospital; patients were called discharged who were simply sent to a nursing home. The sixties were the time of what Breggin called the second wave of lobotomies. At the time, it was being especially advocated for violent behavior as well as a wide variety of psychopathology. Breggin pointed out that the positive outcomes in the second wave were just as untrue as in the first wave.

Among many other facts, Dr. Breggin reported that Walter Freeman, the pioneer of lobotomy, when asked whether it bothered him that approximately two-thirds of lobotomized patients were women, had replied, "How much abstract ability does a woman need anyway?" Further, Freeman had said there were five kinds of patients for whom lobotomy was especially indicated—the poor, the uneducated, Blacks, Jews, and students. (In the 60s students were being obstreperous to authorities, apparently because they objected to being drafted for the Vietnam War.)

Lothar Kalinowsky, the biological psychiatrist, eventually stood up and objected that Breggin should not be making such shameful statements about the great men of psychiatry. Kalinowsky never said that a single fact was not true, but rather that

Breggin should not say such things about the great men of psychiatry, even to other psychiatrists at a professional meeting.

After the meeting I asked Breggin about shock treatment; he said, "Of course, it's terrible. But I can only fight one battle at a time."

Peter Breggin continued to lecture and bring to the attention of many people, including professionals, just how bad lobotomy was. Thanks to Peter Breggin and other decent people, the facts about lobotomy began to surface. (At the time there was even a TV show in which a brain surgeon cured people by performing lobotomies. The textbooks in psychology and psychiatry all referred to lobotomy operations as very helpful, and Moniz had won the Nobel Prize for the development of lobotomy. It was only many years later, after the operation was largely abandoned, that it was discovered that Moniz had beyond question consciously faked at least some of his published data.)

In the 70s the American Psychiatric Association appointed a "blue-ribbon" panel of experts to deal with the growing controversy created by Dr. Breggin. They reviewed the available data and concluded that pre-frontal lobotomy was a very safe and effective treatment when properly used. (They defined an "expert" as someone who had performed a minimum of 12 such operations in the previous year. Obviously, any psychiatrist or neurologist who had a dim view of the operation would have stopped doing it, and was automatically excluded as an expert. Nor did they allow professionals like Breggin who had qualms about the operation to discuss their views with the committee.)

The committee's report was issued about six months before a trial in Michigan (the state in which I live) in 1973. The state was about to lobotomize criminals using heated electrodes inserted deep into the brain and had the supposedly voluntary consent of several incarcerated individuals to undergo this "harmless" operation after which they would be set free. The case was brought by lawyer Gabe Kaimowitz who represented a local poverty law project. When the first prospective patient learned what psychosurgery would really do to him, he withdrew his consent.

Medical, surgical and neurological experts for the defense testified at the trial that the operation was safe and effective. But Kaimowitz brought in Breggin as his main expert. The three judge panel decided, first, that despite its long history there was no clear evidence that lobotomy and other forms of psychosurgery were good for patients; second, that it devastated the mental and emotional functions of the individual; third that it had to be considered a dangerous and experimental treatment which could only be performed with informed voluntary consent, and fourth that no involuntarily confined person, whether criminal or mental patient, could give informed voluntary consent for an experimental treatment, since if you cannot say no, you cannot really say yes. The judicial opinion closely paralleled Dr. Breggin's testimony.

The decision was never appealed, and led to the immediate end of lobotomy in all public institutions in Michigan, and eventually to the termination of psychosurgery in state institutions throughout the country. It also contributed to ending all psychosurgery at federal and Veterans Administration facilities.

Shortly thereafter I noticed that Breggin (1979) had written a book on the bad effects of shock treatment, *Electroshock: Its Brain-Disabling Effects.* I thought to myself that he must now feel the battle on lobotomy was won. The book was a good one, and I told that to Ursula Springer, the publisher. She said it upset many people, but his next book would upset more, because it was on the bad effects of medication.

The book on medication, *Psychiatric Drugs: Hazards to the Brain* (1983) was one of the scariest books I had ever read. Until then I had considered medication as second-rate treatment, but better than nothing. After reading that book, I realized we were creating a population of brain-damaged individuals.

I have heard Peter say that after that book he decided he had done his reform thing, and decided to try to write another novel (he had already written two). But some psychiatric survivor activists were going to appear on the Oprah Winfrey show to talk about the bad effects of hospitalization, shock treatment and medication. Winfrey said they would be more effective if they could get a mental health professional to also talk, and they asked Breggin. He has said that he knew the activists were decent people, so of course he said yes. In the first part of the show the psychiatric survivors spoke eloquently describing the damages caused by institutionalization and the treatments, and in the second part Breggin said that everything they were saying was true, that these were dangerous treatments, and patients and their families had a right to know the dangers before being treated, but they were not being told.

Oprah asked Dr. Breggin how should a person go about selecting a psychiatrist. Dr. Breggin replied, "Very carefully." He urged patients, "Trust the part of you that cares about you. The issue is not how to select a psychiatrist, but how to select a psychotherapist."

As the show closed, Oprah asked Dr. Breggin how should a person go about selecting a psychiatrist. Dr. Breggin replied, "Very carefully." He urged patients, "Trust the part of you that cares about you. The issue is not how to select a psychiatrist, but how to select a psychotherapist." He added that if all a professional does is give you medication, and isn't interested in helping you understand yourself, you are not getting first-rate treatment. You don't have to be impolite, you can take the prescription, but you don't have to get it filled, and you can make an appointment with someone more likely to be helpful. He explained that the organizations that a professional belongs to may help you decide. If they belong to any professional organization that has "electrical" in its title, they are not likely to help you. If they belong to an organization like the American Academy of Psychotherapy, you know they have at least a certain amount of relevant training, a certain amount of personal therapy, and a certain amount of careful supervision of psychotherapy, and therefore they are likely to be helpful.

I know so much about the broadcast because of what happened next. The American Psychiatric Association had a transcript of the broadcast made and sent to the National Alliance for the Mentally Ill (NAMI). The national leadership of that organization filed charges with the medical licensing board of Maryland that Breggin was unethical and should have his license to practice medicine revoked.

Breggin, of course, tried to organize a defense. It was suggested that it would be helpful if academics, as well as other professionals, wrote letters to the licensing board. Psychologist Robert Morgan suggested that if he contacted me I would probably write a letter.

Breggin called me and told me what happened. I said, "I know who you are. I've heard you talk, and I've read your books, and this is outrageous. Of course, I will write a letter."

He sent me a copy of the transcript and of the allegations and I wrote a five page letter pointing out that biological psychiatrists frequently make public statements that most of their colleagues do not agree with, and no one considers that unethical, and that everything he had said I have heard other first-rate psychiatrists say, except they said them to an audience of mental health professionals. Obviously, many other people wrote in support of him to the licensing board as well.

Meanwhile, the American Psychiatric Association had contacted Oprah Winfrey and demanded the right to reply in a broadcast, but that Breggin must not be permitted to reply to them. She replied that they would have to debate Dr. Breggin rather than to take him on in absentia. At first they refused, but then the President of that organization agreed to go on the air. He presented a convincing case, if it were true. But among other things in response to Dr. Breggin's warnings about psychiatric medications, the APA president said that tardive dyskinesia was not a serious or frequent problem. But one of the reasons so much of biological psychiatry hates Breggin is because he does his homework and gets the facts straight. Later in the same broadcast, Breggin pulled out the report of the American Psychiatric Association's committee on tardive dyskinesia. According to the report what the organization's President had just said was not true. Biological psychiatrists and drug company representatives are not used to

The American Psychiatric Association had contacted Oprah Winfrey and demanded the right to reply in a broadcast, but that Breggin must not be permitted to reply to them. She replied that they would have to debate Dr. Breggin rather than to take him on in absentia.

anyone getting up and telling the truth, when they, knowingly or unknowingly, get the facts wrong.

Eventually, Breggin went public and talked to the media about the license attack. Many newspapers ran articles about it, but most important of all, the *New York Times* covered the controversy. The state of Maryland made Dr. Breggin go before a hearing, but was forced to announce that they were dismissing the charges. In a letter to Dr. Breggin, the licensure people declared that he had done nothing wrong, that it was a matter of free speech, and they thanked him for his contribution to mental health in the state of Maryland.

Dr. Breggin's earlier books were addressed primarily to professionals. He had been interested in writing a book for the general public, but had been told there was no market for it. However, now the publishers, having read the *New York Times* article and witnessed his successful handling of the controversy, were seeking him out. This led to his writing *Toxic Psychiatry* (1991) which did reach a mass market.

After *Toxic Psychiatry* came a succession of first rate books, two with his wife Ginger Breggin: *Talking Back to Prozac* (with Ginger), *Talking Back to Ritalin,* the first edition of *Brain Disabling Treatments in Psychiatry, The War Against Children of Color* (with Ginger) and most recently *Medication Madness.* I have used a number of them, in successive years, with my large undergraduate classes in Personality: A Psychoanalytic Approach. For the last few years I have been using a book I consider a classic: Breggin and Cohen (1999), *Your Drug May Be Your Problem.* There are other books which also list side effects, but this is the only book which carefully deals with the issue of withdrawal effects, and how best to safely accomplish withdrawal. I recommend that every mental health professional should have a copy on his or her shelf.

When I first used *Your Drug May Be Your Problem* with my undergraduate class, as one of four required books for the semester, I thought I should probably change it after the first year because it is too technical and therefore probably dull. But when I got student ratings at the end of the term, the students rated it as the best book of the four, which startled me. Then I realized that many of them were on psychiatric medication, and so were many of their friends and relatives. Until they took my course they did not know that there was a down side to medication and that they had an alternative—psychotherapy—that is far more effective as well as safer. I still use the book and 300 students, twice a year, read it.

I have only gotten one complaint from the parents of a student who they said had a withdrawal reaction from stopping a mood stabilizer. (They did not call it a withdrawal reaction, of course, but the return of her "biological illness.") They wrote letters of complaint to the university President, the Dean, and my Department Chairman for my being unscientific and not knowing the data, and consequently being destructive. I eventually talked to them for two hours, and their complaint was that their daughter had bought Breggin and Cohen in the bookstore and acted on it, and the bookstore would not have carried the book if I were not using it in my course. Later, the young woman took my course, and they complained that when she told me she had stopped taking medication and that she was feeling better, I did not tell her that was impossible, and that she should take her medication. It was only when I casually mentioned that NAMI was not an accurate source of information, and that it banned local chapters from sharing any negative information about a medication, that they admitted that they were members of NAMI and believed everything the organization said. Our two-hour discussion seems to have mollified them.

Early on I really admired Breggin's ability to get the media, including the *New York Times,* to pay attention to important but not popular facts. Probably everyone who reads this book already knows about the International Center for the Study of Psychiatry and Psychology. Its creation is not the least of his (and Ginger Breggin's) contributions. It started out as a small group of decent people, who had been influenced by Breggin, and it has kept growing, eventually under Ginger's guidance. What one person can do is limited, what a group of bright, decent people can do is much more impressive. When my wife and I attend the meetings of that organization, there is a feeling of being home. Irrespective of theoretical orientation, every one of its members whom we have met is a bright, decent person whom we can respect and learn from.

> Breggin was even more effective in talking to an audience including ordinary people than in one restricted to professionals. The atmosphere was electric. People who were there have talked about it for years.

Over the years I have learned that decency comes first. A basically decent professional will use anything he or she learns to help people; if decency is lacking, it doesn't matter what he or she knows-- no one will get help.

A number of years ago, the Michigan Psychoanalytic Council decided to sponsor a workshop with Peter Breggin. It makes me feel good that we were the first psychoanalytic institute to invite him. Edward Gibeau, who was the President of the Council, decided that what Breggin had to say was too important to keep hidden. In addition to the workshop for professionals, for which there was a fee, there was a lecture open to everyone, free of charge. The open lecture was better attended (there were people sitting on the floor) by a more varied audience, and Breggin was even more effective in talking to an audience including ordinary people than in one restricted to professionals. The atmosphere was electric. People who were there have talked about it for years.

Of course, Breggin makes many people very angry. Early on, I noticed in reading his book on electric shock treatment that he cited many of the same studies that Kalinowsky cited in his textbook on that treatment. But they cited the findings differently. I looked up several of the studies cited differently, and I talked to the author of one study, who happened to be a friend of mine. In each case, Breggin had cited the study's findings accurately, and Kalinowsky had not. This is what makes his opponents furious. He is bright and he does his homework. Their usual attempts to pretend that scientific sounding statements are automatically scientific do not hold up if there is someone who knows the truth, is willing to say it, and can document what he says.

In short, Peter Breggin has made a difference in the fields of psychiatry, psychology, and mental health treatment. He has made a difference to many patients whose treatment has been less destructive and more helpful, including thousands of people who would otherwise have been lobotomized, and to many more in creating hope that one can receive and one can practice treatments that actually help people.

Bertram Karon, PhD

Bert is professor of psychology at Michigan State University and a leader in the Michigan Psychoanalytic Council. He is an esteemed teacher, a highly regarded researcher and clinical psychologist, a constant support and friend to ICSPP, and the author of Psychotherapy of Schizophrenia.

My Friendship with Peter and His Fight to Protect Children From Psychiatric Abuse

by Brian Kean, PhD

In late 1995 I traveled across the United States and visited middle schools. At each school I interviewed teachers and other educational personnel with a focus on Attention Deficit Hyperactivity Disorder (ADHD). I also presented seminars on ADHD to the community in Oconee County, South Carolina. My first impressions left me with an understanding of how poorly the ADHD construct was understood; particularly the risks associated with long-term reliance on drugs to modify the behavior of children. The other impression from the trip was the extent of medication use in United States schools for the treatment of ADHD. The United States certainly was the centre of the ADHD epidemic. At that time, the model viewing learning and behavior problems of children as a psychiatric disorder was spreading to Australia and other countries. Having worked as a teacher for twenty years in special education in Australia, I viewed with concern the changing model from an emphasis on educational and behavioral interventions to reliance on drug therapies.

I had become aware of Peter Breggin's work through reading *Toxic Psychiatry* and in 1995 I saw him in an Australian documentary entitled Speed for Breakfast. In the documentary, Peter was introduced as "an anti-psychiatrist…a psychiatrist and author who is strongly critical of his own profession and doesn't much believe in the use of drugs at all" (Swanson, 1995).

Peter's opening comment in the documentary provided a succinct critical analysis of the use of drug therapies for the treatment of ADHD:

> Ritalin has been studied for decades now and they have not been able to prove a long-term beneficial effect in children, they have not been able to show improved

> academic performance in children...all they can show is what we know will happen to any animal or any child given Ritalin...they will accept more boring, confined circumstances for a short period of time until the drug wears off. If you give Ritalin to a rat it stops its exploratory behavior, it stops looking inquisitive, it stops being playful, it sits around and gnaws on its bars or marches up and down. It becomes a fit inmate for a cage. We are making fit inmates for cages. We should not do that to our children. (Breggin, 1995)

Peter's comment contradicted everything I had heard from the medical experts promoting ADHD. The mantra had been "Ritalin, Ritalin, Ritalin" as the new biological solution for the parents and teachers dealing with children with challenging behaviors or learning problems. Peter's strong critique of the medical model challenged the promotion of drugs and deconstructed the diagnosis to suggest that all that was involved was the use of drugs for behavior modification.

Peter's account was critical of the imprecision of the diagnosis and the lack of long-term research into the potential risks. His viewpoint saw their widespread use, not as a valid medical treatment, but rather as a method of suppression of a child's spontaneous or undesirable behaviors without adequately identifying the causes. Peter's thesis and advocacy for the rights of the child, combined with his deep understanding of the medical issues and drug effects, provided for the first time an ally in supporting my own research and personal concerns.

Meeting Peter Breggin

In late 1996 I returned for my second visit to the United States. The journey commenced with the presentation of a paper at the Sixth Annual Conference of the Institute for the Study of Postsecondary Pedagogy at State University of New York, New

Paltz. In the week before leaving Australia I attempted to contact Peter Breggin. Numerous Internet and other searches did not result in finding his direct contact details. I had only a few days before leaving. By accident, while searching for Peter, I came across Ginger Breggin's e-mail address. I sent Ginger an e-mail and much to my surprise her response was almost immediate. Peter had agreed to meet with me at his home. I quickly rearranged my travel schedule and worked in a visit to Washington DC.

> What astounded me however was Peter's generosity in giving me unrestricted access to years of research.

Peter had lived in Bethesda, Maryland since 1968. At the time, his home was also his private practice, library, research centre and office for the International Center for the Study of Psychiatry and Psychology. I had booked a hotel in Bethesda. On arriving I rang the contact number Ginger had provided and arranged for a meeting later that day. To my surprise Peter's house was no more than a block from the hotel.

I walked with some trepidation to Peter's house. My expectation was somewhat reserved as I had discussed ADHD with medical practitioners and pediatricians in Australia and my views and concerns were generally dismissed as the medicos believed that the diagnosis was in their domain and that an educator had to conform to the medical model.

To my surprise, Peter and Ginger welcomed me and made me feel that I was a valued guest in their house. Peter and I spent a few hours discussing ADHD. I found it fascinating that this eminent psychiatrist conversed so easily with me and made me feel that my educational perspectives provided valuable insights into the issues surrounding the epidemic of children labeled with the disorder. In the evening Peter and Ginger invited my family to dinner at their house. I was traveling with my wife and teenage daughter and her friend. When we arrived at Peter's and Ginger's home we were welcomed like long lost friends.

My daughter and her friend were taken back when they met Peter. Although they were not familiar at all with his work they were awestruck by his presence. They sensed they were in the company of a great man.

I spent the next few days working at Peter and Ginger's house. Peter had offered me access to his files for my research. The wealth of material and articles I was able to obtain provided the missing links I needed to move forward with my research. What astounded me however was Peter's generosity in giving me unrestricted access to years of research filed by Ginger. Ginger was also so helpful allowing me to photocopy articles and assisting me with the complexity of the filing systems used to chronicle psychiatric research extending over fifty or more years.

In those days, Peter's house in Bethesda, Maryland contained his office. (He now has an office in a building that is separate from his home in Ithaca, New York.) Peter managed to see patients from around 10 AM each day extending into the early evening. Peter's and Ginger's was a work-oriented household. From the beginning of the day the phones rang with calls from media, patients and professional colleagues. It seemed that there was not a minute to lose on their quest to protect human rights from psychiatric abuses.

Seminar at Johns Hopkins

On the third day working at Peter's and Ginger's, Peter came out of his office for a break. He asked me if I wanted to present to his postgraduate counseling class at Johns Hopkins. I was a bit suprised by this unexpected offer but quickly agreed to participate.

Over the next two days I wondered exactly what I would present. I attended Peter's class and watched as he presented for the first hour. His presentation style was interactive and challenging. His one clear objective was to make the students think critically about their role, and to understand the psychopharmaceutical complex and the way their approach in counseling could assist individuals to function and develop in society.

Following Peter, I presented on the reforms necessary in schools to reduce the reliance on the labeling of children with a psychiatric disorder as a result of learning failure and/or behavioral problems in schools.

With honesty that shocks, Peter told me that he thought I was a better teacher than he was. He was a good lecturer, a good psychotherapist, but not as good a teacher in classroom groups, he explained. We talked about how I had been teaching all sized groups for many years, while he had been lecturing and conducting psychotherapy.

After the class Peter and I had dinner together. We spent the evening discussing education and particularly early childhood development. For some reason we both started to talk about our own personal experiences in early childhood and schools while reflecting on the current circumstances in the United States and Australia. I think it was at that point that a true friendship between us commenced.

Living and Working with Peter

The following year I returned to the United States and stayed for two months with Peter and Ginger and their daughter Aly in Bethesda, Maryland. In this period I began to understand the complexity of Peter's and Ginger's working life. Ginger spent hours on the computer managing the ICSPP listserv and dealing with the business side of life as well as establishing a complex repository of documents covering media and a library of journal articles and texts that covered every dimension of psychiatry. She was also the person who reached out the most to newcomers to the reform movement.

I accompanied Peter to many formal events in this period. The most interesting were the interviews for radio or television. Observing Peter in action and the way he managed media was quite a privilege. Peter's style was always confident, well thought through and cutting in his analysis. I watched him perform on a television mini-debate with his strategy focused on delivering key sound bites in order to fit into the media model while remaining strategic in his responses. He often began with a brief deconstruction of the opponent's argument, not targeting the individual, but contradicting or contrasting a point that highlighted a flaw or gap in the other's analysis.

Observing Peter in action and the way he managed media was quite a privilege. Peter's style was always confident, well thought through and cutting in his analysis.

In one interview an ADHD advocate attempted to imply that amphetamines where not dangerous and were as safe as coffee or chocolate. Peter's pithy opening attack declared that this benign view of the stimulants was inappropriate and unethical. He pointed out that these views did not match with the warnings required by the FDA in the official drug labels for prescribed stimulants and ran counter to the severe restrictions placed on the use of these drugs by the U.S. Drug Enforcement Administration (DEA) and the United Nations International Narcotics Control Board (INCB). He reminded them that both the DEA and the INCB repeatedly and adamantly warned about the risk of Ritalin abuse and confirmed that the drug's clinical properties and risks were similar to cocaine. In less than thirty seconds he had destroyed the credibility of his opponent. Then he went on to deliver a rational, compassionate analysis of the needs of children under stress and how drugging only suppressed their problems and did not treat the underlying causes of the childrens' stressors.

During this period of time Peter and I became lifetime friends. Every evening we walked Peter and Ginger's dogs. We talked of many things. Peter was particularly interested in the perspectives held on the United States by someone from Australia. The time spent with Peter and Ginger in this period also involved long discussions particularly concerning the need to address and to prevent the trend of moving the ADHD diagnosis to earlier age groups. During this time, Peter commenced the writing of *Talking Back to Ritalin.* Along with working on my doctoral research in the various libraries in Washington DC, the time was one of developing a stronger and stronger bond with Peter and Ginger.

Every weekend we headed off to Lake Anna. Peter had a holiday house on the lake about two hours south of Washington DC. (A reformer without great income at the time, he had obtained funds to build the cottage from the settlement of a libel and slander suit he brought against a shock doctor.) It was on those visits that I began to understand the complexity of Peter.

He was a man driven by his work, with a work ethic that few, if any could compete with. He was also a man who loved nature, birds, the environment and had compassion and empathy for an incredible number of people. He always welcomed friends and neighbors to his house and enjoyed the celebration of living. Even in the poorer rural communities surrounding Lake Anna, Peter and Ginger had numerous friends. Many held him in awe when they first met him but soon realized that they were dealing with a compassionate person who did not judge but instead appreciated and loved humanity. In the following years I continued each year to attend the ICSPP conference and have always spent time visiting with Peter and Ginger following the conference. I witnessed Peter's legal triumphs, the writing and publication of multiple books and articles, and the ongoing educational efforts by Peter and Ginger in challenging the psychopharmaceutical complex.

Peter's life and professional career are a mirror of his conclusions. Let us all join to support the cause that Peter founded in the early 1970s. On a personal note to my best friend, I hope that you continue with your fight for at least another decade. Peter, without your fighting this battle, the children of the future will have less hope. I also want to thank you for the support you have given me over the past years and wish you and Ginger the very best for the future.

References

Breggin, P. R. (1995). Speed for Breakfast. Four Corners. Sydney: Transcript of Swanson, N. ABC Broadcasting documentary, 12 February, 1995.

Swanson, N. (1995). Four Corners. Sydney: Transcript. ABC Broadcasting documentary, 12 February, 1995.

Brian Kean, PhD

Brian has had thirty-two years' experience in teaching and has held a variety of teaching and consultancy positions in special education and is qualified to practice in all areas of special education. He is currently a Senior Lecturer and Coordinator of Secondary Programs at Southern Cross University in Australia. Brian is a Member of the Board of Directors of the International Center for the Study of Psychiatry and Psychology (ICSPP) and co-Editor-in-Chief of the journal Ethical Human Psychology and Psychiatry.

So, What's Peter Breggin Been Up To?

by Andrew Crosby, MA

My ICSPP-related duties led to a brief e-mail exchange with Peter a while back, and during this, he made reference to a couple of projects he's been working on. It occurred to me that I've had no idea what he's been up to for ... years, actually. Then it occurred to me that, quite likely, you don't know either.

Peter agreed to sit down with me for a talk at our recent conference so we could catch up. We talked about what he's been working on and what makes him happy. I tried to dig for some more riveting stuff, but Peter wasn't having any of that. And, truth be told, I didn't try very hard. You'll see why as we go along. So ... here's what Peter's been up to. You may be surprised. I sure was.

The Work

Peter has a few writing projects in the works, perhaps most significantly a new book. The title is *Medication Madness: A Psychiatrist Exposes the Dangers of Mood-Altering Medications.* It includes 50 to 60 accounts of people who were tragically affected by psychiatric treatment. The book actually began when Peter was updating his 1991 classic, *Toxic Psychiatry.* When he realized how many important clinical stories he had to tell, he set aside updating *Toxic Psychiatry,* and wrote *Medication Madness.*

Peter has also done some updating of other books that has proceeded as planned. He finished working with David Cohen on a new edition of the book they co-wrote and published in 1999, *Your Drug May Be Your Problem,* and the new edition is now available. Peter is finishing up work on rewriting his 1997 book, *Brain Disabling Treatments in Psychiatry* that will be published early in 2008. This completely updated edition will include a section on the spellbinding effect, or intoxication anosognosia (denying intoxication), about which Peter wrote in the Fall 2006 *Ethical Human Psychology and Psychiatry* (Volume 8, Number 3). He also presented on this at the 2006 ICSPP conference in Bethesda, Maryland.

Peter has continued his litigation work as well. He discusses a great deal of his forensic work in Medication Madness. Although he seems to genuinely enjoy the legal arena, he tells me that it is very stressful and time-consuming, so that he continually tries to cut back on this aspect of his activities. He said that his record as an expert in malpractice and product liability cases remains favorable—almost all of them are settled and many that go to court are won. He also testifies in criminal cases on behalf of people driven into violent medication madness by psychiatric drugs. "It leads to good things," Peter says of litigation and his professional witness duties, despite the inherent adversarial nature of these matters.

With that, Peter did something interesting with our discussion—he changed course. It was a quick but natural transition. And although I wanted to pry more into his writing and legal work, it just didn't happen. Good thing. Where we ended up was more revealing than anything I could have facilitated. A heck of lot nicer, too.

The Country Life

In 2002, Peter and Ginger officially stepped aside from the nonprofit ICSPP organization Peter had founded and handed matters over to Dominick Riccio, Lloyd Ross, and the board of directors. They headed for New York State's Finger Lakes Region to enjoy, as Peter referred to it several times during our discussion, the country life in a lake side home.

It seems to have worked out better than they could have hoped. Traveling appeals to many couples who are slowing down (please don't say retired—Peter hasn't retired), but the Breggins appear to have no such aspirations. They are homebodies, it seems, and wouldn't have it any other way. Peter said, in so many words, that he really can't leave home for any length of time. He attended a conference in London this year, for example—for the weekend. He "just had to get back home." Attending the recent ICSPP conference in Arlington was difficult for him as well, made even more so by Ginger's absence. She was busy with family, awaiting the arrival of their first grandchild together. The boy, named Cole, has safely "made his arrival on Earth," according to Peter's recent report.

To hear Peter talk about the country life, his affection is understandable. "In the country, people have a deep sense that you live life the best you can and take responsibility for all your actions," he said. "City people, university intellectuals, don't have that." Where he lives now, people have known each other for a long time, have grown up together. They talk, they listen, and they care. This fosters a sense of responsibility toward one another that much of the Western world has tossed aside or just can't get around to anymore. This holds special meaning for Peter.

Peter has dedicated his work and his life to helping people overcome or avoid conflict. Guided by love, empathy, and other concepts alien to many helping professionals, he has engaged in healing relationships that have actually healed people.

Recall that Peter has dedicated his work and his life to helping people overcome or avoid conflict. Guided by love, empathy, and other concepts alien to many helping professionals, he has engaged in healing relationships that have actually healed people.

Yet his professional life—outside the therapy setting—has also been filled with conflict.

Oh, yes, he's had to fight. He's had to fight to be heard, he's had to fight to work in an ethical manner; he even had to fight to keep his license when attacked by the psychiatric establishment because of criticisms he made of psychiatry on the Oprah Winfrey Show in the late 1980s.

"There were a lot of times I wasn't sure I'd survive professionally," Peter said, his expression revealing that he meant it. ICSPP was born of this conflict, he recalled, as surrounding himself with a solid group of supporters lent credibility to his positions and helped stave off annihilation. Peter then noted that ICSPP has evolved far beyond that, and, following his wife Ginger's initial work as managing director, he credits Dominick, Lloyd Ross, and many others for making that so.

The Spiritual Life

Around this point, I asked Peter about comments he had made during his conference presentation earlier in the day. He had spoken about what psychiatric drugs do the brain, concluding that, "Psychiatrists hate the brain. And child psychiatrists hate children's brains." He had added, "Go meet one. Do they seem to like kids?" Everybody chuckled, and not because that was funny —people just tend to laugh when a covert truth is revealed.

When asked, Peter said he is still angry about what psychiatry is doing, especially to children, and he said it is still important to work against these forces. Next, I asked Peter a question I've asked others. It goes something like, "How do you feel about the effectiveness of current reform efforts? How optimistic are you now, compared to how you felt ten, twenty, or thirty years ago?"

Before reading Peter's response, glance back up to the title of this section.

Now that you're back, here's what Peter had to say: "I don't look at success. I don't think about success or results. It's about living right. It's about doing the right thing."

Peter spoke of his spiritual beliefs, and credited his Jewish history for instilling in him the sense that "things don't necessarily get better—the important thing is to live right." In his writing, he regularly refers to the necessity of principled living. The basic principles, from his view, are responsibility, liberty and love.

There is something extraordinarily logical and touching about the central elements of Peter's life as our discussion revealed them. Peter has engaged in empathic, caring relationships with people who have been harmed; it's been the right thing to do. He has fought when needed, despite his abhorrence of conflict; that has been the right thing to do. Peter founded ICSPP "to have a safe, conflict-free place" within which to work; it was, quite naturally, the right thing to do.

Now, Peter has settled in the country with his family. I didn't have to ask why he chose the country, as he readily offered the information: "I live in the country to be closer to God."

One can only assume—it was the right thing to do.

So **Not** *His Comfort Zone*

Peter has withstood withering attacks and criticism. Though he abhors conflict, he has stood his ground when challenged and has never shied away from a fight that needed to be waged. Strong-willed, quick-witted, and steadfast in his beliefs, he has lived his life as he has intended. He has been unflappable against tremendous odds.

But I know how to rattle him. I know how to shake him up, intimidate him. I've found Peter Breggin's Achilles heel. Well, I didn't exactly find it. It just sort of played out in front of me.

Want to know what it is? Want to know how to make Peter Breggin squirm and try to crawl under the table? Here you go FDA folks—here's how to scare the hell out of Peter Breggin …

Flatter him. Call him "great," "wonderful," "inspirational." Really want to freak him out? Call him a "hero."

In case you're wondering, no, I did not fawn all over him like that. I didn't have to. We had our talk in the hotel lobby area near where presentations were being held at the conference. I didn't have to fawn all over the guy because twenty other people interrupted us to do so.

And, you know, they didn't fawn all that strongly. Indeed none called him "wonderful" or "inspirational" as I suggested; they just sort of implied it. Yet Peter experienced what one might diagnose as flattery-induced agitation. Technically, that's a drug-induced inner agitation that makes it difficult to hold still.

I commented on Peter's reaction, asking something like, "You do realize you can't come to an ICSPP conference and blend into the scenery, right? Why the jitters?"

"I've never been comfortable with stardom," he said, smiling and crossing his arms tightly before him. "Ginger always reminds me of the impact of my work, and I guess she's right." Peter shrugged and added, "I don't know, it's just not my comfort zone."

You needn't take my word for it. By completely random assignment, we were joined by an unbiased, objective observer who supported the premise that Peter's humble manner is as genuine as it is unique.

Tom Bratter, founder and director of the John Dewey Academy in Massachusetts, popped in to say "Hi." And to heap praise on Peter. When Peter swatted his hand at the flattery saying, "Aw, come on," Tom turned to me and said (I am not making this up), "That's why this guy is so great. That's why this organization is so great."

Tom continued: "It's his humility, not taking himself too seriously." Peter tried to change the subject; no dice. "He's responsive, he's supportive," Tom went on. "Most heads of organizations aren't like that."

"Former head," Peter corrected.

"That's another thing," Tom said, jabbing his finger at me. "No other head of an organization would just hand it over to other people to run as they please. Not before they're totally washed up. But Peter did it. That takes humility."

Peter bobbed and weaved, but Bratter added, "Everything Peter said 20 years ago about what would happen has all come true; it's all happened, just as he said it would. He should be apologized to. But no, they still condemn him." Bratter also expressed his contention that *Toxic Psychiatry* "is more valid now than when Peter wrote it. It has survived the test of time."

Demonstrating his gift for colorful language, Bratter said he is often attacked for his own unconventional beliefs. "And you know what I say to them? 'I'm glad you're condemning me. If you were praising me, I'd be [blanked] up like you.'"

Peter agreed with Bratter's positive take on the message behind the criticism, but hastened to add, "I'm just not in-your-face about it like some people." With that, Peter commented that Tom's style is all well and good and works for him. But Peter prefers the conflict-free approach. He really doesn't want to fight anymore. More to the point, perhaps, he no longer feels the need.

Conclusion—In the Comfort Zone

What else has Peter been up to? He spends more time with friends and family. He chats with his neighbors and plays with his dogs. He sleeps in front of the T.V. Along the way, he gets to his e-mail and re-writes a book or two, as well as a whole new one, *Medication Madness.* Battling the world doesn't make the agenda, it would seem, when you're living the country life. We all should be so lucky. Maybe we are so lucky. We belong to the organization Peter founded with the intention of providing a safe, conflict-free place to share ideas. And look at some of those ideas—non-coercive support for people who've been harmed; truly informed consent; a view of human suffering that takes into account the real-world challenges with which we all struggle; healing through relationships.

Perhaps we are not as far along the spiritual path as Peter with regard to contentment. But let's not be too hard on ourselves. We are, after all, on that path.

A question for you: How did you find that path? How did you learn of it?

Each of us has a unique answer, but I ask you to think deeper within that answer. When I asked Peter that question about how reform efforts are going, he spoke of not expecting the world to get better, but rather of living well and doing the right thing. Somewhere in there he also said, "I feel as though I've had a calling. And I've done the best I can. I've answered."

I'm going to go out on a limb and suggest that each of us, no matter how we found ICSPP, has had a calling. At some point we all decided to live right and to do good things.

How about that—There's a little bit of the country life in each of us, compliments of just being part of ICSPP. So let's keep living right. Let's keep doing good things.

Andrew Crosby, MA

Andrew is a social worker who lives and works in northern New Jersey. He writes for and edits the ICSPP Newsletter, *and is an amateur writer. This article first appeared in the* ICSPP Newsletter *(2007, No. 4) and was based on a conversation with Peter and others at the tenth annual ICSPP conference held in October 2007 in Arlington, Virginia. Andrew, who is a Board Member of ICSPP, has another contribution in chapter 14.*

My Experience of Peter Breggin

by Ian Williams Goddard

After my mother, suffering from dementia, was placed on mind-altering drugs, I combed the library for related research. Finding ample reason for concern, I wrote a paper on the topic and submitted it to *Ethical Human Psychology and Psychiatry* (known then as *Ethical Human Sciences and Services.*) It was accepted, and as an unexpected result I was invited to work as a research assistant to Peter and Ginger Breggin, who lived only a few miles away.

From 1999 through 2002 I worked in the Breggin's in-home office in Bethesda, Maryland. I did general office work, managed their extensive medical-research files, and made frequent forays to the National Library of Medicine across the street to procure studies on psychiatric drugs. Peter never argued from conjecture or anecdote, only from peer-reviewed research. His critics learned to avoid him in public debate because they knew that, despite his non-mainstream stance, Peter had the facts behind him.

Working in the Breggins' home office gave me a unique up-close view of the man, Peter Breggin. Perhaps the most notable observation was that here was a man possessed of continuous energy, vision, and focus.

In his complex multifaceted career Peter was absolutely indefatigable. I can't begin to express how true that was. On any given day he'd be seeing patients, doing media interviews (in the office with lights, cameras, and crew or over the phone), hosting visits from professional colleagues, reviewing the latest research, working on books, going to give a lecture or catch a plane. Day after day, year after year. Yet engulfed in such a unique life of nonstop activity he was never hassled or hurried, never frazzled or at wits end—on each rapidly changing task, totally focused, totally present, as if there were no other demands.

Always calm and collected at the center of a cyclone of activity. Never before or since have I encountered such a dynamic person.

Yet in his career Peter was not detached or aloof, he was always there, immediately connected to the people around him. He has an innate sense of the humanity and dignity of each person he encounters. When I'd inform him of some dreadful plight in the news, I could see in him an immediate empathic connection to the people involved. Peter's whole life was a clarion call to just that empathic connection. In fact it was precisely that empathic connection that prevented him from treating people with problems in life as automatons with brain disorders. His empathic vision was impervious to the drug-company-induced illusion that reduces problems in life to brain disorders. That illusion disconnects those in need from those they need. It shifts the locus-of-control from individuals and their interconnectivity with family and friends to faceless and remote drug companies. That delusion systematically dehumanizes us all, and nobody sees that more clearly or helps others to see it more clearly than Peter. It's important to understand that Peter's work on empathy in *Beyond Conflict* (1992)

Peter has an innate sense of the humanity and dignity of each person he encounters. When I'd inform him of some dreadful plight in the news, I could see in him an immediate empathic connection to the people involved. Peter's whole life was a clarion call to just that empathic connection.

and *The Heart of Being Helpful* (1997) reflects the underlying and cohesive continuum, animating the entire humanizing paradigm he defined throughout his career.

Peter's career has been a unique combination of therapy, science, philosophy, spirituality, humanism, and social activism. Reducing further, it represented a rare balance of the intellectual and the emotive, of thought and feeling, of comprehension and caring.

The boundless energy I witnessed in Peter plus his clear and sustained vision is what it takes for someone like him to make a difference on so many fronts for so many years. It's interesting to note that of all the people I've known, those with personal temperaments closest to Peter's were commercial airline pilots. Now there's a group of folks who are unflappably focused, calm, and composed. You're not going to be able to ferry hundreds of human lives through perilous skies every day if you don't have unshakable composure. And come to think of it, in a deep allegorical sense that's what Peter's career was, that of a pilot. A spiritual pilot there to carry people away from a sea of problems and illusions to a land of sanity and solutions. Fly Peter!

Reference

Goddard, I.W. (2000). Concerns About the Use of Buspirone in Alzheimer Patients. *Ethical Human Sciences and Services,* 2, 119-22.

Ian Goddard

Ian has been a research assistant to Dr. Breggin since 1999. He is an artist and writes on a variety of topics. He's currently pursuing a degree in computer science.

The Peter Breggin I know and Love

by Jean Ross

When I hear the familiar voice over the phone say, "Hi, Mom, how're you doing?" I know immediately that it's Peter calling. We end up talking about his latest project, whether it be the rock wall he's building, the manuscript he's finishing for the publisher, or the landscaping he's creating for his beautiful upstate New York home. Our conversations are more like the ones we shared over a cup of tea at Lake Anna; comfortable and caring.

Lake Anna was really, in retrospect, the place where I had a chance to get to know Peter as an individual. His boundless energy was evident from the start. With his pronouncement of his tree planting intentions, followed by his invitation, "Jean, you want to come?" I was ready, dressed in my work jeans and carrying leather gloves borrowed from Ginger, his wife and my daughter. It was during such times of working together that we built a relationship of mutual respect, which later grew into the most natural and familiar love for one another.

Rocks have always been a passion with Peter. Not just stones that you could carry in your pocket, but huge rocks, erratics deposited by the glacier, were the ones that Peter wanted to punctuate his landscape. Those that he had brought in by truck and crane remained at the Lake Anna property, but the rock commemorating their wedding on July 4, 1984 was moved to their home in upstate New York. That is a special rock not to be left behind, a rock that symbolized the great love that Peter shared with Ginger then, now, and always.

When Peter had an idea to protect his land against wave erosion from the lake, he worked diligently to create a rock wall around all his water front summer home property at Lake Anna. Many a time I observed him working hard, sweating but happy, as he carried a rock to be placed in just the right place in his rock wall. Each time Phil and I went to visit Ginger and Peter, I would walk with Peter as he pointed out the changes he had made most recently not only to his rock wall but to the landscaping; adding a tree here, protecting a bush from wildlife there. His love of nature was evident from the first weekend we had together, a passion that has blossomed at his home in upstate New York. Not only does he have a rock wall and boat dock at his new home, but he has created a beautifully landscaped acreage that invites the visitor down newly crafted steps to his home that is built into the hillside overlooking the lake.

Peter's love of nature includes all living creatures, especially birds. Many times Peter has called me just to tell me of a single bird sighting he had made. Not infrequently he stood by his kitchen window, binoculars glued to his eyes, while describing the particular characteristics of the bird he was observing. I have a mental picture of both of us hunched over our respective bird identification books with our telephones glued to our ears, talking long distance, trying to identify this little feathered creature.

Peter's love of nature includes all living creatures, especially birds. Many times Peter has called me just to tell me of a single bird sighting he had made. Not infrequently he stood by his kitchen window, binoculars glued to his eyes, while describing the particular characteristics of the bird he was observing.

No matter where Peter and Ginger live there has to be room for Peter to write his books, many of which he has invited me to proofread. What an honor to have his creation in my hands to read before anyone else has a chance to see his work. What trust he has shown toward me to critique his creation. Many a time as he and Ginger would go for a walk together, I would happily curl up with his most recent manuscript, pen in hand, to make suggested corrections in the margins for him to pursue later.

As a retired elementary school teacher, I am grateful to Peter for his tireless work in protecting children all over the world from drugs, such as Ritalin. While still in the classroom I saw firsthand the use of this drug to mask one young girl's emotional problems resulting from her mother's boyfriends' sexual abuse of her. Without Peter's professional stand against the drugging of children, I am convinced that even more of our children today would be subjected to unnecessary harmful drugs. His voice is a voice of hope to many who cry out for help.

Jean Ross

Jean is a retired teacher who taught elementary school for more than 30 years. She is also Peter Breggin's mother-in-law.

More than 50 Years as the Conscience of Psychiatry

by Ginger Ross Breggin

Peter and I have been married 25 years now, and we have known each other since those heady beginning reform days of the campaign to stop psychosurgery in the early 1970's. I knew when I married Peter that I was marrying my hero.

Since his childhood, Peter has been active as a reformer who protected the vulnerable and advocated for caring, rational human services. In his first year of college in 1954, he began working as a Harvard volunteer on the wards of a state mental hospital. By 1955-1956 he was directing the program that for a time began to revolutionize the concept of the state mental hospital by introducing truly empathic and even loving approaches to helping the inmates. Hence the title of my introduction: More than 50 years as the conscience of psychiatry.

I have had the great gift of watching this man hone his skills and accomplish his goals over more than 35 years. When I first met Peter he was the (righteously) angry young professional in the early 1970's with a jaw-dropping command of his subjects.

His knowledge ranged from a command of psychiatric history, to little known knowledge of the influence of psychiatry on Nazi Germany and the Holocaust, to a far-ranging and detailed grasp of the science of the damaging effects of bio-psychiatry. Simultaneously Peter was able to intimately practice and publicly discuss the healing effects of psychotherapy and other human-relationship-based approaches to helping persons in emotional crisis. Many of these topics would become the later subjects of his books, articles and seminars.

Throughout our marriage I have worked closely with Peter and have seen countless clients come to him wounded, confused, deeply disturbed. Although I do not work in my husband's clinical practice, I often become acquainted with his patients in the waiting room, sometimes bringing them refreshment, sometimes chatting with them. I have witnessed the growth and healing of these many people whom we have had the privilege to have in our lives.

Simultaneously I have watched my husband step up, take a moral stand, and speak publicly to the abuses of his field as a scientist and an eloquent presenter. I have watched him jeered and catcalled by other psychiatrists who support shock treatment during his invited scientific presentation at the electroshock consensus conference at the National Institutes of Health (NIH) in the late 1980's. I have watched him taunted and belittled by CHADD leadership during the NIH Consensus Development Conference on Diagnosis and Treatment of Attention Deficit Hyperactivity Disorder in the late 1990s where he was again an invited scientific presenter.

I have watched my husband step up, take a moral stand, and speak publicly to the abuses of his field as a scientist and an eloquent presenter.

Most frightening to us were the six months during which Peter's medical license in Maryland was under attack. In 1987 the biopsychiatric and drug-company-supported parents' group NAMI made a formal complaint—misrepresenting Peter's public comments on an Oprah show—to the medical licensing board. When we received the notice of the investigation we faced the possibility that Peter might lose his license and thus his livelihood. Although it would have been a gross injustice, we were not naïve and knew that such injustices occur, especially when aimed at silencing important critics such as Peter was becoming.

Fortunately, NAMI's ill begotten attempt to silence Peter instead resulted in Peter being fully exonerated by the state licensing board and praised for his service. The national media attention generated by NAMI's unjust action resulted in major book publishers becoming interested in Peter's first popular book. Thus, Peter's bestseller *Toxic Psychiatry* was born.

Peter has tirelessly maintained his dignity, his poise and his empathy during these difficult times. He has drawn always from the science background from which he reaches his conclusions and never allows himself to be goaded into overstating his positions.

It might be enough to be a gifted therapist and a determined scientist as well as an inspired reformer and inspiring speaker. But Peter has also had the ability to carry his message to the public—well beyond the cloistered walls of his own profession or the arena of science itself. In this way my husband has enabled millions of persons throughout the world to be better warned of the potential hazards involved in being "treated" by biopsychiatry.

From *Oprah* to *Larry King Live, Sixty Minutes, 20/20, Court TV, Primetime, The O'Reilly Factor, Hannity and Colmes, the Rush Limbaugh Show, PBS* radio and television, *Radio Pacifica,* as well as hundreds of other talk shows and news shows, Peter has carried his message to the media and to the public. Virtually every significant print media outlet in the U.S. and many abroad have carried Peter's message including *Time Magazine, Newsweek, Forbes, Wall Street Journal, New York Times, Washington Post* and *Los Angeles Times.*

My husband is actually a private man. I have not ever seen him seek the spotlight merely for his own aggrandizement. He has always maintained a deep awareness of the millions of wounded and damaged human beings who are the victims of biopsychiatry, including involuntary treatment, drugs, electroshock and psychosurgery.

Peter remembers the millions of psychiatric patients who have suffered irreversible neurological damage such as tardive dyskinesia that has disfigured and crippled them, and the electroshock victims who have had permanent mental disabilities and memory loss with months to years of their lives obliterated. He carries with him the awareness of the countless children and adults who have become violent or suicidal on the SSRI antidepressants such as Prozac and Paxil. He never forgets the millions of children, some mere infants, some in utero, being emotionally and sometimes physically scarred through their exposure to stimulants as well as stronger psychiatric drugs such as antidepressants and the so-called antipsychotics.

Because Peter knows there are better ways to help these children and adults suffering emotional distress or crisis, he feels compelled to speak out about the brain damaging effects of the biopsychiatric approaches. These dangerous and flawed physiological approaches are neither the best nor should they be the last resort of mental health professionals and their patients.

Behind his ability to speak so clearly and confidently about these issues is my husband's precise scholarship and scientific command of the field of biological psychiatry as well as the related fields of psychotherapy, psychology and social work. When Peter was invited back to *Oprah* to debate the president of the American Psychiatric Association (APA), he was able to prove through his detailed knowledge of the APA's own published guidelines that the president of the APA was lying on the TV show about tardive dyskinesia statistics in an attempt to downplay the damage done by the so-called antipsychotic drugs. Peter was able to unmask the untruths on the air in the middle of that Oprah show because he had brought the APA book onto the set, anticipating the possible need to document his statistics.

Peter's ability to precisely explain how the science of his field fits into individual circumstances has enabled him to become a top-notch medical legal expert. Working with some very fine attorneys, Peter has been able to help achieve justice for many individual human beings who have been damaged by negligent psychiatric treatment. He has also been able to shine a spotlight on drug company malfeasance through worthy product liability suits in which he has participated as a medical expert.

Does Peter ever relax? Of course he does, in his own fashion. After seven solid hours at the computer writing his next book or working on a legal case, my husband will put on jeans and an old shirt and go move some small boulders around our yard, along with lots of mulch. Or he will spend a few hours filling several 30-gallon bags with weeds he pulls by hand. Occasionally he may fish for a while, until he catches a beautiful brown trout or a large-mouth bass. If hook extraction proves traumatizing to the fish, he quickly loses his taste for fishing, as he finds the fish beautiful and likes returning them to the lake whole. This empathic response has led to a number of our lures being modified so that the barbs are removed making it easy for caught fish to jump off the lure before being landed. Mostly he's given up fishing in favor of going down to the water at sunset, watching the lake waves, enjoying the evening birds, visiting with neighbors and playing with our Shelties.

We do like eating out. Our palates are probably underdeveloped and our preferred restaurants are the local diner near our home in the country and a diner in Ithaca. Sitting across from one another with cups of coffee and a satisfying plate of food lets us catch up, share new ideas about ongoing projects and talk about our lives together. Our children and now our grandchild are favorite subjects. When we aren't engaged in our own intense discussions we enjoy seeing our neighbors at the restaurant.

Meanwhile, in addition to his professional accomplishments as scientist, speaker, therapist, and reformer, I have watched my husband produce more than a dozen of his 20-plus books and dozens of peer-reviewed articles. His prodigious command of the material as well as his lightening writing ability (both the physical act of typing at over 100 words per minute and composing so quickly and so well) is breathtaking. These skills along with the advent of computers help explain his output.

One of the greatest gifts has been the number of individual professionals who have become cherished colleagues and friends. Life's demands don't allow enough time together but you are always with us in spirit and we draw strength every day from your support and friendship.

Peter founded the International Center for the Study of Psychiatry and Psychology (ICSPP) in the early 1970's as a support network of professionals and opinion leaders for him as he worked successfully toward stopping the resurgence of psychosurgery. Eventually ICSPP grew into a support network that boosts the morale and shares information among hundreds of professionals and laypersons concerned about psychiatric reform. The expanding scientific and reform work by a growing number of ICSPP members has been deeply gratifying and encouraging. From the scientists among you to the practitioners, to the parents who are speaking out, to the professionals who increasingly enlarge their own spheres of influence, and to those who have been injured by biological psychiatry, we draw strength and feel appreciation for your accomplishments. And your friendship always comforts us.

There is one additional quality that helps to explain my husband's accomplishments. He often claims that he has been able to achieve so much because he is incredibly persistent (some might even say, downright stubborn). But his character is more multifaceted than that. I believe that in addition to being my hero, Peter is a genius. He has gifts that he has honed and developed and drawn upon that enable him to have the positive impact he has on the lives of so many millions and upon our very world. I am grateful every day to be able to share in this amazing man's life and in his work.

Ginger Ross Breggin

Ginger Ross Breggin has co-authored two books with her husband: the bestseller Talking Back to Prozac *and* The War Against Children of Color. *She also coedited* Dimensions of Empathic Therapy *with her husband and an educator. For more than a decade she was Director of the International Center for the Study of Psychiatry and Psychology (ICSPP.org), when she developed the annual international conferences, newsletter and membership that exist today. She also conceived and co-founded ICSPP's scientific journal,* Ethical Human Psychology and Psychiatry, *and served as its first managing editor. She has been responsible for shaping the thrust and direction of the organization, as well as for maintaining it on a daily basis. Her outreach efforts have encouraged many professionals in the difficult task of creating a more ethical, caring approach to mental health problems. At the center's year 2000 international meeting, she was given the ICSPP Humanitarian Award "in recognition of unswerving resolve and advocacy on behalf of human rights and of providing the foundations for ICSPP's effectiveness." In addition, she has worked with her husband on numerous reform projects in psychiatry, including management of the successful campaign to stop the federal violence initiative, a racist program aimed at finding genetic and biochemical causes for violence in inner city children. A former journalist, editor, and public relations consultant, she continues to work closely with her husband in the development of his books and projects. While attending American University, she won the Honors Program award for the best social sciences research paper of the year in the university. She is also an award-winning photographer. Ginger is a proud mother and grandmother.*

Chapter Two

Reforming the "Snake Pits"

Introduction

Peter had just begun his major in American history and literature (an honors program) as a freshman at Harvard when a friend asked him if he wanted to volunteer at the new Harvard-Radcliffe Mental Hospital College Volunteer Program at nearby Metropolitan State Hospital. Eventually Peter became a director of the ground-breaking program, lectured about it to professional conferences, and formulated and helped to write a book describing the successes of volunteers in working with the most disturbed psychiatric inmates.

These experiences led Peter to go to medical school to become a psychiatrist. He did not anticipate that, within the next several years, psychiatry would become so dominated by pharmaceutical interests that the idea of volunteers offering caring human services as a treatment for disturbed hospital patients would become anathema.

The volunteer program flooded the hospital with hundreds of college students. In addition, Peter created a special case aide program where students worked with individual patients and he convinced the Harvard faculty to turn it into a seminar for academic credit. His understanding that caring relationships were the key to emotional recovery was strengthened by this experience. Both the larger group program and the case aide program are described in excerpts including those from *The President's Joint Commission on Mental Illness and Health* (1961) and the *Saturday Evening Post (1957).* Excerpts follow:

The President's Commission Lauds and Recommends the Harvard Volunteer Program. The Joint Commission on Mental Illness and Health, *Action for Mental Health* (1961, pp. 90-91).

The positive effects of this well-conceived and progressively systematized effort to improve the human condition and total outlook of rejected patients were readily apparent. Colorless, drab, despair-filled wards became brightly decorated, cheerful halls where patients, students, and increasingly the attendants talked, sang, smiled, and even laughed. Chronic patients became more active and enjoyed normal social contacts. By spending time with patients, the students learned information of therapeutic use to the doctors and the doctors in turn asked for help with certain patients. The volunteers were particularly useful with patients whose acute symptoms had long since subsided and who were ready for discharge except that there had been no one to prepare them for outside living. By the end of the first year, 11 of 15 patients visited by student case aides were released from the hospital, some to come back later, but others to remain in the community. The student assumed responsibility for meeting the patient's family, investigating placement in rest homes or job possibilities, and visiting the patients after their release.

Each volunteer had the same problem, whether working with an individual patient or a group: how to develop a relationship that would work toward the patient's recovery. Group discussions and professional consultation gave the volunteers the help they needed.

Helping State Mental Hospital Patients as a Harvard College Student Volunteer. "They Befriend the Mentally Ill," ***Saturday Evening Post,*** **October 5, 1957.**

Simply by being warmhearted, these volunteers from college campuses rescue mental patients from the abyss of loneliness. The doctors themselves heartily approve.... The college boys and girls, ranging in age from eighteen to twenty-four, are not only livening up the general social tempo of the hospital's "back" wards. Many are working intensively with individual patients who need emotional support in preparation for discharge, assisting them in locating jobs and places to live in the community.

Initiated and conducted entirely by students with little if any formal faculty backing, the project has won the warm endorsement of leading psychiatrists, including the hospital's superintendent, Dr. William F. McLaughlin; Dr. Jack R. Ewalt, Massachusetts Commissioner of Mental Health; and Dr. Milton Greenblatt, research director at the Massachusetts Mental Health Center, who serves as the volunteers' professional advisor...

Doctor McLaughlin says the students have benefited at least half of his 2000 patients, many of whom are seriously regressed schizophrenics....

Doctor Ewalt, noting that the Metropolitan State Hospital has the best discharge record of any hospital in his department, is inclined to give the students a large share of credit for this achievement. "If it can be adequately supervised," he added, "I would heartily recommend this program to other states. Student volunteers could do a lot to make up for the nationwide shortage in professional personnel, which today is the most urgent problem facing our mental-health administrators."

[P]atients would not have to play cards alone, or pretend to phone friends, or look for [imaginary] visitors with a pair of binoculars, if there were more volunteers; students like Larry and Michael Dohan, Peter Breggin and Peter Keese—the two Pete's were cochairmen of the Harvard program last semester....

....Although the type of therapy in which the students are participating is simple and logical in principle, Doctor Greenblatt points out, it has received all too little emphasis in recent years. The neglect has been due in part to personnel shortages and partly to preoccupation with shock therapy, psycho-surgery and the new drugs. All of these treatments have been highly useful, but more patients could be returned to life outside the hospital if they were given more opportunity for "resocialization" inside the hospital.

"Moreover, in a great many patients," Doctor Greenblatt says, "the psychosis which originally brought them to the hospital years ago has long since 'burned out.' One can now ask, how much of their trouble is 'patient disease.' Their motivation has run down for lack of social stimulation in the hospital atmosphere. The students provide just such a social stimulation—and very effectively. It has been estimated that a third of the patients now in mental hospitals could be discharged if this kind of attention could be made available to them."

Opposing Abuse and Promoting Caring Psychosocial Interventions. "A Psychotherapist Puts Down 'Shrinks" by Caryl Rivers, *The Washington Star*, August 3, 1976.

Peter Breggin's interest in the treatment of mental patients began when he was a [freshman] at Harvard in the late '50s and took part in a program in a state mental hospital. "It was very apparent to me that a lot of the patients' problems were caused by the hospital; they were suffering from their role as patients. They were drugged, humiliated and locked up against their will."

He was part of a group who worked with supposedly burnt-out patients in the back wards. Eleven of the 15 "incurable" patients were out of the hospital inside of a year....

Deciding to go to Medical School. "An Introduction by the advisors to the student volunteer program" by Milton Greenblatt, MD, Professor of Psychiatry, Harvard Medical School, and David Kantor, MSW in *College Students in a Mental Hospital—An Account of Organized Social Contacts Between College Volunteers and Mental Patients in a Hospital Community* by Carter C. Umbarger, James S. Dalsimer, Andrew P. Morrison and Peter R. Breggin (1962).

The four authors of this [book], all of whom were undergraduates at Harvard, contributed actively, as well as speculatively, to the Volunteer program. Carter Umbarger, Andrew Morrison, James Dalsimer and Peter Breggin all served it in leadership roles; it was Peter Breggin and Andrew Morrison who were instrumental in having an undergraduate course based on volunteer work at Metropolitan State introduced at Harvard. All four have continued their studies at the graduate level. It is characteristic of the career commitments made by the most highly motivated among the volunteers that Morrison, Dalsimer and Breggin entered medical school....All four have continued to occupy themselves with the problems of the mentally ill, and the care that is provided for them.

Residency Training. Robert Seidenberg, MD, Clinical Professor of Psychiatry, State University of New York, Syracuse, NY, 1987. From a letter written to the medical board in defense of Dr. Breggin during the attack against his medical license (chapter 5).

It is my pleasure to have known Peter R. Breggin, M.D. for over twenty–five years both as a student and colleague. I do not exaggerate when I say that Peter Breggin was the brightest and most capable resident in the life of our resident program here at Upstate SUNY. Even then he displayed the scholarship, erudition, and most of all, the unique sensitivity to human values so vital to our field.

I have followed his career closely, having read his books and scholarly papers. Those of us who have studied the history of the assaults against the brain through the centuries applaud Peter's clarion call for professional restraint. And, he has almost single-handedly succeeded in eliminating the shameful practices in the surgical and electrical fields. We are now in the midst of a chemical attack on brain tissue; here again because of his particular insight and expertise, it was clearly his professional responsibility to alert both practitioners and patients to the dangers of current therapies and to the existence of an alternative approach.

A Venture Into Fiction

After finishing his medical and psychiatric training, as well as two years on the staff of the National Institute of Mental Health (NIMH), Dr. Breggin went into private practice and teaching in 1968 and quickly published two novels, *The Crazy from the Sane* (1971) and *After the Good War* (1972). He had worked many years on *The Crazy from the Sane*, which tells the story of a young psychiatrist's crushing disillusionment with his profession.

By contrast, *After the Good War* was written in less than a year. It has been classified as "psychiatric science fiction" and received the largest advance that the publisher, Stein and Day, had ever given for a work of fiction.

Both books received good reviews but Dr. Breggin's love for writing fiction would soon be set aside in order to stop the return of lobotomy and newer forms of psychosurgery (chapter 3). Excerpts from reviews of Dr. Breggin's two novels follow.

Breggin's *"After the Good War"* Gets Record Advance. Stein and Day, Fall Catalog 1972.

Stein and Day has paid the highest fiction advance in its history for this novel, for good reason.

Retaining Humanity. Review of *The Crazy from the Sane* by Todd Gitlin, *Psychology Today,* February 1972.

The patients are beautifully drawn: in the desperate excesses of their feelings they try to keep their humanity while they resist the imprisoners....

Recommended for Psychiatrists. Review of *The Crazy from the Sane,* by Henry E. Jones, MD, psychiatrist, in *Reason,* August 1972.

Although anyone would enjoy the story and gain a perspective on the psychiatric profession, I particularly recommend the book to psychiatric residents, psychiatrists and psychotherapists.

Like Brave New World. Review of *After the Good War* by Paul Varnell, *Reason,* October 1974.

Taken altogether, the book is a clever and thought-provoking performance, told with sufficient distance and detachment so that the reader is prevented from watching the plot too exclusively and is encouraged to reflect on what he is reading. Breggin's ideas about the necessary nature of childhood, the development of the "self," the category "human being," and individuality properly understood (the real topics of this book) are well worth brooding on.

A Clever Book. Review of *After the Good War* by Cecil Richmond, *Indianapolis Star,* January 14, 1973.

...it's a clever book without being too slick, humorous without being ridiculous, and acutely apropos without being absurd.

Faint-hearted Beware. Review of ***After the Good War*** by William B. Hill, S.J., Chief Editor, ***Best Sellers Magazine,*** July 1, 1973.

Breggin takes contemporary trends and uses their own terms to satirize them cruelly and accurately. He strikes at a permissiveness which is based on the loss of all tradition at a fearfulness that places tremendous emphasis on conformity. It is a very clever work, but should be read only by those who are already steeped in the ugliness that it castigates.

Chapter Three

Stopping the Resurgence of Psychosurgery

Introduction

Dr. Breggin discovered in 1971 that lobotomy and newer forms of psychosurgery were being revived and promoted throughout the world. Dismayed, he decided to move beyond his psychotherapy office and his career as a writer into the wider arena of political reform on an international level.

At first it seemed few cared. Dr. Breggin eventually developed sufficient media coverage, along with a coalition that included U.S. Senators and Congressmen, that stopped the resurgence of this destructive "treatment" throughout much of the world. Dr. Breggin inspired and wrote the legislation that led to the Psychosurgery Commission. He also helped to write legislation calling for a ban on federal funding for psychosurgery, and while it failed to be passed, it drew media interest and had a chilling effect on the surgery. He testified before the U.S. Senate and several times in court against the treatment and wrote newspaper and peer reviewed journal articles criticizing psychosurgery.

The anti-psychosurgery project took up a large portion of several years of his life and he continues to look upon it as one of his most successful reform efforts. Where there were dozens of psychosurgery projects in the United States, Canada and Europe in the early '70s, now there are a very few that keep a low profile.

As a part of his international effort to stop psychosurgery, he developed the following projects during the 1970s:

- In 1972, Dr. Breggin founded the International Center for the Study of Psychiatry and Psychology (ICSPP.org) with a board of directors including psychiatrists and other mental health professionals, lawyers, consumers and several members of the U.S. Congress. In recent years, Dr. Breggin and his wife arranged for an orderly transition to new and younger leaders.

- Dr. Breggin wrote federal legislation to ban federal funding of psychosurgery that was introduced by the Congressional Black Caucus and other members of the U.S. Congress and Senate. The legislation did not pass but it had a chilling effect on any further funding for psychosurgery. He originated the idea and worked with members of the U.S. Senate to create the federal Psychosurgery Commission that investigated and eventually declared the treatment experimental and unsuitable for routine clinical application.

- Dr. Breggin helped to bring about and testified at the Kennedy Hearings on psychosurgery.

- He testified as the primary medical expert in the landmark legal case *Kaimowitz v. Department of Mental Health* in Michigan, a 1973 trial before a three-judge panel. Drawing on Dr. Breggin's ideas, the court's final opinion effectively stopped all psychosurgery in America's state mental hospitals (see ahead).

- He made innumerable TV and radio appearances, and hundreds of print media interviews, against psychosurgery. He also addressed professional conferences, including the American Psychiatric Association, the National Institute of Mental

Health (NIMH), the National Institutes of Health (NIH), the National Institute of Neurological Disease and Stroke (NINDS) and Harvard Medical School.

- He wrote numerous articles about psychosurgery for the public and the profession (e.g., Breggin 1972a-e, 1973a&b, 1975a&b, 1980, 1981b&c, 1983c).

- More recently, Dr. Breggin became the consultant and medical expert in the first successful psychosurgery malpractice case with a $7.5 million verdict against the Cleveland Clinic in June 2002. The Cleveland Clinic stopped performing psychosurgery and only two medical centers in the United States have been identified as continuing to conduct these mutilating procedures.

By the time it was over, Dr. Breggin's anti-psychosurgery campaign had stopped most projects in the United States, Canada and Europe. He was especially grateful to see an end to the "research" of O. J. Andy at the University of Mississippi in Jackson who had operated on several dozen black children as young as age five, planting multiple electrodes into their brains to stimulate them and then to burn psychosurgical holes in their frontal lobes and limbic system. His efforts also stopped a federally funded psychosurgery project on adults conducted in Boston by Harvard psychiatrist Frank Ervin and Harvard neurosurgeon Vernon Mark under the sponsorship of another Harvard neurosurgeon William Sweet.

The following section and numerous others throughout this book provide excerpts from the media, scientific journals, and related sources about Dr. Breggin's reform work. They are supplemented by commentaries from his colleagues. The media section in this chapter is especially rich with documentation of his efforts.

Media Supports Breggin Campaign

Breggin Unleashes Criticism. "Psychiatry as a Tool of the State," by Robert Trotter, *Science News*, February 17, 1973.

Concern about the misuses of psychiatry is not confined to incidents in the Soviet Union. In the United States, an outspoken Washington psychiatrist, Peter R. Breggin, last year unleashed a torrent of abuse on psychosurgery.

***Newsweek* Covers the Start of the Campaign Against Psychosurgery. "Psychosurgery Under Fire," *Newsweek*, March 27, 1972.**

With the advent of tranquilizer drugs in the early 1950s, the brain operation known as lobotomy fell into relative disuse. And that, most people agreed, was a good thing. For while a lobotomy, which involves severing nerve fibers in the brain's frontal lobes, frequently serves to give a psychotic relief from his symptoms, it is also all too apt to dull his emotions and intellect.

Tranquilizers, however, are not a total answer to the problems of psychosis and so, in recent years, neurosurgeons have developed more precise methods of "psychosurgery" that are said to remove symptoms of extreme psychosis without the lobotomy's appalling side effects. But now a Washington, D.C. psychiatrist is questioning both the methods and the motives of today's psychosurgeons. He charges that many of the 400 to 600 psychosurgical operations carried out annually in the U.S. involve patients whose disorders are far from extreme, and that the result of the procedures is to leave the patients docile and tame.

..."At worst," states Dr. Peter R. Breggin in a highly controversial article in *Medical Opinion and Review*, psychosurgical operations "are irreversibly damaging to the patient's self. At the very least they are blunting the patient's emotional responses."

...At the crux of the issue is the ongoing controversy over the cause of major psychiatric illness. According to the neurosurgeons, the cause is usually biological...Breggin disagrees. "Mental patients are largely victims," he says, adding however, that where biological function is the cause there is still no justification for interfering haphazardly with the brain's biology.

***Time* Acknowledges the Anti-Psychosurgery Campaign. "Psychosurgery Returns," *Time Magazine,* April 3, 1972.**

Now, psychosurgery appears to be undergoing a renaissance. Though various old-style lobotomies have been abandoned, some doctors are turning once more to surgery to control the emotions...

There are those who believe that brain surgery has sinister implications. Dr. Peter Breggin, a Washington D.C. psychiatrist, thinks that any operation that alters the personality partially kills the individual and should therefore be outlawed. He also suggests that doctors are operating on emotions, indiscriminately calming down prisoners, mental patients, and hyperkinetic children to make them easier to handle, and tranquilizing neurotic housewives....

***Science* Acknowledges the Psychosurgery Debate. "Psychotherapy: Legitimate Therapy or Laundered Lobotomy?" *Science,* March 16, 1973.**

If any single individual is responsible for getting the [psychosurgery] issue out in the open, it is Peter Breggin, a Washington psychiatrist who writes "brave new world" novels about psychosurgery. Breggin opposes any and all psychosurgery on the grounds that the operations have a general blunting effect on emotions and thought processes and that there is no theoretical or empirical justification for any of them.....

Federal Legislation to Put a Moratorium on Funding Psychosurgery and on Practicing Psychosurgery in Federal Facilities. In the U.S. Senate, Senator J. Glenn Beall, Jr., on behalf of himself, Mr. Dominick and Mr. Buckley in support of S.J. Res. 86, Joint Resolution to suspend projects involving psychosurgery, *Congressional Record,* Volume 119, No. 49, the 93d Congress, First session, March 29, 1973. Senator Beall met personally with Dr. Breggin who recommended and helped to write the proposed legislation.

Mr. President, I am sending to the desk a joint resolution that would, if enacted, declare a 2-year moratorium on the use of Federal funds and Federal facilities in projects involving the medical procedures known collectively as psychosurgery or psychiatric surgery... Mr. President, my interest was aroused last year when I read an article entitled "Eerie Brain Surgery—A curse, or a Blessing." ... Dr. Peter R. Breggin, a practicing psychiatrist in the District of Columbia, vigorously raised the ethical issue of psychosurgery with several of its practitioners. ... Dr. Breggin, who has emerged as a prominent spokesman in opposition to psychosurgery, expressed another area of concern when he summed up his views stating that:

> The real issues are not scientific or technical. The real issues are moral, political and spiritual. What is a man—a machine, device, a space filled with molecules? ... And how should man best live—under the control of others through behavioral modification, or to the best of his capacities within an environment that respects his freedom and his unique human and spiritual quality?

Early Successes in Stopping Psychosurgery. "Spectrum" by M. Stanton Evans, CBS Radio Network, April 1, 1974.

The [International Center for the Study of Psychiatry and Psychology] was founded three years ago to combat attempts to alter patterns of human consciousness and behavior by the use of surgery, drugs and other mind-destroying practices. On the findings of the Center's executive director, Dr. Peter Breggin, these appalling techniques have begun to spread quite widely in recent years.

Breggin cites case histories of people blinded by pre-frontal lobotomies, children whose brains have been coagulated by electroshock and prisoners submitted to mutilating operations. Other topics of concern to Breggin and his cohorts include "the massive use of drugs and electroshock in prisons and hospitals, the drugging of hyperactive children….and the use of biologic psychiatry to explain and control….dissent and violence."

A principal goal of the Center has been to halt federal funding of experimentation with human beings, and it has scored some notable successes. The National Institute of Mental Health has terminated a one million dollar research grant in support of psychosurgery, and turned down another request of similar magnitude. The Law Enforcement Assistance Administration has said it will no longer support psychosurgery projects, and a new federal prison facility has curtailed plans for behavior modification activity.

It is understandable that the Center has attracted broad support. For what is at stake here is the very question of human personality itself, versus the chilling view that human beings can be treated as objects of experimentation….

The Ralph Nader of Psychiatry. "Peter Breggin: the Ralph Nader of Psychiatry," ***The Drummer,*** **Philadelphia, February 1975.**

Peter Breggin is a crusader, not a dreamer. He's the 38-year-old Ralph Nader of psychiatry, and he's put an entire field of psychiatric research and development—psychosurgery—on the defensive. Breggin, a psychiatrist himself, thinks psychosurgery should be outlawed. The psychosurgeons, of course, defend their practices vehemently....

When Breggin first became aware of the reappearance of psychosurgery as a psychiatric cure, he thought it was being performed only in rare cases. But he set out to research and document its use anyway. What he found startled him: 600 to 1000 such operations each year. He compiled details of almost 100 of them in a research document titled "The Return of Lobotomy and Psychosurgery."...

Breggin isn't satisfied with his successes in stopping psychosurgery, nor does he confine his tactics to hoping and crying out.

"I think we've put a real stopper on psychosurgery, but that's just a tiny skirmish," Breggin warns. "The battle against psychiatric fascism is just beginning."

A "Little Murder." Report by Gary Grassel, ***The Advocate*** **(An Independent Paper Published by and for HEW Employees), April 1972.**

Dr. Breggin calls psychosurgery "a little murder" that "partially kills the self."

Dr. Breggin, who has been chiefly instrumental in revealing the present resurgence of psychosurgery, strongly opposes lobotomy and psychosurgery and believes that only Federal legislation can put a stop to these mutilating operations. He urges interested people to write in support of such legislation to their Congressmen...

The Battle of Boston

Boston became the most hard-fought arena in the anti-psychosurgery campaign as Dr. Breggin zeroed in on stopping the experimental surgery, for the control of violence, being conducted by three highly connected Harvard professors—neurosurgeon Vernon Mark and psychiatrist Frank Ervin with the help of neurosurgeon William Sweet who was director of neurosurgery at the famed Massachusetts General Hospital (MGH). Dr. Breggin traveled to Boston many times to appear on the radio and TV, and to lecture at Harvard College, Harvard Medical School and other academic centers. A great deal of credit goes to *Boston Globe* reporter Jean Dietz who dared to cover the controversy and to give voice to Dr. Breggin's criticisms of several of the most powerful physicians in her hometown and in America.

Attracting Nationwide Attention and Taking the Campaign to Boston. "Brain Surgery—Therapy or Tampering" by Jean Dietz, *Boston Globe,* April 17, 1972.

Dr. Peter Breggin, the young Washington, D.C. psychiatrist who has attracted nationwide publicity with his campaign against psychosurgery, was in Boston recently to debate his claim that researchers here are fostering brain operations to "pacify" potential radicals and "convert rebellious females into docile housewives." "Investigations show that the majority of these pacification operations are being performed on women," Breggin contended at an exclusive interview. "They blunt the emotions and subdue behavior by reducing the drive system of the individuals and pulling the roots out of their intellectual life."

"You can't tamper with the frontal lobes without reducing all creativity, a person's perseverance as well as the ability to get angry."

Virtually a One-Man Effort. "Senate Urged to Kill 'Brain' Study" by Jean Dietz, *Boston Sunday Globe,* September 24, 1972.

Until this week, the drive against so-called "psychosurgery" has been virtually a one-man effort by Dr. Peter R. Breggin... Breggin has charged that the $1 million proposition to continue the study of violent behavior related to brain disease supports the type of "brain surgery for criminals and other violent individuals" now being conducted at Boston City Hospital in affiliation with Massachusetts General (MGH). ... "I thought we had them stopped. This item in the bill took me by surprise," Breggin said Friday. ...

According to Breggin, Sweet and Mark advocated the use of amygdalotomy, a neurosurgical operation in which small portions of the brain are destroyed by electrodes, for the cure or control of violence associated with psychomotor epilepsy.

Breggin says the operation "has nothing to do with epilepsy." He claims that the operation "blunts the emotions" in anyone, whether they suffer from epilepsy or not. He describes the procedure as a "partial deadening of the individual, a partial murder of the living person."

Dr. Breggin Thanks the *Boston Globe* and Challenges the Psychosurgeons. "Brain Surgery," Letter to the Editor by Peter R. Breggin, MD, *Boston Globe,* October 20, 1972.

I want to commend you on Jean Dietz's thorough and unbiased coverage (Sept. 24) of the controversial brain surgery for violence being performed at Boston City Hospital by Drs. Vernon Mark and William Sweet.

The US Senate has now added significant restraints to the original allocation of $1 million for the continuation of their work. Specifically, Sen. Warren Magnuson; Chairman of the Senate Appropriations Subcommittee Labor-HEW, which allocated the money, has placed a letter in the *Congressional Record* re-instructing the National Institute of Health "to delay this funding at this time" until the Institutes can conduct an investigation into the "several disturbing published reports" about the work at Boston City Hospital.

The Institute has replied that it will form a task force to investigate the problem.

Meanwhile, to alert the public further to the personal and political dangers inherent in this work, I want to repeat my long-standing offer to join in a public debate in Boston any day, any evening with anyone representing the position that brain surgery should be used for the control of violence.

The Anti-Psychosurgery Campaign Heats Up. "Boston's Psychosurgery: Success and Controversy" by Jean Dietz, *Boston Globe*, January 21, 1973.

Dr. Peter Breggin, a young Harvard-trained psychiatrist who practices in Washington, D.C., contends that at least 1000 patients in the US have been recent victims of so-called "psychosurgery" defined as destruction or mutilation of healthy parts of the brain in order to affect the individual's emotions and personal conduct.

The work of Dr. Mark and his former psychiatric colleague Dr. Frank Ervin has been a prime target for Breggin's attacks, collated in two lengthy articles inserted in the *Congressional Record* by Rep. Cornelius E. Gallagher of New Jersey.

"Mini-lobotomy" is Breggin's catchall term for describing various operations performed by a number of surgeons, a vague phrase which particularly angers most doctors. Of all forms of new surgery, Breggin calls Mark's amygdalotomy "the pacification operation par excellence" because he says the amygdala is the major "moderator and switchboard for the entire limbic system and hence for all emotions and drives, and even for all higher level activities through its connections to the frontal lobes."

"Destroying the amygdala to cure one symptom such as violence makes no more sense than bombing a railway center to stop one passenger on one train," contends Breggin. "The symptom may be knocked out, but many other tracks and greater numbers of humanity will be brought to a halt."

"A Clockwork Orange? Psychiatric Experimentation on Prisoners," was the topic of a conference held at the University of California Medical Center in San Francisco where Dr. Breggin spoke on the technique, applications and politics of brain surgery.

"Psychosurgery is the quintessence of the technological control of human beings," Breggin told the audience. "It has powerful potential for the future as well as grave political implications, which are already evolving."

At a conference in Houston on "Neural Bases of Violence and Aggression," Breggin made national headlines with charges that psychosurgeons, including the Boston group, are "promoting mutilative brain surgery under the academic umbrella of pure research."

The issue had become so hot by last month that Boston University undergraduates turned out in a blinding snowstorm at the start of exam period to hear Breggin share his fears of "a new wave of lobotomies" aimed at "relatively well functioning individuals who live at home and hold jobs or who are diagnosed as neurotic women or as the new breed of prison revolutionaries."

The Kennedy Hearings

On his many trips to Boston, Dr. Breggin confronted Senator Ted Kennedy, Chairman of the Senate Committee on Health, by demanding in the media that Kennedy hold hearings on psychosurgery and come out against it. Kennedy, in fact, did not want to criticize the medical establishment, especially several of the most influential and respected psychiatrists and neurosurgeons in Boston who were under attack from Dr. Breggin. Meanwhile, Dr. Breggin received an anonymous brown envelope with pictures and medical records demonstrating that Rosemary Kennedy had been lobotomized.

Threatened with the prospect of Dr. Breggin releasing these documents at a time before anyone knew the story, Kennedy held hearings. Dr. Breggin was invited to testify; but Kennedy actively defended psychosurgery. In the following news story, the *Boston Globe* covers an interchange between Dr. Breggin and psychosurgeon O. J. Andy at the Senate hearings:

Drs. Breggin and Andy Debate at the Kennedy Hearings on Psychosurgery. "On Surgery in Mental Ills" by Charles E. Claffey, *Boston Globe*, February 24, 1973.

Washington—Medical experts differed radically yesterday on whether the practice of psychosurgery is helpful or harmful to patients with mental disorders....

Dr. Andy argued that there are many patients who do not respond to drug therapy for their mental ills, but for whom surgery has beneficial results. Some drugs, he added, have detrimental side effects.

Dr. Peter R. Breggin, a Washington physician, challenged Dr. Andy's findings, and characterized surgery to correct mental disorders as a form of "mutilation of the brain." He said that some of Dr. Andy's statements were "outright false," and stated that any type of psychosurgery "should be made illegal."

"It is time to take the power over mind and spirit away from the professionals. Lobotomy and psychosurgery is an ethical, political and spiritual problem. It should be controlled through the democratic process, not through professional review. It should be made illegal," Dr. Breggin said.

Signaling a Grave Danger. "Opponent Sees 'Grave Danger' in New Psychosurgery Effort by Hub Team" by Jean Dietz, *Boston Globe*, May 24, 1973.

There is "grave danger" that there will be tests of the effectiveness of psychosurgery on violent and potentially violent persons in the Boston area....

Dr. Peter Breggin, who directs the Project to Examine Psychiatric Technology at the Washington School of Psychiatry, told a meeting at Harvard Medical School that a Boston City Hospital group is seeking a $1 million grant from the National Institute of Health to fund a new study of "violence and psychosurgery and hormonal research on dangerous persons."

Breggin identified the local group, headed by Dr. Vernon Mark of Harvard Medical School, as "people who have lied in reporting the success of their cases in books and in medical journals."

Other doctors in the group seeking new funds are Ira Sherwin, John Lyon and Dietrich Blumer, according to Breggin, who calls for outlawing psychosurgery in the United States.

The Washington psychiatrist made a sweeping series of statements comparing the investigations of the Neuro-Research Foundation of Boston to the "maltreatment of mental patients in Nazi Germany."

He said members of the foundation including Mark, Dr. William Sweet of Massachusetts General Hospital and Dr. Frank Ervin, now Professor of psychiatry at University of California in Los Angeles, have obtained large Federal grants in the past.

Breggin spoke after an active day of radio, newspaper and television interviews, and efforts to obtain the records of one of Mark's former patients from Massachusetts General Hospital.

The Thomas R. Story

Dr. Breggin was critical of the work by neurosurgeon Vernon Mark, psychiatrist Frank Ervin, and neurosurgeon William Sweet. Examining their publications, Dr. Breggin concluded that the doctors were misrepresenting their own facts about their most famous case, Thomas R.

The mother of psychosurgery victim Thomas R. only discovered what had happened to her son when a friend told her that it sounded like Dr. Breggin was describing her son when publicly criticizing the psychosurgeons. Up until that moment, Thomas' mother thought that her son was completely disabled by severe schizophrenia.

In fact, Thomas R. had been a brilliant engineer who was having conflicts with his wife when his wife's psychiatrist sent him to Vernon Mark's psychosurgery project. Although Mark, Ervin and Sweet had claimed that they cured Thomas of his violence literally without any side effects, they had destroyed his mental functioning, turning him into a chronically disabled psychotic mental patient who spent most of his time on the wards of a VA hospital.

Nor was there any prior record of violence, other than throwing a can of food on one occasion without hitting anyone. Thomas was hiding his head under newspapers in fear of being assaulted by Boston doctors when Dr. Breggin met and evaluated him at his mother's home on weekend leave from a chronic VA ward.

Dr. Breggin obtained Thomas' medical records and assisted his mother (Thomas' guardian) in finding a lawyer to sue Mark and Ervin. Because of his involvement in exposing the damage to Thomas and in bringing the suit, Dr. Breggin did not testify.

Harvard doctors lined up to support the experimental psychosurgery as if it were routine medical care and the malpractice suit was lost. But the publicity devastated Mark and Ervin, and contributed to the demise of their psychosurgery project.

Mark and Ervin Are Sued by Mother of Thomas R. "Hub Psychosurgery Draws $2 Million Suit" by Jean Dietz, *Boston Globe*, December 10, 1973.

The complaint charges the doctors with "publicly disclosing the private facts of the plaintiff's life in an objectionable manner." It states that the doctors presented "the plaintiffs life and medical history to the public eye in a false light without prior consent" with the result, it says, that Mark and Ervin "have been unjustifiably enriched."

The case has been a topic of discussion here since the visit of Dr. Peter Breggin, a Washington psychiatrist who came to Boston on Nov. 27 for a speaking engagement at Tufts.

Breggin, who has conducted a nationwide campaign against psychosurgery, said he received a letter from the patient's mother in which she wrote: "I am the mother of a patient of Dr. Mark and Dr. Ervin…The poor guy has been almost a vegetable since. I wonder if you would be interested in checking his case. We know he was destroyed by that operation."

Breggin said he came to Boston "to make sure the press knows about the case."

He said he also wanted to announce formation of a new, nonprofit "Center for the Study of Psychiatry" in Washington, D.C.…

Banning Psychosurgery—The Groundbreaking Kaimowitz Case

Citing Dr. Breggin's testimony, the three-judge panel in the psychosurgery case *Kaimowitz v. Department of Mental Health* banned psychosurgery in Michigan's state mental hospitals, effectively stopping all psychosurgery in state hospitals in the United States. Prior to making their decision, the judges released the patient despite the state hospital's contention that he was so dangerous that only psychosurgery could facilitate his release.

Taking the Anti-Psychosurgery Campaign to Court. "Psychosurgery Will Face Key Test in Court Today," *The New York Times*, March 12, 1973.

Detroit, March 11—For the last 18 of his 36 years, Mr. L. has lived the life of a forgotten man. An alleged murderer and rapist who is reported to have a life-long history of uncontrollable rages, he has spent all his adult years behind the locked doors of a state institution for the criminally insane.

Until three months ago there seemed little chance that this man, who is said to have above-average intelligence, would ever be considered sufficiently 'cured' to be released. Then he was selected to participate in a research project in which brain surgery might be used to try to control his violent behavior.

But no sooner was this door to a possible new life opened than it was shut by a court suit that challenged the project on ethical, legal, and medical grounds.

Tomorrow a three-judge panel in Wayne County Circuit Court here will begin to hear the precedent-setting case [brought by attorney Gabe Kaimowitz], thrusting Mr. L. into the center of a mounting national controversy over the use of brain surgery to erase the symptoms of otherwise untreatable behavioral and emotional disorders.

At the center of the controversy is a debate over the purpose, effectiveness, side-effects—indeed, the very nature—of psychosurgery, a modern technique by which tiny portions of tissue deep in the brain are destroyed through surgery, electricity, radiation or ultrasound.

....The case here is part of a continuing struggle by some lawyers and doctors....to bring psychosurgery under tight public control, if not ban it altogether.

A leader in this fight has been Dr. Peter R. Breggin, a physician and novelist who is on the staff of the Washington School of Psychiatry and who entered his objections at great length into *The Congressional Record* last year.

Among the fears of those who have joined Dr. Breggin's cause are that psychosurgery might be used as a weapon for controlling violent prisoners, institutionalized patients or political activists (such a suggestion was raised in connection with the 1967 Detroit riots) and that medicine might use psychosurgery as an "easy way out" instead of trying to correct underlying social causes of mental illness and providing conservative psychotherapy for all who need it....

But before any electrodes could be implanted in Mr. L's brain, Gabe Kaimowitz, a civil liberties lawyer on the staff at Wayne State University, filed a suit contending that the patients at Ionia (all potential subjects in the study) were being unconstitutionally detained and should be released; that no person involuntarily detained could consent to any form of experimentation, and that psychosurgery, in any case, was against public policy and must be stopped.

"Psychosurgery is designed to correct or control behavior," Mr. Kaimowitz said. "There is no manifestation of disease or illness as we know it ....

Liberating the Potential Psychosurgery Victim. "Mental Patient John Doe Ordered Freed," ***Detroit News,*** **April 5, 1973.**

A 37-year-old state mental patient, who once faced experimental brain surgery to control his supposed aggression, will be freed next Monday unless further legal action blocks his release....

Threats Against Dr. Breggin

Psychosurgeons and psychiatrists who supported psychosurgery reacted with a variety of threats against Dr. Breggin and his anti-psychosurgery campaign. In May 1973 Dr. Breggin attended a seminar put on by several psychosurgeons at the annual convention of the American Psychiatric Association in Hawaii. The psychosurgery advocates were very disturbed to see him in the audience.

When Dr. Breggin presented evidence against psychosurgery, the panel was enraged and one of the surgeons, M. Hunter Brown, indirectly threatened his life. Fortunately, Dr. Breggin's tape recorder picked up the entire exchange. Some of the media, including the famous columnist Jack Anderson, then wrote about the threats. Soon after, legislation was passed in California requiring informed consent for psychosurgery, including independent medical evaluations. The medical board criticized M. Hunter Brown when he failed to comply, and he stopped doing psychosurgery.

"Get Breggin" by syndicated columnist Jack Anderson, *Washington Post,* June 11, 1973.

The nation's most outspoken foe of psychosurgery, psychiatrist Peter Breggin, has been warned that several ex-convicts are out to "get" him. Apparently they believe in the psychosurgery he opposes to probe the brain and modify violent behavior. Breggin calls this "partial murder" because it blunts the patients' personality. The warning that ex-inmates might seek reprisals against him, Breggin says, came from a California psychosurgeon who claims to have performed 300 behavioral operations. Breggin quotes Hunter Brown as telling him: "I am in close correspondence with some prisoners at San Quentin, sixty of whom wish to have psychiatric surgery. The word has gotten around that the first man who is paroled—and this is a real risk, Peter, seriously—the word is to 'get Breggin.' This is the truth and I can document it."

At least three members of Congress including Sen. James Buckley (Cons-R-N.Y.) and Rep. Ron Dellums (D-Calif.) have written to California Attorney General Evelle Younger expressing concern over the alleged threats.

Libel and Slander

At the same seminar put on by the psychosurgeons and their advocates at the annual meeting of the American Psychiatric Association in 1973, a powerful Boston psychiatrist named Leo Alexander slandered Dr. Breggin in front of the entire audience of professional persons.

Dr. Breggin had already been critical of Alexander on two counts: First, Alexander supported lobotomy; and second, he had been the American medical and psychiatric investigator at the Nuremberg Trials and had failed to bring even the most brutal of Hitler's psychiatrists to justice. In addition, prior to World War II, Alexander had co-authored a book that openly praised Hitler's eugenic programs.

To add insult to injury, Alexander later falsely claimed to have written the Nuremberg Code when in fact he had nothing to do with it. Alexander must have felt the pressure of Dr. Breggin's criticism and responded by libeling him in medical journals and slandering him at the psychosurgery meeting in Hawaii where the psychosurgeon M. Hunter Brown also threatened his life.

Armed with the same tape recording that caught M. Hunter Brown's threats, Dr. Breggin brought a libel and slander suit against Alexander. The pro-lobotomy electroshock psychiatrist settled for $30,000 in 1973, at the time an enormous sum for Dr.

Breggin who was barely surviving economically during the early years of reform work.

Psychiatry Strikes Back. "A Psychotherapist Puts Down 'Shrinks" by Caryl Rivers, *Washington Star*, August 3, 1976.

Dr. Peter Breggin relaxes in the backyard of his suburban home....He is casually dressed in sports shirt and slacks and his full face is friendly and open. He does not look like a heretic. He is one; or that is how he thinks others perceive him.

Breggin is one of the country's most outspoken critics of psychiatry. He has vigorously attacked the profession for psychosurgery—operating on the brain—and for the use of electroshock, the practice of jolting mental patients with electric shock to help "cure" them.

Breggin, a [psychiatrist] psychotherapist himself, has been denounced, attacked and defamed—he accepted a $30,000 out-of-court settlement after he sued another psychiatrist for libel....

Psychiatry on the Defensive. "Peter Breggin's Private War" by Robert J. Trotter, *Human Behavior*, November, 1973.

A whole field of psychiatric research and technology has been put on the defensive by one man. The field is psychosurgery, a form of brain surgery used to modify behavior. The man is Peter Roger Breggin, a 37-year-old psychiatrist and novelist who works in Washington, D.C. For the past two years, he has been saying that all forms of psychosurgery should be outlawed because they represent the grossest kind of mutilation of brain tissue. The surgeons, of course, feel their work is a scientifically sound method of treating some cases of mental illness....

There is no doubt that the lobotomies were effective in calming and controlling the patients but, explains Breggin, "destruction of frontal lobe tissue is immediately reflected in a progressive loss of all those human functions related to the frontal lobes—insight, empathy, sensitivity, self-awareness and so on." And follow-up studies of these patients show that surgery did not help them at all. "In fact," says Breggin, "they were severely brain damaged and there was a high mortality rate."

The man who has been so vocal about what he calls "one of the horrors of psychiatry" is surprisingly soft-spoken and almost gentle. But when he makes his numerous charges against psychosurgery and psychiatry, he becomes a different more intense person. He changes from warm and playful to hard and serious. Breggin is a small man with deep-set eyes, wavy salt-and-pepper hair and a trim athletic body. Under most circumstances—in his small office at the Washington School of Psychiatry, in a restaurant or at home—he is completely at ease. Discussing himself, the weather or almost anything except psychiatry, he speaks in a relaxed, quiet voice. But when the talk turns to the thing he says he knows most about, psychiatry, he goes through a perceptible change. He sits forward a bit, his green eyes open wider and he begins to speak a little louder and faster. The words and ideas begin to fly. When he gets started on psychosurgery, he can go on nonstop for a half hour or more punctuating his monologue with names, dates, facts, figures, quotations, and

The man who has been so vocal about what he calls "one of the horrors of psychiatry" is surprisingly soft-spoken and almost gentle. But when he makes his numerous charges against psychosurgery and psychiatry, he becomes a different, more intense person.

journal references. During such discussions, Breggin's otherwise ever-present smile and sense of humor begin to fade. It becomes quite clear that psychiatry and psychosurgery are things he feels strongly about.

"The 1930s in psychiatry," Breggin says, "were very similar to what we are getting into again. The notion was that there was such a thing as mental illness, that it was biological and genetic and that people should be castrated and given lobotomies. I think it is a continuation of the behavior modification approach to human beings. The move goes from drugs to electroshock to psychosurgery and castration to extermination. Germany simply had the most advanced psychiatry at the time and came up with the Final Solution. And the history of the Final Solution confirms what I have more recently found in the campaign against lobotomy and psychosurgery: psychiatry cannot be left alone to police itself."

How can a man who feels this way about psychiatry call himself a psychiatrist and continue to see patients? Breggin says there are alternatives to what is usually called psychiatry.... "To me, the basic principle is that, given a free society, people will develop these alternatives. If the problems of guilt, shame, anxiety, depression and psychosis were not under the control of this viciously totalitarian system that we call psychiatry, lots of alternatives could be implemented....

"What I hope to do is actually cut into this psychiatric hegemony, monopoly and power," he says. "You know, if psychiatry didn't have the alternatives of involuntary treatment, electroshock, drugs and psychosurgery, psychiatry might even develop some alternatives."

Where will the attack on psychiatry lead? Breggin has formed a Nader-like institute, the Center for the Study of Psychiatry, that will provide an alternative for people to turn to on issues of psychiatry and behavior modification. As a nonprofit research and educational organization, it will examine the impact of psychiatric theory and practice upon personal freedom and privacy, individual rights and civil liberties….

As Peter Breggin puts it, "Institutional psychiatry is an oppressive force. And once you begin to face oppression, it becomes both a personal and a political process. You become interested in the overall oppression in society. You become a freedom fighter."

Peter Breggin's Humanism in Clinical Behavioral Science: the Early Years

by Robert J. Grimm, MD

In late 1972 Stevie Remington of Oregon's ACLU asked me to review an Oregon legislative proposal, S.B. 298 by Senator Halleck, to regulate lobotomy and Electro-Convulsive Therapy (ECT) on patients in state institutions. At the time, I thought that lobotomies—invented by Edgar Moniz in 1936 and widely practiced in the United States (Freeman & Watts, 1942) through the early 1960's—had gone the way of the Dodo and been replaced by drug treatments.

By this time in 1972, Vonnegut's *Titans of Siren* (1959)—the use of brain stimulation for mind control had been published; Kesey's *One Flew Over the Cuckoo's Nest* (1962)—the dreary side of mental institutions in that era was scheduled to be filmed at Oregon State Hospital (1974); Crichton's *Terminal Man* (1972) was in the bookshops—brain stimulation to prevent a temporal lobe epileptics rage attacks (which don't exist in epileptics), and Opton and Stender's concerns regarding psychosurgery and brain stimulation on California prisoners—"A Clockwork Orange at UCLA")— was being circulated.

Vernon Mark and Frank Ervin's *Violence in the Brain* (1970) was published three years after their famous letter (with W. Sweet of Harvard) in JAMA (1967) recommending that the black leaders of the Detroit riots ought to have their brains examined (literally) for EEG substrate abnormalities underlying their putative anger. At the time, the neurosurgery service at Boston City Hospital offered experimental stereotaxic amygdalotomies, Mark and Ervin's program for the bona fide aggressive. Overarching the times: Aldous Huxley's *Brave New World* (1939) and *Brave New World Revisited* (1966), freshened by Orwell's *1984,* were road maps to such dark futures.

Brain control was in the air.

At the time into a conventional teaching and research life, and running a residency program, my awareness of the medicalization of mental illness, let alone its implications, was about zero. I had read Huxley and Orwell but their message had been mindlessly filed despite their relevance to the very experimental work I was doing at the time; viz. I trained monkeys to perform a repetitive task, e.g., to touch a sequence of elevator-like buttons. When they did this up to speed, they were rewarded by a brief electrical stimulus from implanted electrodes in their pleasure center. During performances, I recorded the discharge from engaged single cerebellar neurons. *Brave New World* or *1984* were nowhere in sight.

In response to the ACLU request about psychosurgery, I curtailed my work and learned that women with intractable hand-washing compulsions had the option in one Portland hospital of having a coagulating depth electrode placed in cingulate gyrus to destroy the alleged hand-washing center, promising a more hopeful future. I canvassed colleagues, students, mentors, and acquaintances regarding lobotomies, read the literature of the day, including Peter Breggin's 1972 *Congressional Record* anti-lobotomy piece (Breggin, 1972a) and his other writings about the Boston City amygdalotomy program for treating "violence" (e.g., Breggin, 1972b, 1975). I knew then I was not alone. Here was a comrade-in-arms with a wider, deeper view, sensitive to the im-

I knew then I was not alone. Here was a comrade-in-arms with a wider, deeper view, sensitive to the implications of psychosurgery, drugs, and brain stimulation aimed at fixing errant brains.

plications of psychosurgery, drugs, and brain stimulation aimed at fixing errant brains rather than a progenitor, dysfunctional society.

I provided the ACLU with a position paper in opposition to both psychosurgery and brain stimulation in all adults, not just the institutionalized, and so testified in the Oregon Legislature. This angered S.B. 298's author Senator Halleck who said, "If you don't like this bill, write it yourself." Together with my colleagues Dr. Don Rushmer and Henry Craword of the Oregon Medical Association (to provide a bit of political cover), we did just that. In essence, S.B 298's rewrite said that psychosurgery could be done in Oregon on adults if four conditions were met: (1) The psychiatric diagnosis was clear; (2) all available therapies had failed; (3) there was a truly informed consent regarding the nature of the proposed procedure; and (4) that said procedure was established in the literature and curative for the specific psychiatric condition. Viewed as eminently sensible, S.B 298 passed both houses of the Oregon legislature without a dissenting vote and was signed into law by Governor McCall. As the fourth provision was unsupportable by the psychosurgery literature of the day, the revised bill ended lobotomy in Oregon in 1973. The hand that guided me was Peter's.

After the passage of the Oregon lobotomy bill, I was called by Philadelphia lawyer Lawrence Elliot Hirsch to testify in a trial on a young man left partially paralyzed after his 3rd lobotomy. The year was 1975. The CT scan of his brain was unforgettable: his frontal cortex had been replaced by a cyst and he had no ability to edit old memories.

As it turned out, Peter was also on the case and we met. The impact on me of our meeting amplified my understanding of the ethical issues associated with lobotomy and other mind-altering practices, and for me, opened mind-brain-social realities in clinical neuroscience, psychopharmacology, and the adverse consequences of brain drugs. In the lobotomy trial, the defendant died, bringing to the fore an old Pennsylvania statute that "thou shall not speak ill of the dead."

During a recess, I met old Dr. James Watts, Walter Freeman's collaborator in *Prefrontal Lobotomy* (1942). I asked him about a comment in their book "..that some people suffer from too much frontal cortex." "Oh yes," said the courtly Virginian, "Walter always talked like that." With this confirmation of the power and trajectory of Peter's work to alter American psychiatry, my life was thereafter changed in teaching and clinical work with the neurologically impaired.

> Men like Peter Breggin are crucial to the sanity and survival of our culture....They illuminate and preserve the deepest, elemental pieces of the human spirit.

At an invited talk "Neural correlates of reason & liberty" that I gave in December 1974 at the University of Michigan, Ann Arbor, neurology chief Russell DeJong asked me to his office to tell me of a neurology resident at the University of California-San Francisco named John Friedberg. John had gotten into trouble in his residency after publicly attacking ECT as brain damaging. Faculty psychiatrists asked for his head and he was summarily dismissed.

John reapplied to University of Michigan to finish his training. DeJong said John's application was "too controversial ...could you take him in Portland?" I wrote to John, had him visit, and said we would take him if he promised to keep me out of hot water. He agreed. But for one slight sidestep in his senior year at Oregon Health Science University (OHSU)—picketing a visiting ECT lecturer—John was as good as his word. He finished the program and later his neurology boards. In recent years, he has been a leader in the fight to abolish lethal injection in death penalty cases.

Dr. Friedberg is but one of my residents protected by the reach of Peter's effect on my teaching, social renaissance, and support of unpopular ideas in specific venues.

Years later, in April, 1994, I flew to Austin, Texas to speak to a Texas Legislative committee against proposed use of ECT on adolescents. I testified, (1) How on earth could one obtain an informed consent in a child or adolescent? and (2) As there was no clinical evidence of the short- or long-term effects of ECT on kids, it should not be done. Peter also testified. The proposal from the Texas Psychiatric Association was defeated.

Peter's long shadow on my life continued. And at about the same time, it even reached into my family. When my wife, child psychiatrist Nancy Grimm, applied to OHSU to finish her adult training in psychiatry, she was asked, "Dr. Grimm, do you share the views of your husband?" She made it crystal clear she was capable of thinking for herself and was promptly accepted.

In this short piece reflecting on the influence of Peter's work and writing on my career, his fundamental humanism, vision, and unceasing efforts in writings and teaching to sensitize and protect us from 1984s and Brave New Worlds of our own making—centered my thinking in the 1970s.

Now, in a country where 45 million Americans have no health coverage, where the average face time with physicians is 5-15 minutes, where molecular biology safely dominates neuroscience, and physicians are trained to diagnosis faults in the individual and not the society that has fostered them–Peter's insistent focus on the human condition has been steady and reliable.

Men like Peter Breggin are crucial to the sanity and survival of our culture, centered as they are on the oldest dictum of Medicine. They illuminate and preserve the deepest, elemental pieces of the human spirit.

I count it as one of the riches of my life to know and to have been guided by the first among them in Peter Breggin's humanism in clinical behavioral science: They teach one to look deeper than the science and technology of medicine.

Currently, issues such as torture, transcranial magnetic stimulation, vagal nerve stimulators, persistence of ECT and cingulotomies to rid an individual of their particular demons, and a cascade of drugs aimed at fixing the behavior of adults and children are weekly in the neurology trade newspapers on my desk. Old and new threats require a continued infusion of Peter Breggins into medical training and health policy.

The Breggins of medicine are critical to keeping medical practices relevant in a troubled world where altering brains to accommodate dysfunctional societies is the danger.

The Breggins of medicine are critical to keeping medical practices relevant in a troubled world where altering brains to accommodate dysfunctional societies is the danger. Peter saw it all thirty-five years ago and has worked tirelessly to foster alternative, humane changes in treatment of the vulnerable to prevent structural or chemical alterations of their brain. We remain in his debt.

Eventually, I was involved as a medical expert in a lawsuit against Harvard's amygdalotomy program. At the request of attorney Bill McDaniels of the Califano law firm in Washington, D.C., I was asked to examine one of the Mark and Ervin cases (Thomas R., in Mark and Ervin's *Violence and the Brain)*, a young Irish genius who took a recently divorced friend into his home. The friend promptly took up with Thomas R's wife and the domestic row that followed came to the attention of the local parish priest, fresh from a hospital internship at Boston City Hospital, the site of Harvard's psychosurgery program for the violent under Mark and Ervin. Peter had made Thomas R. a national cause (e.g., Breggin, 1972b; 1975; see the media coverage of these events earlier in this chapter) after Thomas' mother and guardian empowered Peter to interview her son and to obtain his medical records, to make public his evaluation, and to find an attorney to take the malpractice case. Because he was so personally involved in publicizing the case and bringing about the lawsuit, Peter did not feel he was in a position to testify as an independent expert.

Between the row in the Thomas R. household, and the parish priest's talking Thomas R. into seeking treatment at Boston City Hospital, a certain transmogrification of the facts had ensued, e.g. name-calling, object-throwing, and fist-shaking (in Boston traffic) were translated as violence. Thomas R. was admitted. After several weeks, he signed consent for the procedure (believing it was the only way he was going to get out of the place) and underwent bilateral stereotaxic electro-coagulation of the amygdala. Shortly thereafter he was released, and promptly disappeared from Boston.

He was picked up months later on a rural road in Iowa, walking along in bare feet and wearing an aluminum foil helmet. He explained to the State patrolman that Harvard had sold his brain codes to Yale. Jose Delgado, at the time a professor at Yale, had visited the Boston City program when Thomas R. was there and Thomas remembered Delgado's discussion about brain stimulation and control, word-for-word. I flew to Boston, and examined Thomas R. before the trial. He was ambulatory but vacant inside with zero memory of anything, including his family.

In the trial that followed, the first question Harvard's attorney, John Dorr, asked me when I was on the witness stand was "Dr. Grimm, have you ever heard of Harvard Medical School?"

With the King-can-do-no-wrong defense, Harvard won the suit, but lost the battle. The amygdalotomy program at Harvard was ended.

References

Breggin, P. (1972a). The return of lobotomy and psychosurgery. *Congressional Record,*118, E1602-E1612. Republished with a new introduction in Breggin, P. (1982). The return of lobotomy and psychosurgery. In R. Edwards (Ed.), *Psychiatry and Ethics,* pp. 350-352. Buffalo: Prometheus Books.

Breggin, P. (1972b). Psychosurgery for the control of violence–including a critique of the work of Vernon Mark and Frank Ervin. *Congressional Record,* 118: E3350-E3386. Revised and republished in Breggin, P. (1975). Psychosurgery for the control of violence: a critical review. Chapter IV in Fields W. and Sweet W. (Eds), *Neural Bases of Violence and Aggression.* St. Louis: Warren H. Green.

Breggin, P. (1975). Psychosurgery for political purposes. *Duquesne Law Review,* 13, 841-862.

Crichton, M. (1972). *Terminal Man.* New York: Bantam Books.

Dow, R., Grimm, R. and Rushmer, D. (1974). Psychosurgery and brain stimulation: the legislative experience in 1973. In I. Cooper, M. Riklan and R. Snyder (Eds.), *The Cerebellum, Epilepsy, and Behavior.* New York: Plenum.

Freeman, W. and Watts, J. (1942). *Prefrontal lobotomy,* Springfield: Charles C. Thomas.

Grimm, R. Advocacy of psychosurgery and intra-cranial brain stimulation in the involuntarily committed: Medical, legal, and ethical objections. ACLU statement to Senate Human Resources Committee Hearings on SB-298, Oregon Legislature, March 20, 1973.

Grimm, R. (1976). Brain control in a democratic society. In W. Lynn Smith and A. Kling (Eds.) *Issues in brain/behavior control.* New York: New York: SP Books

Huxley. A. (1938). *Brave New World.* New York: Penguin.

Huxley, A. (1958) *Brave New World Revisited.* New York: Harper Colophon Books.

Kesey, K. (1959). *One Flew Over the Cuckoo's Nest.* New York: Bantam Books, 1959.

Mark, V. and Ervin, F. (1970). *Violence in the Brain.* New York: Harper & Row.

Mark, V., Sweet, W. and Ervin, R. (1967, September 11). The role of brain disease in riots and urban violence. *Journal of the American Medical Association,* 201, 217.

Opton, E. and Stender, F. A clockwork Orange at UCLA. Committee Opposing Psychiatric Abuse of Prisoners, 5406 Claremont Ave, Oakland, California.

Orwell, G. (1949). *1984.* New York: Brace, Jankovic Publishing Co.

Vonnegut, Jr., K. (1959). *The Sirens of Titian.* New York: Dell.

Robert J. Grimm, MD

Bob finished an undergraduate degree at Antioch College and master's and medical degrees and an internship at the University of Michigan with post-doctoral work in physiology and biophysics at the University of Washington. His neurology residency was in Portland, Oregon. The years 1970-1995 in Portland were spent teaching neurology and running a brain research lab. He has had a private neurology practice since 1973, the year he co-authored the Oregon bill outlawing psychosurgery, and the year he first met Peter Breggin. A substantial courtroom experience followed involving cases of individuals injured by lobotomy and ECT (through 2000). Bob remains in full-time clinical practice and currently researches the issue of individuals who do not recover from a whiplash. Since 1959, he has been married to the former Nancy Ross, a Johns Hopkins medical school graduate and former child psychiatrist. Bob's latest book, Neurology Work *(in press) describes his career in neurology. In his work opposing all practices to control brain by medical, surgical, and electric techniques presides the humanity and thinking of Peter Breggin.*

A Loving Essay on Breggin

by David B. Stein, PhD

In the academic year 1973 to 1974, I did my psychology internship at The University of Mississippi Medical School. Much of the outstanding literature in behaviorism during that time period was the product of some of the best researchers who made up the faculty of the school.

However, it did not take me long to become disenchanted with what I was observing. The faculty cranked out data like a factory production line, but unfortunately few worked directly with the patients, and quite frankly I doubted that they would do much good even if they did any direct intervention. All that they seemed to care about was publishing and the furtherance of their careers without any of them expressing one shred of concern for the wellbeing of the patients.

The greatest atrocities that I was observing were the product of neurosurgeon Orlando Andy who placed electrodes into the brains of children and adolescents, stimulated them experimentally, and then burned holes inside their skulls. I saw this monster butcher children and teenagers who acted out in the institution and just about anyone who had the misfortune to be referred to Dr. Andy.

Worst of all were those eminent researchers at the university who knew what was going on and who did nothing about it! Just as a side note, these same eminent researchers, some thirty years later, are now in high positions of power and yet they still are doing nothing, even though they are well aware of the abuses of psychiatry and psychology. All that seemed to matter to them was the furtherance of their careers, or as Mel Brooks says, "Let's protect our phony bologna jobs, boys!"

As a result of the efforts of someone named Peter Breggin to publicize Andy's atrocities, a committee was formed to monitor the neurosurgeon but they still gave him permission to butcher anything in his path. But this pesky psychiatrist named Peter Breggin did not give up.

I had no idea who Peter Breggin was, but being only a student, I cheered on who ever this upstart was. It gave me hope that there was someone out there who really cared. The big shots certainly did not give a damn. Nonetheless, in the early 1970s Breggin's efforts led to the termination of Andy's psychosurgical experiments.

After completing my internship and during the intervening years I heard little about what was happening at the U. of Mississippi Med School. I knew that many of the big shots spread out to positions at prestigious universities.

> I called my publisher, and shouted into the phone, "I found the person that I want to write the forward—a Dr. Peter Breggin! How can we find him?"

Eventually, I became an academician. I became interested in the treatment of children and teenagers without the use of psychiatric drugs. One of my best sources was again someone named Peter Breggin. I had my second book published by Wiley, Jossey-Bass Publishers, but I had no one to write the forward, and this being my first really serious book, I wanted someone whom I respected. I walked into my second office at Barnes and Noble, and right at the entrance was a pile of books titled, *Talking Back to Ritalin: What doctors aren't telling you about stimulants for children.* I stayed up all night reading the book. How in the world did I miss this wonderful piece of work? I called my publisher, and shouted into the phone, "I found the person that I want to write the forward—a Dr. Peter Breggin! How can we find him?" In less than an hour my phone rang and Dr. Breggin calmly said that he would love to read my manuscript and would let me know as soon as possible if he would be willing to do what I so eagerly requested. The next day, he accepted. Oddly, it took me several days to realize that I had cited this writer numerous times. I just did not immediately make the connection.

I was overwhelmed when Dr. Breggin (he was not as yet Peter to me) called and asked me to come to Bethesda and meet some lovely folks. A few weeks later, I drove up, checked into the hotel down the block from the Breggin's house, and called to let Dr. Breggin know that I was in. He said he would walk over to meet me on the street. This big shot writer was going to walk over to meet this neophyte? I walked down the street and spotted this beautiful and gentle face with a great big grin on it aimed right at me. We greeted and hugged each other. I was so excited that as we walked to his house I did not hear a word he was saying.

We entered his humble and very warm home, and a new world opened up to me. No longer was I alone. No longer was I going to feel like a misfit outcast. A new tradition began of frequent meetings at the Breggin's home. Living room discussions with some of the most amazing people became a part of my life. I craved discourse with people whom I respected, and suddenly here it was. I entered a world of discussion, debate, disputation, exchange of ideas but, even more importantly, mutual respect, dignity, and ethics. I met some of the most amazing people. Eileen Walkenstein, who constantly kept egging me on to debate Mike Valentine, was a delight, but no one beats Valentine in a debate and she knew that. The elegant and handsome David Cohen was almost always present. Steve Baldwin, who would become one of my closest friends, and who would tragically die a few years later, would lend so much energy and brilliance.

I could write entire texts about the others: Loren Mosher, Bill Bruck, Fred Baughman, Ron David, Jake Johnson, Clement Vontress, Larry Plumlee, Milton Shore, Jerry Miller, Ron Hopson, Richard DeGrandpre, and Doug Smith. I cannot forget the power of the gentle smile of Kevin McCready. It was so much fun to eat from the bowls of carefully washed grapes that always seemed to be present, and talk and talk and talk. I could not believe that I was in the same room with all of these brilliant minds and deeply caring souls.

One thing was clear. None of us could do our contributions, i.e. our books, our essays, or our articles, without the giant upon whose shoulders we stood—Peter Breggin.

One thing was clear. None of us could do our contributions, i.e. our books, our essays, or our articles, without the giant upon whose shoulders we stood—Peter Breggin. It was he who spent countless hours in the NIH medical library painstakingly going through the mountains of misinformation and disinformation and making sense out of it all and thus allowing us to produce our good works. I doubt that any of us could have made sense, as he has, of the overwhelming volume of gobbledygook. We desperately needed his scholarship to help us with ours.

It was during one of these evening discussions that I realized that Peter Breggin was the same Peter Breggin who dogged the outlandish Orlando Andy some twenty–five years earlier. I later had to frequently travel to Mississippi, and during one of these trips I discovered that Orlando Andy was alive and still butchering people. I had to tell Peter, I could now call him as friend

Peter, about Orlando. I watched his blood pressure rise, and I saw the determined look that that son of a bitch was not going to be in operation for long.

Peter warned me during the earliest part of our friendship that it would not be long before I would become a target from those who were growing rich at the expense of the health and wellbeing of children. Indeed, it came. Many of Peter's closest friends and allies became targets, but we had something during those years that Peter did not have earlier. We had each other. Later the good Lord brought a marvelous lady into his life, Ginger, who had the razor sharp intelligence and a locomotive's energy to support him and work side by side with him.

I could never have made it were it not for the friends and support of the members of the International Center for the Study of Psychiatry and Psychology.

How, I have often wondered, especially before his having Ginger, did Peter Breggin survive the onslaughts directed at him? I could never have made it were it not for the friends and support of the members of the International Center for the Study of Psychiatry and Psychology (ICSPP), the organization he founded during those early years of living room meetings.

Peter took the heat during the earliest years of his being a reformer alone. I cannot imagine how he survived without himself becoming one of the mental patients he so boldly protected.

I am so glad that Peter has been such an important part of my life and such an incredible inspiration. My only regret is that we did not meet during the early Mississippi years of my internship.

However, I count the blessing that he is here now. I shall continue to devour every word that he writes and treasure every moment that I can spend with him.

David Stein, PhD

David is a professor of psychology at Longwood University, Farmville, Virginia. He is the author of four books on effective medication-free cognitive/behavioral treatment of ADHD, including Ritalin is Not the Answer: A Drug-Free Practical Program for Children Diagnosed as ADD or ADHD, *a bestseller. David won an award at the 1998 American Psychological Association Convention as one of the top ten research presentations. In addition to his teaching, researching and writing he is a Diplomate in Forensics and is an active consultant to the Virginia State Police.*

Chapter Four

Opposing Shock Treatment

Introduction

In 1979 Dr. Breggin published his first medical book, *Electroshock: Its Brain-Disabling Effects,* the first and only medical book devoted to evaluating the harmful effects of ECT. It took a courageous, independent medical publisher, Springer Publishing Company, to dare to bring out this book. In this section, the retired owner of the company and the former editor-in-chief describe the drama and importance surrounding their decision to publish the book.

Over the ensuing decades Dr. Breggin remained a staunch opponent of ECT and in 1985 he was asked to be the sole scientific presenter on brain damage and dysfunction caused by the "treatment" at the NIH Consensus Development Conference on Electroconvulsive Therapy. He has written many articles and book chapters updating his criticism and his call for the profession to abandon shock treatment (for example, 1980, 1981a, 1984, 1986, 1998d; 1987 with de Girolamo).

Dr. Breggin's most recent and detailed analysis of ECT is contained in a chapter in *Brain-Disabling Treatments: Drugs, Electroshock and the Psychopharmaceutical Complex* (2008). He has been a medical expert in many ECT malpractice suits and in June 2005 he was the medical expert in the first malpractice trial to bring a jury verdict in favor of a patient injured by shock treatment (see www.breggin.com). More recently, Dr. Breggin was the medical expert in another ECT malpractice suit that settled for an amount in excess of $1 million.

The "Treatment" that Refuses to Go Away. "Electroshock Treatment: Safer and Quicker Than Drugs?" ***The New York Times,*** **December 21, 1979.**

Despite an image that suffers from graphic, often frightening accounts in movies, newspapers, magazines and in the writings of some psychiatrists, electroshock treatment persists....The use, and alleged abuse, of electroshock arouses conflicting views from former mental patients, public interest groups and psychiatrists....

Dr. Peter Breggin of Bethesda, Md., author of the book: *Electroshock: Its Brain-Disabling Effects,* said that shock patients suffered structural brain changes and learning difficulties that lasted the rest of their lives....

Empirically Strong: Review of ***Electroshock: Its Brain-Disabling Effects*** **by Nancy B. Burrell,** ***Library Journal,*** **March 1, 1980.**

Researching definitive literature on the subject of electroshock therapy (ECT) has been a trial for librarians and doctors alike. Psychiatrist Breggin takes an authoritative and comprehensive stand against ECT as he makes sense of the jumble of contradictory literature that has appeared since its invention in 1938. The author contends that despite substantiated memory loss, pathologic brain damage, and even death subsequent to treatment, the proponents of ECT have ignored the problem to the point of not citing important literature, carrying on lopsided experiments, and even accusing patients of exaggerating the after-effects....An empirically strong work which also deals with the ethical and philosophical issues involved.

More on the Anti-ECT Campaign. "The Electric Shock Debate" by Sandy Rovner, ***The Washington Post,*** **January 30, 1985.**

....Breggin, a Bethesda psychiatrist, one-time Harvard Medical School psychiatric fellow and for several years a full-time psychiatric consultant at the National Institute of Mental Health, sees ECT as the "lobotomy of the '80s." His book *"Electroshock: Its Brain-Disabling Effects"* published in 1979, hypothesizes that the apparent improvement in mood and the lessening of manic or psychotic symptoms is symptomatic of brain damage, not a marker of improvement. "Head injury, carbon monoxide poisoning or sniffing glue can produce euphoria," says Breggin. "It is an artificial high typical in the early stages of brain damage. The shock doctors say the depression has lifted. It hasn't lifted, the ability [to perceive it] has been destroyed."

Testifying as a Scientific Expert at the 1985 Consensus Development Conference on ECT. "Panel Calls ECT Effective in Narrow Range of Mental Illness, but Side Effects Significant" by Calvin Pierce, *Clinical Psychiatry News,* July 1985.

Electroconvulsive therapy can be an effective short-term treatment for a narrow range of severe psychiatric disorders but has significant side effects, has been under-investigated, and is still the most controversial treatment in psychiatry, a panel concluded at a National Institutes of Health consensus development conference....

Dr. Peter Breggin, a psychiatrist in private practice in Bethesda, Md., and a vocal critic of ECT, insisted that "electroshock works by damaging the brain" and urged the panel to recognize that ECT combines brain damage caused by the seizure with brain damage caused by electrical trauma.

The panel denied that ECT causes neuronal cell death but said the memory deficit caused by ECT "may represent alterations in neuronal function that are not detectable with present methods."

Dr. Breggin responded, "I think it's an advance in psychiatry," that the panel formally acknowledged the occurrence of memory deficits after ECT....

Electroshock Damage. "Electroshock: Fifty Years Later" by Russ Rymer, *Hippocrates,* March/April 1989.

"How do I know these techniques aren't new?" Peter Breggin asks. "Because I was giving modified ECT at Harvard in 1963, and it's the same old thing. It's as dangerous as it ever was." Breggin is perhaps the foremost among ECT's critics, a psychiatrist who takes time out from his Bethesda, Maryland practice to speak against shock at conventions and on talk shows and to testify against it in court. "ECT is inherently damaging to the brain," Breggin says, "for a very simple reason. The combination of electricity and seizures is bad for the brain."

While shock doctors maintain that Breggin's accounts of the effects of shock therapy are misleading and anecdotal, they have a harder time refuting his observation that there is no solid theoretical explanation for ECT's effectiveness....

"It [ECT] is so uncomplicated, it's embarrassing," says Breggin. "ECT causes organic brain syndrome. It's in DSM-III. Look it up." DSM-III, the diagnostic bible of the American Psychiatric Assocation, describes organic brain syndrome as any generalized disorder of the brain. One common feature of brain damage is a temporary delirium, feeling of well-being, and feeling of release from physical or mental ailments. Another feature is temporary or permanent amnesia....

Shocking Many Psychiatrists. Ursula Springer, PhD, *The History of Springer Publishing Company* (2008). Published by permission of Springer Publishing Company.

Our publications in psychiatry were relatively few—numbering about 30 by the year 2000. Yet they were authored by prestigious scholars. One psychiatrist who became a longtime friend of Springer Publishing Company was Peter Breggin, MD.

In 1979 we published his book *Electroshock—Its Brain-Disabling Effects.* The book aroused shock effects among many psychiatrists. One of them—a leading proponent and practitioner of this lucrative procedure—approached me in our exhibit booth during a convention pointing his finger toward me saying furiously: "So, you are the publisher of his book (pointing to *Electroshock*). You will have on your conscience suicides of depressed persons who were not helped by electroshock treatments, etc. I will see to it that all my psychiatry colleagues boycott your company and its publications!" A truly dramatic moment that I managed to survive (and to enjoy!).

Also by Dr. Breggin, we published in 1983 a volume that required careful screening to prevent possible lawsuits by rich pharmaceutical companies: *Psychiatric Drugs—Hazards to the Brain.*

Fortunately, no dire consequences followed. Still, for years later we received phone calls from individuals, often one in prison or a mental institution, asking for this book to clarify their own brain problems.

These Breggin-authored books could only be published by an independent publisher with some courage to buck lucrative medical practices. No major corporate publisher would dare to do that. Cheers to independent and risk-taking publishing!

Compassion is the Basis of All Morality

by Carole Saltz

Certainly to this day if I had to briefly number the projects I've worked on with the greatest reach or influence or impact on a field, Peter's first two books for Springer Publishing Company—on the devastating effects of ECT and on the major tranquilizers—would be there: *Electroshock: Its Brain-Disabling Effects* (1979) and *Psychiatric Drugs: Hazards to the Brain* (1983). Or, if I had to briefly number the projects I feel most proud to have worked on (because these two categories are not necessarily the same), Peter's books for Springer would be there.

Working with Peter on those two manuscripts helped shape me as an editor and publisher—taught me not to be afraid to tell the truth. But working with Peter on those two manuscripts also taught me that if you're going to tell the truth (especially a truth that no one wants to hear), you'd better be very afraid—afraid enough to check your work obsessively and to make sure that you've got it just exactly right.

I have come to realize just how unusual it was to work with an author who wanted constant critique of his work, who thanked me for every question I raised.

Years later, I have come to realize just how unusual it was to work with an author who wanted constant critique of his work, who thanked me for every question I raised, who was never annoyed or offended at being pushed to explain more, to describe more, to supply more detail and more truth. The process of editing those books was tough and it was laborious but it was also joyful.

Part of that joy was certainly about being challenged intellectually. I remember arguments of the very best kind—open and important because they drove the work to make it stronger. The back and forth was uncompromising and would continue until the questions were completely answered. This was a necessary part of the process but few authors in my now considerable experience really want you to tell them the truth. Peter always did and with that wonderful curiosity and enthusiasm of his, looked forward to the next round.

Knowing that this work of Peter's was good and could do good for others was joy of a different kind. It gave me something to aspire to as an editor and publisher and as a human being. Sometimes I hear an insistent voice in my head (I promise, I don't hear voices very often but when I do I'm usually very grateful), reminding me of what's wrong with our world. At least some of the tones of that inside voice are Peter's—filled with indignation at injustice and ethical impropriety and willing to take on the bad guys no matter what the cost. I'm sure that voice has informed important moments for me both professional and personal, moments when I've chosen in one way or another to tell a truth or take a stand despite the risk.

For that, I am most grateful and for having a small role in bringing Peter's work into the world.

Carole Saltz

Carole was the senior editor at Springer Publishing Company when Peter Breggin published his first two medical books with the company. She is now the Director of Teachers College Press in New York City.

Chapter Five

Winning the Medical License Attack

The Oprah Incident

In 1987 Dr. Breggin was invited by Leonard Frank, Rae Unzicker and other representatives of the psychiatric survivor reform movement to join them on The Oprah Winfrey Show. During the show Oprah was very sympathetic and supportive of their criticisms of psychiatry, and the TV program became the most effective public education effort in the history of the psychiatric reform movement. At the end of the show, in response to a question from Oprah, Dr. Breggin said that patients do not have to start taking psychiatric drugs from doctors whom they do not trust.

Organized psychiatry, led by the American Psychiatric Association (APA) and the National Alliance for the Mentally Ill (NAMI), was outraged by the success of the show and especially by the venue it provided for Dr. Breggin's views. Both APA and NAMI resented Dr. Breggin's previous disclosures about their dependence upon pharmaceutical company funding, as well as his criticism of their unbridled support for drugs, electroshock, lobotomy and involuntary treatment.

The APA and NAMI demanded equal time with a full hour of their own on The Oprah Show. Courageously, Oprah refused and instead invited the President of APA, psychiatrist Paul Fink, to debate Dr. Breggin for an hour. The debate was an overwhelming victory for Dr. Breggin—and no national figure in psychiatry would ever again consent to debate him. The humiliated APA and NAMI responded by organizing an attack on Dr. Breggin's medical license in his home state of Maryland with NAMI bringing a complaint about Dr. Breggin's television remarks.

The attack backfired. The publicity surrounding the assault on his license took Dr. Breggin's reform efforts from the media shadows into the media spotlight and his eventual victory led to the writing and publication of *Toxic Psychiatry* (1991). The response of so many people who came to his support revived Dr. Breggin's morale and further inspired his reform efforts.

Transcript of Dr. Breggin on the First Oprah Show. "Inappropriate Treatment for Psychiatric Problems" The Oprah Winfrey Show, April 2, 1987.

OPRAH WINFREY: Should mental treatment be voluntary or involuntary? You are about to hear some incredible mental hospital horror stories from people who were institutionalized against their will and faced with forced drug treatment and painful shock therapy....

WINFREY: Joining me now is a psychiatrist who believes that the psychiatric community is out of control. He has led reform meetings against psychiatric abuse of patients that are forced to take mind-damaging drugs, electroshock treatment, and lobotomies. He is the author of "Psychiatric Drugs: Hazards to the Brain."

Welcome Dr. Peter Breggin to the show....

At the very end of the show, Oprah and Dr. Breggin had the following exchange that was cited in the attack on his license:

WINFREY: I was saying to you, Doctor, during the break, if you're in need of a good psychiatrist, how do you know how to find one? Because certainly there are some good ones out there.

DR. BREGGIN: Well, stop thinking psychiatrist and think psychotherapist. It could be a social worker, a clinical psychologist, or a psychiatrist. In my opinion, if the person belongs to an association that says "electrotherapy" in it or "biological psychiatry" in it, it's not my viewpoint. I'd stay away from them. If the person belongs to, say, the American Academy of Psychotherapists, at least—which is not mostly psychiatrists. It's mostly psychologists and social workers—at least you know the person knows how to do psychotherapy or has had some training in it.

But basically, tune into yourself. You judge the therapist. Don't let the therapist...

WINFREY: (interrupting) How do you judge when the reason why you're going is because your judgment is impaired?

DR. BREGGIN: [closing comment] Find the little part in you that loves yourself and see if you're being loved by your therapist. See if that person cares for, supports you. If that person offers a drug, don't even say, "No, thank you." You can take the prescription and go. Don't fight about it. Don't get into trouble. But go. Don't take the drugs. And relate to people who care for you as a person. That's the whole key. That's the starting point...

Ginger Joins the Fight

After the license attack began, Peter's wife Ginger decided to fully devote herself to her husband's defense and eventually to all of his reform efforts. Drawing on her background in public relations and journalism, she generated enormous media coverage of the license attack. Many observers have stated that the media coverage stymied the efforts to attack Dr. Breggin's medical license and hence to stop his reform work.

Following the license attack, Ginger began to work fulltime on behalf of her husband's psychiatric reform efforts and for many years she managed the International Center for the Study of Psychiatry and Psychology (ICSPP), building it into an international organization with hundreds of members, an annual meeting, a newsletter and finally a peer-reviewed journal, *Ethical Human Psychology and Psychiatry.*

Associated Press Covers the License Attack. "Doctor Opposed to Drugging Mentally Ill Fights for License" by Jerry Estill, *Associated Press,* September 20, 1987.

Washington—A psychiatrist who says too many of his colleagues are too quick to prescribe powerful drugs for mentally ill patients is fighting for his medical license after expressing those views on national television.

Dr. Peter R. Breggin's appearance Tuesday before Maryland state medical licensing authorities stems from a complaint filed by the National Alliance for the Mentally Ill.

In an April 20 letter to Maryland officials, Laurie M. Flynn, executive director of the private organization known as NAMI, alleges that Breggin urged all psychiatric patients to stop taking their medications....

Although Breggin's views are well known—he is the author of two books challenging the use of electroshock and drug therapy and worked for the National Institutes of Health—the particular comments that prompted the NAMI complaint were made April 2 during the closing minutes of an Oprah Winfrey show....

It was that response that NAMI contends amounted to Breggin urging "All psychiatric patients across America" to stop taking their prescribed medication....

Breggin himself characterizes the dispute as "basically a political issue attempting to stifle someone who spent 20 years on reform work for psychiatric patients." ...

About two-dozen psychiatrists from across the nation have written to Maryland authorities in support of Dr. Breggin. Most support his ideas. Others say that while they are not necessarily in total agreement with Breggin, his ideas are well enough founded to merit serious consideration.

Fighting Back! Support Letters Pour In

At the urging of his attorney, Ralph Temple, Dr. Breggin sent out a request for letters of support to be sent to the state licensure agency that was evaluating the complaint against him. Within a week or two, dozens had arrived. According to attorney Temple, he had never seen so many positive, personally written letters generated on behalf of anyone under attack. Three letters are from Congressmen and a Senator who joined the Board of Directors of ICSPP in the early 1970s and who continued to support Dr. Breggin's reform efforts in 1987 when the license attack began. Here are excerpts from some of the dozens of letters sent in support of Dr. Breggin:

A Leader in Social Reform. U. S. Congressman Louis Stokes (Dem-Ohio).

I have known Dr. Breggin and have been familiar with his reform efforts in psychiatry since we first worked together on patient rights issues in 1971. I was glad to join his distinguished Board of Directors at that time and have remained on the Board ever since. Over the years, I have had the opportunity to be reminded of his continuous and highly successful efforts on behalf of some of this nation's poorest and most vulnerable people, including state mental hospital patients, the institutionalized mentally retarded and those exposed to potentially damaging treatments. I know Dr. Breggin as a sincere and responsible physician devoted to the public good...Dr. Breggin is a leader in social reform.

Responsible for Many Advances. U. S. Senator Steve Symms (Rep-Idaho).

I have been on the Board of Directors of the Center for the Study of Psychiatry since 1971 and have remained in touch with Dr. Breggin's reform activities in psychiatry since that time. Dr.

Breggin is a champion of patient rights and honesty in psychiatry. He is a respected member of the medical community and the author of many scientific books and articles. He is responsible for many advances in the field of medicine in the last two decades.

Stopping Psychosurgery. U. S. Congressman Ronald V. Dellums (Dem-California).

Dr. Peter Breggin first came to my attention in approximately 1970, when he took a public stand against the use of psychiatric brain surgery on retarded children in custodial institutions in Mississippi. Dr. Breggin went on to discover a planned "new wave" of lobotomy-like operations putting at risk the helpless inmates of our public institutions. At the time I held a press conference in support of his reform work and consulted with him and proposed relevant legislation. The National Commission on Psychosurgery and Senate hearings on psychosurgery were the direct outcome of Dr. Breggin's efforts. Psychosurgical operations on patients came to a halt largely as the results of Dr. Breggin's efforts educating Congress and the public.

I joined Dr. Breggin's Center for the Study of Psychiatry as a Member of the Board of Directors at the time and have remained on the board ever since. I am aware of his ongoing efforts on behalf of the mentally ill, the retarded, prisoners and others who have few enough champions in this society. In the District of Columbia and in Kentucky, for example, he has recently been active on behalf of the rights of indigent hospitalized patients. It is rare indeed for a psychiatrist to devote himself for so many years to such difficult public issues.

No Longer Controversial. Bertram Karon, PhD, Professor of Psychology, Michigan State University.

As a professor of Psychology who has been involved for many years with the training of Clinical Psychologists and Psychiatrists, and with research on treatment processes, it was with astonishment that I learned that you were reviewing the medical ethics of Dr. Peter Breggin, one of the most ethical and ethically concerned psychiatrists in the United States. I do not know Dr. Breggin personally, but his credentials are first rate, and his work is deservedly highly regarded nationally.

I first became aware of Dr. Breggin in the early 1970's, during the so-called "new wave" of psychosurgery, when well-known psychiatrists were advocating both in the mass media and in professional publications and meetings, the use of psychosurgery not only for schizophrenia and auditory hallucinations, but also for aggressiveness, delinquency, sexual deviation, obsessive-compulsive disorders, and even hyperactivity.

At a meeting of the American Psychiatric Association, Dr Breggin presented some of the evidence about psychosurgery. It was, of course, controversial. I was struck that one well-known psychiatrist went so far as to say that Dr. Breggin should not have made these statements (at a professional psychiatric meeting) because it was "disrespectful" to the "great pioneers" in the field of psychiatry. Dr. Breggin served a useful purpose in bringing to the attention of psychiatry and other mental health professions the actual state of the evidence with respect to these procedures.
His views, which were controversial at that time, are now considered "middle of the road" and agreed to by most psychiatrists today. His reading of the evidence, while not fashionable at the time, proved to be factually accurate.

He has continued to be a professional conscience to the field, and has continued to be concerned about side effects and iatrogenic disorders. This does not make for pleasant reading, and he makes all of us uncomfortable. But his is a useful and necessary role.

We (the mental health professions, including psychiatry) need to know about the negative aspects of the treatments we use or recommend. His critiques are always factually accurate, even if they are not what we would like to hear. His book on the negative aspects of electric shock treatment was, of course, disturbing to those psychiatrists for whom this treatment represents a major part of their practice.

In a number of instances, the way he cited empirical studies differed from other secondary sources and textbooks. For several important studies where this was the case, I took the trouble to go back to the original publications or the original researcher to find out which version of the empirical finding was accurate.

With respect to every study I checked, Dr. Breggin's account of the findings was more accurate than the alternative source. That this was consistently so was very impressive.

Dr. Breggin has performed, and continues to perform a valuable public service, even if he makes us uncomfortable. It would be hard to argue that telling the truth is unethical.

While it would undoubtedly be an unfair comparison, to threaten or remove Dr. Breggin's medical license for saying publicly that there are dangers connected with psychiatric medications, would seem like General Motors threatening Ralph Nader with private detectives for saying publicly that the Corvair was a dangerous car. It was a bad mistake for General Motors and this would be an equally bad mistake.

Stifling free discussion of the controversial issues almost always implies guilty secrets to the outsider. The side effects of medication are a scientific issue, and in science controversy must not be stifled because it is inconvenient or economically unrewarding.

A Well-Trained Psychiatrist. Richard H. Phillips, MD, Professor and Director, Adult Psychiatry Clinic, Department of Psychiatry, State University of New York, Upstate Medical Cen-

ter, Syracuse, New York. Dr. Phillips taught Dr. Breggin during his residency.

Dr. Breggin is a well-trained physician and psychiatrist who has been in practice for many years. He is respected in the field, and I know of no instance in which he has ever been accused of harming one of his patients.

Supporting the Bill of Rights. Robert S. Mendelsohn, MD, author of *Confessions of a Medical Heretic.*

You have made—and are continuing to make—a major contribution to the health of American citizens by telling them the truth about modern psychiatry.

I know you will receive the support of all citizens who believe in the Bill of Rights more than psychiatric voodoo. Please count on me for any help I can provide—personal, courtroom testimony, media visibility, or whatever...

A Personal Friend and Colleague. Jay Salwen, MD.

In the many years I have known Dr. Breggin, his friends and his colleagues there has never been any question of Dr. Breggin's ethical standards on either a personal or professional level. If everyone were as forthright and honest and open as Dr. Breggin, we would all be better off by far.

Honored, Not Censured. Eileen Walkenstein, MD, psychiatrist and author.

I believe Dr. Peter Breggin should be complemented and honored for the work he is doing and for his daring to speak out in accordance with his conscience, his critical intelligence and his professional experience.

"Unhuman" Treatment. Jay Haley, Former Clinical Professor of Psychiatry at the University of Maryland and Howard University.

There is nothing that [Dr. Breggin] said that I would not agree with after 30 years training therapists... Many people in this field are concerned about the brain damage caused by shock and anti-psychotic drugs, as well as the often unhuman manner of those who dispense this treatment.

Where Others Dare Not Look. Roger Manus, Attorney, Carolina Legal Assistance, Raleigh, North Carolina.

I am a staff attorney with Carolina Legal Assistance (A Mental Disability Law Project). We provide free civil legal services to persons of low income who have mental retardation or who have received psychiatric treatment. In our work, we tend to focus on those cases which raise issues concerning discrimination or the human service delivery system.

Dr. Breggin has worked with and consulted with my colleagues and me over several years as an expert on psychiatry and psychiatric drugs. At my request, Dr. Breggin testified before the Mental Health Study Commission of the North Carolina General Assembly and was very warmly received on the subject of my concerns about the damaging effects of psychiatric drugs. Many sectors of the electronic and print media also found his message important. We even arranged to have a videotape made of his lecture concerning psychiatric drugs so that this important information could be disseminated more widely. Dr. Breggin has done much with little or no compensation. This represents his sincere personal commitment to public interest reform. I have also observed that he has a very real and personal concern for individual patients. I and many others know him as a responsible, ethical, and scholarly physician who looks where others dare not look and speaks directly amidst the deafening silence and half-truth.

The Finest Qualities. Ava Crow, attorney, and her staff, State of Kentucky Protection and Advocacy, Louisville, Kentucky.

When the public is clamoring about physicians' incomes, competency, ethics, and lack of compassion, Dr. Breggin can be used as an example of a physician who exemplifies the finest qualities of the medical profession.

Outspoken Patients' Rights Advocate. Norman S. Rosenberg, patients' rights attorney, Washington, District of Columbia.

For many years, Peter Breggin has been an outspoken patients' rights advocate. In his writings and public appearances he has expressed opposition to psychosurgery, electroconvulsive therapy, and the use— especially some psychiatrist's overuse— of chemical interventions. While controversial, Breggin's opinions reflect a view shared by others in the mental health community, including respected psychiatrists and professionals from other disciplines as well as consumers.

A Real Patient Advocacy Group. Rae Unzicker, Coordinator, on behalf of the NAMP Coordinating Committee.

The more than five hundred members of NAMP [National Alliance for Mental Patients] respect Dr. Breggin's right to voice his opinion; moreover, we support his opposition to forced treatment. Further, we recognize that mainline medical-model psychiatrists have had, and continue to have, more than ample opportunity in the media to promulgate their points of view.

More Support from the Psychiatric Survivor Movement. Leonard Roy Frank for NAPA (Network Against Psychiatrist Assault), Berkeley, California.

Many former psychiatric inmates and rights activists with a particular concern about abuses in the field of psychiatry have made ample use of Dr. Breggin's writings to support the position that ECT should be abolished and that psychiatric drugs should never be used without written informed consent from the intended subject....

Since 1972, Dr. Breggin has on many occasions contributed his time free of charge to members of NAPA and other movement organizations for consultation purposes regarding issues of common concern.

His contributions extend beyond the borders of the United States. His writings are widely read among former psychiatric inmates and concerned people in Canada and Australia, and in Europe, where his books have been translated into other languages.

Dr. Breggin has taken a courageous public stand for human rights in psychiatry and against dehumanizing and damaging psychiatric treatments. In doing so, he has performed a major service for people labeled "mentally ill" and the community at large.

Another Close Colleague. Lawrence Tirnauer, Ph.D., psychologist and President, American Academy of Psychotherapists.

I have known Dr. Breggin personally for many years. We have referred patients to each other and have consulted with each other on difficult cases. We recently presented a workshop together at a national meeting of the American Academy of Psychotherapists , (AAP) concerning how to work with difficult patients. Even before he was elected to the AAP membership, Dr. Breggin was invited by to present his views on psychiatric medication at one of our national meetings. I have also heard Dr. Breggin speak on other occasions and I saw him on The Oprah Winfrey Show.

I know Dr. Breggin to be an extremely honest and ethical physician. While his views are controversial, they receive considerable support in many areas of the mental health profession. The presentation of his views has been very beneficial to the AAP, to the mental health profession and to our patients in general.

Highly Respectable. Larry O. Gostin, Executive Director, American Society of Law and Medicine.

I am writing in support of Peter R. Breggin, M.D., the author of *Electroshock: Its Brain Disabling Effects*, and *Psychiatric Drugs: Hazards to the Brain*. As you know, there is a broad range of opinions within the psychiatric community on the subject of psychiatric drugs and the benefits of non-drug psychological care for emotional distress. I believe Dr. Breggin's position to be highly respectable, and worthy of serious consideration among professionals and the informed public.

A Complete Victory

The license attack was turned into a complete victory for Dr. Breggin and an affirmation of his work and his reputation. The licensure board apologized for attacking Dr. Breggin on a matter of freedom of speech and thanked him for his contribution to mental health in the State of Maryland. The media attention and the victory greatly increased Dr. Breggin's visibility and credibility and led to the book contract for *Toxic Psychiatry* from one of the nation's largest publishers.

Dr. Breggin Won't Be Bullied. "Free Speech on Science," editorial, *Courier News*, Kentucky, September 28, 1987.

In April, psychiatrist Peter Breggin of Bethesda, Md., appeared on a television talk show and said he opposed drug and shock therapy for the mentally ill.

Then the National Alliance for the Mentally ill, which endorses the use of anti-psychotic drugs, complained to the Medical and Chirurgical Society of Maryland that some psychiatric patients who had heard Breggin's comments stopped taking their medications. So the medical society ordered Breggin to appear before a committee for possible revocation of his license.

Last week the committee, in a closed-door session, grilled Breggin for an hour. Fortunately, the panel recommended against revoking his license—but not before Breggin was forced to explain his action and present hundreds of documents and statements of support from other psychiatrists. His accusers weren't even at the meeting.

Breggin hadn't told anyone to stop taking medication. He had merely repeated a position he's held for 30 years as a member of the reform movement in psychiatric care. His sin, in the alliance's view, was stating his case on national television.

Such intimidation stifles free scientific inquiry, the give and take that helps scientists hone in on the truth. It also treads on free speech, as guaranteed under the First Amendment.

Apparently, the medical society's committee wasn't too proud of its role in all this. It asked Breggin not to announce its decision on his license to the media.

Breggin did anyway; he will not be bullied. But who knows how many other professionals will tame their views in public because of the treatment Breggin had to endure.

Dismissing the Whole Affair. "Medical Probe: Penalty is Ruled Out for Bethesda Psychiatrist," *The Sun,* Baltimore, Maryland, October 1, 1987.

Dr. Hilary T. O'Herlihy, Chairman of the State Commission on Medical Discipline, called [Dr. Breggin] to tell him the decision.

"It was the recommendation of the (Maryland) attorney general, and the commission agreed, that the complaint was not in our jurisdiction," Dr. O'Herlihy commented last night. "For that reason, we dismissed the whole affair and expunged it from the commission's records."

NAMI is a Sore Loser. "Licensing Panel Takes No Action Against Psychiatrist" by Scott Shane, *Baltimore Sun,* September 24, 1987.

Encouraged by his apparent victory in a medical licensing hearing, Dr. Peter R. Breggin predicted yesterday that the controversy over his remarks against psychiatric medication on the Oprah Winfrey show "will result in the best airing there's ever been of the abusive practices of psychiatry against patients."

The Bethesda psychiatrist said he had been told at the conclusion of the hearing before Maryland medical licensing authorities last Tuesday that he would not be punished for his televised statement.

But Dr. Breggin, 52, who appeared shaken after an hour and 15 minutes before the Physician-Patient Relations Committee of the state medical society, denounced the proceeding as "intimidating" and offensive to his right to free speech, despite its outcome...

A spokesman for NAMI said the group was disappointed by the panel's decision...

Confirmation from the "Newspaper of Record." "Psychiatrist is Cleared in Ethics Case," Science Times, *The New York Times,* October 13, 1987.

A Maryland psychiatrist did not commit a "legal violation or ethical impropriety" when he appeared on a television program and advised patients not to take prescribed medications under certain conditions, the Maryland Commission on Medical Discipline has ruled. ... The commission would not comment on the case but, in a letter to Dr. Breggin, Dr. John B. Dehoff, assistant executive secretary of the Maryland Department of Health and Mental Hygiene, found "that this entire matter is essentially a freedom of speech issue." The commission voted to dismiss the complaint and remove it from the records, the letter said.

Put Simply. "Doctor is Cleared By Medical Board in Oprah Show Fuss," ***Mad Lib,*** **November 1987.**

NAMI—0 Breggin —1...

ATTACKS CONTINUE

Attacks on Dr. Breggin from the psychopharmaceutical complex never wholly abated. In 1998 an attorney who had hired Dr. Breggin as an expert asked him to obtain affidavits from respected professionals confirming his credentials. Although these were never needed or used in court, they provide additional testimonials about Dr. Breggin and his work.

Several affidavits were from dear friends and colleagues who died at the height of their careers (see chapter 12). Others were from colleagues who appear elsewhere in this biography. Here are three additional supporting affidavits:

If We Truly Care...Raymond C. Russ, PhD, psychologist, Editor of the ***Journal of Mind and Behavior.***

It is my opinion that Dr. Peter Breggin's work in the areas of psychopharmacology and drug side effects, methodology and field testing of anti-depressants, issues relating to subject-selection, attrition, and experimental control, is of enormous importance and of the highest quality. Dr. Breggin is the author of several books and peer-reviewed articles, which by their nature scrutinize the psychiatric "status quo." Thus, it may not be surprising that certain members of the psychiatric industry may try to claim otherwise — but any scholar and researcher familiar with Dr. Breggin's work must take his concerns into account if we are to truly care about those persons entering into psychiatric treatment.

Dr. Breggin is of the highest character, a frontrunner in volatile and sensitive areas, a true leader in a politically charged arena.

His knowledge of the scientific process is precise — he couples that with humaneness and a concern for those who for whatever reasons may not adequately be able to fend for themselves. His work cannot be dismissed.

Thoughtful and Thorough. James S. Gordon, MD, psychiatrist, former Chairman of the White House Commission on Complementary and Alternative Medicine and Director of The Center for Mind-Body Medicine, Washington, DC.

Peter Breggin, MD has done extremely useful and thorough reviews of the literature on the use of psychotropic drugs. Dr. Breggin has been a major force in helping psychiatrists to take a critical look at a variety of aspects of research on psychotropic drugs and medical practice. Dr. Breggin's work is often referred to by my psychiatric colleagues in scientific meetings as well as in conversation.

Dr. Breggin is a thoughtful and respectful presenter of his point of view. I have presented to our psychiatric colleagues with him and have found discussions with him to be thought-provoking and helpful.

I have been impressed by the thoughtfulness and thoroughness of Dr. Breggin's work with patients with psychiatric disorders whom I have referred to him.

Doing What is True for Troubled Human Beings. Fred A. Baughman, Jr., MD, neurologist, El Cajon, California.

I have known Dr. Peter R. Breggin through his books and publications for 15-20 years. I have known him personally for 6 years. As a neurologist/child neurologist with a research background, who has discovered and described real diseases, I have observed, with alarm, psychiatry's ties to industry and their not-unrelated propensity to invent "diseases," blaming (and drugging) the patient-victims.

Dr. Breggin is a persistent, effective critic of biologically oriented psychiatry, documenting its near total lack of scientific validation, while calling for less psychopharmacology and polypsychopharmacology and a return to more humane, more scientific psychotherapies.

Dr. Breggin understands, as few in medicine do, how readily the brain can be rendered dysfunctional or permanently damaged. In fact Dr. Breggin knows more about the brain/mind and the patient than any psychiatrist I have ever known.

Chapter Six

Stopping the Federal Violence Initiative

Introduction

In 1992 while her husband was away lecturing, Ginger Breggin heard on the TV news that Frederick Goodwin, the most powerful psychiatrist in the federal government, had made racist remarks, comparing inner-city children to monkeys in a jungle who just want to have sex, reproduce and kill each other.

Goodwin at the time was head of ADAMHA, the administrative umbrella for all of the government's psychiatric and drug addiction research and service agencies. During the ensuing controversy, Goodwin was first demoted to director of NIMH but eventually was forced to resign from the government.

Remembering her husband's close alliance with the Congressional Black Caucus during the anti-psychosurgery campaign, Ginger called U. S. Congressman John Conyers (Dem-Michigan), then the current chairman of the caucus, to request that he obtain the entire transcript of Goodwin's remarks. When the Breggins met with Conyers' staff and read the transcript, they found something much more ominous than a string of racist remarks; they found a racist program, called the Youth Violence Prevention Initiative or simply the Federal Violence Initiative.

Goodwin was preparing a funding proposal to Congress that would organize all of the government's health agencies, including NIH, NIMH and the CDC, to research the genetics and biology of violence. Specifically, the new initiative would seek to find genetic predispositions and biochemical imbalances in inner city children that would explain their violence. This in turn would lead to biological treatments. The Breggins saw this as racist and eugenical, and compared it to events in Nazi Germany where genetic and biological explanations were used to justify the murder of mental patients and then the murder of Jews and other "undesirables."

Peter and Ginger Breggin organized an international campaign to stop the Federal Violence Initiative. Much like his earlier anti-psychosurgery campaign, Dr. Breggin went to the media, spoke at every opportunity from Harlem and Watts to Howard University and the University of Southern California, and before the annual meeting of the U.S. Congressional Black Caucus. He helped to organize a coalition involving many leaders of the African-American community. At the same time, the federal Genome Project was promoting a national conference on the genetics of violence, which the Breggins also viewed as scientifically invalid and racist since no gene for violence has ever been located and since environmental factors so clearly account for violence among youth in America's urban centers.

Peter and Ginger Breggin's successful campaign ended the Violence Initiative and forced an NIH-wide formal examination of all federally-funded studies relating to violence. It also caused a temporary cancellation of the Genome Project conference, which later was reorganized to include political and scientific dissent. Stopping the Violence Initiative was Dr. Breggin's most successful reform effort since the anti-psychosurgery campaign in the 1970s.

As in the license attack, Ginger Breggin played a major role especially in regard to reaching out to the media and to like-minded professionals. Peter and Ginger Breggin told the story of this reform effort in *The War Against Children of Color* (1994, updated in 1998).

The following news article quotes Goodwin's notorious remarks that drew the attention of the Breggins:

"Jungle Fever—Is Violence in the Genes?" by Judith Reitman, *The Village Voice*, August 17, 1993

If you look, for example, at male monkeys, especially in the wild, roughly half of them survive to adulthood. The other half die by violence. That is the natural way of it for males, to knock each other off and, in fact, there are some interesting evolutionary implications of that because the same hyper-aggressive monkeys who kill each other are also hyper-sexual, so they copulate more....Maybe it isn't just the careless use of the word when people call certain areas of certain cities "jungles"....Dr. Frederick K. Goodwin, director, Alcohol Drug Abuse and Mental Health Administration, in referring to the "Violence Initiative." February 11, 1992

They keep a close watch on Fred Goodwin at the National Institute of Mental Health these days, and his Violence Initiative project is officially "dead." But its premise—that violence is rooted in genetics—remains the core of federal mental health policy at the NIMH. And Goodwin's philosophy is the driving force behind controversial youth violence programs that according to opponents will cost the federal government $400 million over five years, beginning in 1994.

The ill-fated Violence Initiative would have authorized the government to identify inner-city children as young as five who are biologically prone to violence, and then treat them with powerful drugs....

Dr. Peter Breggin, director of the Center for the Study of Psychiatry [and Psychology], predicted, "The Violence Initiative will turn the inner cities into Third World pharmaceutical drug markets."....

[Representative John] Conyers requested details from HHS on the initiative and the primate studies to which Goodwin referred. Despite repeated requests, nothing was forthcoming. In fact, Conyers' staff was told by Health and Human Services:

"There is no Violence Initiative." It would take a General Accounting Office investigation, demanded by Conyers, to reveal that the program did, in fact, exist: even then, information was scant….

As pediatrician Kenneth Stoller, codirector of the American Association for Science and Public Policy, observes: "Poor maternal bonding, dysfunctional families, feelings of helplessness in a climate of bigotry and intolerance are set–ups for later violence. We don't need animal studies, we need compassionate social intervention."….

***The New York Times* Takes Notice. "New Storm Brews On Whether Crime Has Roots in Genes" by Daniel Goleman, *The New York Times,* September 15, 1992.**

The cancellation of an academic conference on genetics and crime this month has cast into spotlight a long-simmering scientific debate on the roots of crime and how it can best be prevented….

The objections to the conference were led by Dr. Peter Breggin, a Washington psychiatrist who charged that the meeting was part of a "violence initiative," a Federal research agenda that he said included finding a genetic marker that would identify children at high risk of becoming criminals, and plans to deter them through medications….

Dr. Breggin said his accusations were based on remarks made by Dr. Frederick Goodwin, director of the National Institute of Mental Health, at a meeting of the National Mental Health Advisory Council on Feb.11. Controversy over a statement by Dr. Goodwin at that meeting, which seemed to compare inner cities to jungles, led to his resignation as head of the Alcohol, Drug Abuse, and Mental Health Administration.

At the meeting, Dr. Goodwin spoke of planning for a "violence initiative," which, among other goals, would seek to find biological correlates of violence in males, detecting them early in life, and seeking to prevent their expression. He also asserted that adoption studies had shown that genetic factors in violence and aggression were "very strong."

Dr. Goodwin declined to be interviewed.

Goodwin Resigns

After resigning from the Alcohol, Drug Abuse, and Mental Health Administration, the umbrella organization above all mental health and drug addiction agencies, Goodwin became director of NIMH. Soon after, amid the escalating controversy over his violence initiative, he was forced to resign from the federal government, losing his status as arguably the most powerful psychiatrist in the world.

Canceling the Conference. "Meeting on Possible Links Between Genes and Crime Canceled After Bitter Exchange—U. Of Maryland organizers call off conference after NIH declines to release grant money," ***The Chronicle of Higher Education*****, September 16, 1992.**

A conference to explore potential links between genes and crime has been canceled after an exchange of bitter accusations between its organizers and the National Institutes of Health....

The meeting was attacked by critics as a promotion of inaccurate and racist views that could be used to brand black people as genetically predisposed to crime. The conference organizers said they had wanted to provide an opportunity for rigorous criticism of research on a possible genetic basis for such traits as alcoholism and aggression....

"Any attempt to cloak this conference in issues of peer review, academic freedom, freedom of speech, or any other lofty concept is pure deception," said John W. Diggs in a September 4 letter to the university. Mr. Diggs is deputy director for extramural affairs at the NIH. He told administrators at Maryland that the institutes would not release money for the meeting....

Mr. Diggs' letter said the conference organizers had "grotesquely distorted the nature and the scope of the meeting that was originally approved through the peer-review process." In an interview, Mr. Diggs said that the organizers had tilted the meeting's brochure toward the view that a genetic basis for crime exists and that they had given the impression that the NIH supported that view. Mr. Diggs said the NIH had an obligation not to spend government money on such a meeting....

Even before the NIH suspended financing for the conference in late July, Mr. Waserman had conceded that the conference's brochure and title, "Genetic Factors in Crime," overstated the potential connection between crime and genetics and that both the title and the brochure needed to be changed.....

The critics are celebrating the meeting's cancellation but say that many other similar research and policy initiatives by the federal government still need to be halted.

"The battle has hardly begun," said Peter Breggin, director of the Center for the Study of Psychiatry, based in Bethesda, Md. "The conference was simply the most visible and obviously atrocious example of an attempt to blame crime on the brains and genes of little black children instead of addressing racism and poverty in America."

Dr. Breggin said he was helping to organize opposition in Baltimore, Los Angeles, New York, and Washington to a federal "violence initiative." Officials planning that program at the National Institute of Mental Health, which is about to become part of NIH, said the initiative would not emphasize biological factors in violent behavior.

Speaking in Harlem. "Genetic Link to Violence Assailed—Psychiatrist says blacks are target" by Jamie Talan, *New York Newsday,* September 28, 1992.

Mention inner-city violence and Dr. Peter Breggin sees red. The Harvard-trained psychiatrist stood before 500 people in a packed Harlem auditorium one evening a few weeks ago and told them the government is gearing up to target 100,000 black children nationwide as biologically prone to violence. Then, Breggin claimed, the government will force these schoolchildren to take drugs designed to keep them calm.

"The problem does not lie in the brain or genes of little black children," Breggin said last week from his home in Bethesda, Md. "It is an obscene idea to go into the inner cities and screen for violence on the basis of biological markers. Kids don't have conditions, they live in conditions."

The government denies that there are any plans to drug anyone, or even any programs to identify a mass of violence-prone children. But federal agencies have already spent tens of millions of dollars to study violence and are hoping to spend even more in its proposed Youth Violence Initiative, a bureaucratic centralization of all scientific, medical and social studies on violence. Those expenditures are enough to feed fears among blacks....

Breggin has been at the forefront of a campaign to stop the Youth Violence Initiative. He has met with Los Angeles leaders of the street gangs the Bloods and the Crips, urging that they lobby to prevent federal funding of the Youth Violence Initiative. Breggin also has won support from the Congressional Black Caucus, which held its annual meeting in Washington over the weekend....

Drugs for Aggression? "Impassive Restraint" by Grant Clauser, *Rx Perspective*, April 17, 1995.

[W]hen employing powerful drugs to help manage aggressive patients, opportunities for controversy surface.

"What you're doing with the elderly is you are hurtling them toward dementia, and you're putting them in a chemical straightjacket," said Peter Breggin, MD, executive director of the Center for the Study of Psychiatry in Bethesda, MD. The rate of patients developing the stereotypical muscle spasms of tardive dyskinesia as a result of haloperidol are as high as 20 percent after a year of treatment. After a few years the rate rises to 50 percent, said Breggin. Tardive dyskinesia is associated with dementia, he added, "so these neuroleptic drugs can cause dementia."

Breggin, who has authored a number of books on the subject of psychopharmaceuticals…advises that any responsible physician should avoid as much as possible the use of drugs to manage aggressivity in patients. "Drugs can temporarily suppress a person, but short of just knocking them down and clouding their senses, there aren't any drugs that are particularly effective in controlling violence," observed Breggin….

Killing a $400 Million Dollar Racist Program. "Study to Quell Violence Is Racist, Critics Charge—Leader Defends Plan to Spend $400 Million" by Karen Schneider, *Detroit Free Press*, November 2, 1992.

The battle began with Dr. Frederick Goodwin, the federal government's top psychiatrist. America's inner cities, he said in a speech last February, are like jungles, and the behavior of kids who live there is like violent and hypersexual monkeys.

Met with a firestorm of protest from across the country, Goodwin apologized and was reassigned to another post in the Department of Health and Human Services.

But his comments land like a cloud over the federal government's plans to spend $400 million over five years to try to reduce violence among young people. Opponents call the project racist and promise a furious fight if it comes before Congress for funding next year.

If opposition doesn't kill it, the Department of Health and Human Services in 1994 will launch the Youth Violence Initiative, an unprecedented nationwide effort to identify youths at risk of committing violence and finding ways to prevent it.

Dr. Louis Sullivan, secretary of health and human services, says the project is a public-health approach to violence, no different from the government's all-out attack on smallpox in decades past.

After researchers determine which kids are at risk, they will develop special programs to help them involving schools, parents, teachers, day camps and possible psychiatric treatment.

Those assurances have done nothing to placate black activists and mental health experts around the country. They charge that Violence Initiative is a racist attempt by the government to take control of young black children. And they contend the government is trying to prove that racial minorities are biologically prone to violence...."

***Time Magazine* Identifies Dr. Breggin as Leader of the Opposition. "Seeking the Roots of Violence" by Anastasia Toufexis, *Time,* April 19, 1993.**

....Investigators of the link between biology and crime find themselves caught in one of the most bitter controversies to hit the scientific community in years. The subject has become so politically incorrect that even raising it requires more bravery than many scientists can muster. Critics from the social sciences have denounced biological research efforts as intellectually unjustified and politically motivated. African-American scholars and politicians are particularly incensed; they fear that because of the high crime rates in inner cities, blacks will be wrongly branded as a group programmed for violence.

The backlash has taken a toll. In the past year, a proposed federal research initiative that would have included biological studies has been assailed, and a scheduled conference on genetics and crime has been canceled....

[Biological findings] may be essential to understanding, and perhaps eventually controlling, chronic wrongdoers, argue proponents of this research. "Most youth or adults who commit a violent crime will not commit a second," observes [psychologist Jerome] Kagan. "The group we are concerned with are the recidivists—those who have been arrested many times. This is the group for whom there might be some biological contribution." Kagan predicts that within 25 years, biological and genetic tests will be able to pick out about 15 children of every thousand who may have violent tendencies. But only one of those 15 children will actually become violent, he notes. "Do we tell the mothers of all 15 that their kids might be violent? How are the mothers then going to react to their children if we do that?

It is just such dilemmas that have so alarmed critics. How will the information be used? Some opponents believe the research runs the danger of making women seem to be "prisoners of their hormones." Many black scholars are especially concerned....

The controversy began simmering more than a year ago when Louis Sullivan, then Secretary of Health and Human Services, proposed a $400 million federal research program on violence.... The program was shelved before being submitted to Congress, and one reason may have been the reaction to an unfortunate statement by Dr. Frederick Goodwin, then director of the Alcohol, Drug Abuse, and Mental Health Administration. Commenting about research on violence in monkeys, Goodwin said, "Maybe it isn't just the careless use of the word when people call certain areas of certain cities 'jungles.'" African Americans were outraged. The ensuing furor forced Goodwin to resign....

Soon after that episode, the federally endowed Human Genome Project agreed to provide the University of Maryland with $78,000 for a conference on violence. When the program's organizers announced that [it] would look at genetic factors in crime, opponents torpedoed the meeting....

Dr. Peter Breggin, director of the Center for the Study of Psychiatry [and Psychology] in Bethesda, Maryland, who led the opposition that scuttled the conference, has no apologies. "The primary problems that afflict human beings are not due to their bodies or brains, they are due to the environment," he declares. 'Redefining social problems as public health problems is exactly what was done in Nazi Germany."...

Taking on the Psychiatric Holocaust. "Death for the Mentally Ill? Counseling is the Best Treatment, Psychiatrist Claims," ***Huntington Herald Press,*** **November 11, 1988.**

The extermination of millions of Jews during World War II still shocks the world, but what internationally-known psychiatrist Peter R. Breggin says about the fate of thousands of mentally ill Germans before and during the war is equally disturbing, though little known.

Breggin, who has done years of research on the subject, says thousands of mentally ill patients were exterminated in the years immediately before the war, killings that actually set the stage for the slaughter of millions of Jews in what is now known as the Holocaust.

And Breggin says the lessons learned about euthanasia a half-century ago are still valid today as countries renew the debate about the legality of mercy killings. The lesson, he believes, is to oppose euthanasia, just as strongly as he has criticized electroshock, [psychosurgery] and drug treatment for mentally ill patients.

The War Against Children of Color

The War Against Children of Color (with Ginger Breggin, 1994, updated 1998) received a number of endorsements:

From a DC Health Official: Joye M. Carter, MD, Chief Medical Examiner, Washington, DC.

Flabbergasting and important information. This book needs to get out into the community. We can use this information in understanding and preventing violence among our youth.

From an Expert in Genetics: Leon Kamin, PhD, chairman of the Department of Psychology, Northeastern University, and coauthor of *Not in Our Genes.*

Sounds a necessary alarm.

Uncomfortably Persuasive. Jonathan Kozol, author of *Savage Inequalities* and *Letters to a Young Teacher.*

Terrifying data conveyed in the calm and sober voice of an experienced and respected physician and researcher. A brilliantly controversial and, for me, uncomfortably persuasive work—and a major contribution to our understanding of racism as it infiltrates our society and culture.

The Plight of Children and America. Samuel F. Yette, author of *The Choice* and former professor of journalism , Howard University.

The Breggins write knowledgeably and passionately not only about the sad, new plight of American's children, but also, inevitably, about the plight of America herself.

Read This Book. Louise Armstrong, author of *Kiss Daddy Goodnight* and *And They Call it Help: The Psychiatric Policing of America's Children.*

Before singing one more anthem to children as our nation's hope, we should all read this book.

An Epidemic of Troubles. James Hillman in *The Soul's Code—In Search of Character and Calling* (1996).

The War Against Children [of Color], as Peter and Ginger Breggin entitle their recent book, threatens American children with an epidemic of troubles caused by the methods that would cure them of their troubles. The familiar evils of other ages reappear in the guises of helping programs, pharmaceutical prevention, and apartheid segregations. It's all back again—eugenics, white racism, sterilization, forced removal, banishment to beggary, punishment, and starvation. As in colonial days, drugs to ease the coolies' pain and increase their indifference will be provided by those who cause the pain.

Chapter Seven

Exposing Drug Company Influence

Introduction

In 1983 Dr. Breggin published *Psychiatric Drugs: Hazards to the Brain,* the first medical book devoted wholly to the dangers of psychiatric drugs, especially their impact on the central nervous system and mind. Eventually it grew into the first and second editions of *Brain-Disabling Treatments in Psychiatry.* The most recent edition was published in 2008.

Breggin's medical books developed the theme that all psychiatric treatments disable the brain and diminish mental functioning. In the most obvious medication example, the so-called antipsychotic drugs disrupt neurotransmission to the frontal lobes causing lobotomy-like apathy and docility. This is the opposite of a genuine therapy that enhances the individual's capacity for thinking, feeling, autonomous action and the pursuit of higher ideals.

Dr. Breggin's 1983 book alerted the profession to the danger of tardive dyskinesia in children, a subject that until then was almost taboo. Caused by neuroleptic or "antipsychotic" drugs, tardive dyskinesia is a potentially devastating neurological disorder with disfiguring and, in the extreme, disabling abnormal movements. *Psychiatric Drugs* also alerted the profession to the danger of dementia produced by longer-term exposure to neuroleptic drugs, a subject most psychiatrists still try to deny or to avoid. In 1983 Dan Rather built an hour-long TV news feature around the book. Because of the book and media attention that Dr. Breggin generated, the FDA felt compelled to respond by developing a new class label warning about tardive dyskinesia for all of the antipsychotic drugs. The FDA-approved label (also known as the package insert) is very influential and appears in the *Physicians' Desk Reference.*

In 1991 Dr. Breggin elaborated on the psychopharmaceutical complex in *Toxic Psychiatry.* A series of books followed, including *Talking Back to Prozac* (with Ginger Breggin, 1994), *Talking Back to Ritalin* (revised, 2001), *The Ritalin Fact Book* (2002) and the *Antidepressant Fact Book* (2001).

Dr. Breggin's most recent book, *Medication Madness: A Psychiatrist Exposes the Dangers of Mood-Altering Drugs* (2008) vividly presents dozens of dramatic cases of individuals driven into bizarre and destructive behaviors and madness by psychiatric drugs.

Another recent book, *Brain-Disabling Treatments in Psychiatry: Drugs, Electroshock and the Psychopharmaceutical Complex, Second Edition* (2008), provides a more in-depth scientific analysis behind his concepts of brain-disabling treatments and medication spellbinding.

Since his earliest medical books, Dr. Breggin has continued to develop the brain-disabling principle of psychiatric treatment. It states that all physical treatments in psychiatry—drugs, electroshock and psychosurgery—disable the brain, and that none improve brain function.

Recently, he has added the theory of medication spellbinding (technically, intoxication anosognosia) which helps to explain why so many people take so many different kinds of psychoactive drugs despite the fact that they do more harm than good. Physical interventions that disrupt brain function, including all psychiatric drugs, tend to hide their damaging mental and emotional effects from the injured individual, rendering the medicated person unable to detect the adverse effects or to properly identify them as caused by the drug. Some people end up believing that they are doing better than ever when they are doing worse, and a number end up committing acts of suicide, violence or criminality that would ordinarily have appalled them when drug-free.

Decades of media coverage have helped to carry Dr. Breggin's observations to the public and professionals alike. Excerpts of some of the media coverage, along with book endoresements and book reviews follow.

***Time Magazine:* Psychiatry's Chief Gadfly? Contents page, *Time,* October 10, 1994.**

Taking Potshots at Prozac: Psychiatry's chief gadfly claims pills don't help mentally ill.

***Time* says Breggin is Prozac's Worst Enemy. "Prozac's Worst Enemy" by Christine Gorman, *Time,* October 10, 1994.**

[Breggin] has earned impressive academic credentials, published a string of books and shown up on Today and The Oprah Winfrey Show. Many patients rave about the doctor. "He's a wonderful person," says one satisfied customer. "He cares so much about his clients. He gave me the will to get better."...

Breggin didn't start out to be a renegade. As his book jackets proudly point out, his background is pure establishment: Harvard College, Case Western Reserve Medical School, a teaching fellowship at Harvard Medical School. But early in his career, he became deeply disturbed by the treatment of psychiatric patients, particularly the many long-term residents of mental hospitals who spend their lives in a drugged-out state.

In 1972 Breggin declared his rebellion, launching the Center for the Study of Psychiatry in Bethesda, Maryland, as a way to push for reform.

The FDA Plays Catch Up with Dr. Breggin. "FDA to Review Risks of Antidepressants in Adults" by Jeanne Lenzer, *British*

Medical Journal, **October 9, 2004.**

The US Food and Drug Administration (FDA) announced last week that it will examine whether antidepressants pose a similar risk of increased suicidal thoughts among adults as they do for children, by reanalyzing data for adults....

Psychiatrist and clinical psychopharmacologist Dr. Peter Breggin, who first described the risks of violence and suicide induced by selective serotonin reuptake inhibitors in his book *Talking Back to Prozac,* published in 1994, welcomes the review. "The stimulant effects of antidepressants that cause mania, agitation, insomnia, and akathisia could be causing deadly reactions," he told *BMJ.*

America's Most Outstanding Critic. "Your Turn" by Kathy Fountain, Fox TV 13, Tampa, Florida, July 7, 2008 (available for viewing on www.breggin.com).

A man unafraid to challenge the American medical system. ... Years before these [antidepressant suicide] warnings became general knowledge, my guest was sounding the alarm about the dangers of these drugs. Peter Breggin is probably America's most outstanding critic.

Can Psychiatrists Offer Psychotherapy? "Psychiatrists Ill Prepared to Treat Crises—[Says] U.S. Doctor" ***The Gazette,*** **October 16, 1992.**

"Psychiatrists are among the worst-equipped professionals to help people deal with emotional crises," U.S. psychiatrist Peter Breggin said yesterday.

The job would be better left to lay people... "The healing process is, astonishingly, simply being with another human being," he said.

"The whole antidote to feelings of terror and fear and violence is someone being there."

People in crisis need a friend more than they require drugging or confinement to a psychiatric ward, he said....

Breggin got a chuckle out of his audience when he talked about the power of feeling wanted. Sometimes his dogs sense when he's feeling down and jump on to his lap, making him feel like the most important person in the world. "Basically, if you are more like a Shetland sheepdog than a psychiatrist, you will be very successful."....

Warning About Withdrawal Symptoms. "A Big Letdown? Lawsuits charge that quitting the popular antidepressant Paxil cold turkey can cause terrifying symptoms," ***People,*** **May 12, 2003.**

[L]ike Prozac and Zoloft, the drug [Paxil] relieves depression by ensuring the free flow of serotonin, a chemical that transmits crucial information between brain cells. But Paxil leaves the body far more quickly than its cousins, which can make quitting that much harder, especially for people particularly sensitive to serotonin fluctuations. "Skip a dose," says Dr. Peter Breggin, author of *The Antidepressant Fact Book,* "and you could get symptoms the same day."...

A List of Dangerous Labels. "Rewriting the Dictionary of Madness" by Ann Japanga, ***Los Angeles Times Magazine,*** **June 5, 1994.**

Is the Diagnostic and Statistical Manual of Mental Health Disorders a work of pure science or just a list of dangerous labels?

Patients walk into Peter Breggin's office and lay their diagnosis on the couch: They're depressed. They're anxious. They're sure they have a measurable, palpable illness, with shape, substance, gravity, consistency.

"A little boy came in with his parents and I asked him: 'Do you know why you're here?'" Breggin says.

"Yes. I'm here because you're the doctor who doesn't believe I should take Ritalin for my ADHD [attention deficit hyperactivity disorder]."

"Well, you've got it close," Breggin answered. "I'm the doctor who doesn't think you've even got ADHD."

It isn't surprising the boy was already identifying himself by his mental disorder. Psych-speak pervades our culture. Folks bandy about psychiatric labels in espresso bars and in school lunchrooms, at supermarkets and on talk shows; we diagnose ourselves and we tag each other: I'm the manic; you're a little obsessive-compulsive. Some of these we pluck from the magazines, others from self-help books. Because the labels are so often intoned, they've come to seem as substantive as a diagnosis of pneumonia or diabetes.

"The public believes these things are real," says Breggin, director of the nonprofit Center for the Study of Psychiatry in Bethesda, Md., and author of the soon-to-be-released *"Talking Back to Prozac."* "They come into my office thinking they have 'it.' People scream at me: 'I have clinical depression!'"

Though everyone seems to believe that mental illnesses have a biochemical basis, Breggin points out that no one has ever been able to prove that these illnesses—such as depression, panic disorder and even schizophrenia—are biological conditions. All the psychiatric community knows is that some patients respond to drugs; some psychiatrists acknowledge that they are treating symptoms rather than a quantifiable illness.

"How do you convince [patients] that a bunch of guys just made this stuff up?" asks Breggin exasperatedly. "They made it up." The renegade psychiatrist did at least manage to convince his young patient that he didn't have an immutable, classifiable "it." Says Breggin: "That boy left here singing for the first time in months."

A Psychiatric Journal Beholden to the Drug Companies. "Upjohn Willingly Settles for Silence" by Kim Cobb and Ste-

ven R. Reed, *Houston Chronicle,* September 11, 1994.

In his book *Toxic Psychiatry,* Dr. Peter Breggin of Bethesda, Md., revealed another example of the late Dr. Daniel X. Freedman using the *Archives of General Psychiatry* to further a hidden agenda on behalf of Upjohn.

Breggin contended that a 1988 article about an eight-week study of Xanax, a panic disorder drug that is the chemical cousin of Halcion, misled readers. The introductory summary, Breggin wrote, described only the more encouraging first four weeks of the trial without mentioning that it had gone on for four additional weeks with far less promising results.

Freedman then tried to obstruct publication of a letter in which 11 psychiatrists and psychologists criticized Upjohn's Xanax studies, according to Breggin.

One of the 11 said that Freedman delayed publication of the letter for 14 months after the original article appeared and refused to publish a "damning table" showing Xanax was almost ineffective at eight weeks.

"Freedman rejected as unfounded any skepticism about his own dual role as a consultant to Upjohn and editor of the journal publishing the Upjohn-sponsored research..." Breggin wrote. "Freedman applied the terms 'Marxist' and 'paranoid' to concerns about drug company influence over research."

Breggin Exposes Prozac. Book Review of *Talking Back to Prozac* by Chris Goodrich, *Los Angeles Times,* September 25, 1994.

"[P]rozac," writes Dr. Peter Breggin, "constitutes a toxic interference into the brain. If it feels good, it means that the individual prefers impaired brain function to normal brain function." Passages like that have made Breggin, author of the best-selling *"Toxic Psychiatry"* and other books, unpopular with the pharmaceutical industry, and *"Talking Back to Prozac"* won't make him any new friends in the field...though it does vindicate many patients who have had unpleasant experiences with psychiatric medications....

Decades as a Reluctant Warrior. "Warriors in Waiting" by Martha Sherrill, *The Washington Post,* September 1, 1995.

We are drowsy, slumbery. A dead perfect quiet, a peace, comes to Washington over Labor Day weekend. The insanity has long stopped. A cease-fire has been struck. The marble corridors of Capital Hill are empty, the soldiers of party politics have taken off for their home states. The lobbyists have gone too, transporting their favors and boozy dinners to the beach....

But here and there you might find a few left. The political animals, the die-hards...Some people in politics have little else in their lives. They are the strange swamp warriors, living for combat, for scraps and intrigue....

"You have to have a willingness to endure conflict. You really have to relish conflict," says [Ralph] Nader of the personality of the long-term successful advocate. "You have to be able to insulate yourself from discouragement and defeats, and have a rebound characteristic...."

Peter Breggin, a psychiatrist based in Bethesda, has given up the hostility that shadowed him for decades as a reformer. "I made a spiritual decision in life that I no longer wanted to get anybody....and I don't want to be working out of anger. And it's a lifelong struggle."

In the old days he was a classic angry young man, he says. But now, looking back, he thinks he just felt bad for other people, had empathy he didn't know what to do with....

"But I was so naïve! I was so young! And so angry!" he says. "And I was so shocked when the psychiatric community came up against me."

No longer shocked or naïve—or so young—Breggin has been fighting the psychiatry establishment for decades. First he protested state-performed lobotomies, then electroshock therapy. More recently he's been writing books, *"Toxic Psychiatry"* and *"Talking Back to Prozac,"* and fighting the use of drugs to treat emotional problems. Along the way, he has endured lawsuits, attempts to revoke his license and frequent dismissals from the media.

Sitting in his cluttered home office in Bethesda, a brown cozy cave of a place with leather chairs and wooden carvings, Breggin seems like a pleasant and satisfied man. Happy....he seems very alive and has a cheeriness that contradicts his image as a fighter.

What keeps him in the struggle? Childhood memories? Nostalgia for his college days? "Personal issues aren't the best motivator," he says in his soft voice. "You don't last that way. It's exhausting. Your ego is always getting bruised. It's involved in winning and losing, and you lose too much. That's how you become a miserable human being."

What then?

"Principles," he says. "I've lived a life which, for better or worse, I've attempted to live by principles. Sometimes I've flubbed them very badly, too. But I believe in the principles of doing certain things—and that seems hard for your average press person to deal with. People don't want to believe that life is a matter of principle, yet I don't see how else you could live."...

Breggin dreams about giving it all up, about being free from testifying in lawsuits and giving interviews like this one. He dreams of spending more time with his grown kids, his wife, Ginger, his dogs. But every time Breggin tries to retire, and he's tried several times—bought a country house, wrote a novel, wrote a play—something always happens to pull him back into the fray.

"Each time there's some signal that I'm supposed to keep going, like some horrendous new attack on me," he says. "Probably any reformer gets into these spiritual wonderings about what's going on in the universe that keeps them in their work.... But in all of us, there's probably some sense there's something beyond us, something making us do it."

And so it is—for a tiny percentage of us. It's a calling, a faith. An inexplicable desire. "It feels like I'm doing it," says Breggin, "almost against my will."

Not Many Fighters in Psychiatry. "Just Saying No to Drugs," *Baltimore Sun*, Oct. 9, 1987.

Dr. Lawrence Tirnauer, a clinical psychologist from Chevy Chase who is president of the American Academy of Psychotherapists, praises his friend. "In the field of psychiatry, there are not that many fighters. And as long as I've known him, Peter has fought to help people avoid psychiatric abuse."

Antipsychotic Drugs Cause a Chemical Lobotomy. "Mental Illness from Psychiatric Drugs?" by W. Herbert, *Science News*, October 1, 1983.

The powerful tranquilizers that are commonly used to control schizophrenic psychosis and to manage problem behavior may in some cases be doing as much damage as good....

Peter Breggin, a Bethesda, Md. psychiatrist and author of the recently published book, *Psychiatric Drugs: Hazards to the Brain*, argues that the evidence is overwhelming; psychiatrists, he says, simply cannot admit that they have effectively "lobotomized" millions of patients with chemicals that are toxic to the brain. The euphoria that [pro-drug] doctors report is a symptom of dementia, or general brain deterioration, Breggin says; in fact, he adds, the literature on tardive dyskinesia reveals that most people with the movement disorder are also demented. The euphoria changes to apathy as the brain continues to deteriorate, Breggin says, and ultimately the chemical damage to the frontal lobes accomplishes the same thing as psychosurgery. Only a lobotomized patient would be indifferent about a disorder like tardive dyskinesia, as most older chronic schizophrenics are....

A Chilly Embrace. "Drugs vs. the Couch" by David Gelman, *Newsweek,* March 26, 1990.

The discovery of new medications for emotional disorders stirs a debate between traditional talk therapists and the advocates of 'biopsychiatry'...

As Freud foresaw, biology and psychiatry have met. They have, moreover, embraced, and brought forth a robust new discipline called biopsychiatry that strongly emphasizes the neurological underpinnings of emotional illness.

Yet the embrace is rather chilly. Many traditional talk therapists have taken readily enough to prescribing medications like Prozac....

On the other hand, some therapists can't help feeling that the trend to neurology threatens their long-held sovereignty over matters of the mind...

If there is a biological bias these days, it is most clearly reflected in psychiatric education... [A] Washington-area psychiatrist who sat on a panel conducting student board examinations last week, says he found himself "distressed about young people coming through and all they talk about is drugs. They don't talk about patients." That was already happening a quarter of a century ago, according to psychiatrist Peter Breggin, who recalls that when he entered training in 1966, he spent only one hour a week learning how to be a "talking doctor." The rest of the time the emphasis was on drugs and electroshock...

Red Flags at Eli Lilly. "Bitter Pill for the Maker of Prozac" by Kelly O'Meara, *Insight,* April 29, 1991.

A case study that linked the popular antidepressant Prozac to suicidal tendencies has opened the gates to lawsuits....

Approved by the Food and Drug Administration in December 1987, Prozac has captured 20 percent of the antidepressant market, has treated more than 3 million people in 45 countries and is expected to gross $1.1 billion for Lilly this year.

But the capsule that Newsweek magazine featured splashily on its cover last summer as a 'miracle drug" with few of the unpleasant side effects of older antidepressants has found its way into the police beat stories of newspapers as a "miracle defense" in murder cases and as a purported cause of suicide....

About 70 civil lawsuits over Prozac have been filed against Lilly in state courts across the country. Most accuse the company of failing to test the drug properly before releasing it and of not warning physicians that a small percentage of people could become suicidal or violent. Lending credence to these allegations, lawyers say, are some 12,400 reports of adverse effects on file with the FDA, including self-mutilation, suicidal obsessions and homicidal thoughts....

What gave rise to the suits was a case study published in the American Journal of Psychiatry 14 months ago in which Dr. Martin H. Teicher of the Harvard Medical School observed six patients who were depressed but free of suicidal tendencies. He noted that they developed "intense, violent suicidal preoccupation after two to seven weeks" on Prozac. Two other case studies show similar results.

But researchers have not explained how Prozac, whose chemical name is fluoxetine hydrochloride, could cause such behavior. The drug works on a neurotransmitter in the brain called serotonin....

Prozac maintains high levels of serotonin in the synapses for a longer time. Flooding the brain in this way shuts down the brain's own production of serotonin, resulting in low levels that trigger aggressive behavior, says Bethesda, Md. Psychiatrist Peter Breggin, a longtime critic of drug and shock treatments for the mentally ill.

"This should have set off terrible red flags at Eli Lilly," says Breggin, who will be an expert witness in several [Prozac related] cases.

High Level Imagining. "Better Therapy Through Chemistry?" by Laura M. Markowitz, *The Family Therapy Networker,* May/June 1991.

[F]or family therapists, who have harbored a deep skepticism about psychotropic drugs since the earliest days of the field, the issue is not so much whether Prozac causes clients to suicide or become violent, but rather how to think about this new development and its impact on the practice of therapy....

"The medical theory of depression is high level imagining," argues psychiatrist Peter Breggin. "We don't have sound evidence that psychiatric disorders are related to genetics or biochemistry. Notions of clinical signs of depression are utter nonsense. Weight loss and sleeplessness are not an indication of a biological disorder; even chimpanzees in the wild lose weight and become irritable and physically dilapidated if they experience loss. Then they are nurtured by another chimp, they perk up and start eating and sleeping, and recover."....

The greatest danger of a drug like Prozac for family therapists may not be the violent side effects alleged in the court cases, but its potential to undermine the broad view of context that has been the hallmark of the field....

Psychiatric Judgment Impaired. "Can Drugs Treat the Mind?" *Glamour,* August 1991

[C]ritics of biopsychiatry say psychiatrists have several not-so-disinterested reasons for advocating drug treatment, which can produce addiction and other unpleasant or dangerous side effects.

In recent years, psychiatrists have lost much professional turf to psychologists, clinical social workers and counselors—that is, non-M.D. therapists—who can provide the same services they do for far lower fees. The ability to prescribe drugs, which for the most part, only M.D.s can do, gives psychiatry an apparent edge over the competition.

But as Peter Breggin, MD, documents in his upcoming book, *Toxic Psychiatry,* psychiatrists' ability to evaluate the worth of drug therapy may have been compromised by the close ties between the profession and drug companies which fund psychiatric professional meetings, journals, and even research....

Larry King Live! Duncan Campbell, Producer, Larry King Live, November 6, 1991.

Dear Dr. Breggin,

Thank you once again for taking the time to be a guest on Larry King Live!

As usual, we have been hearing many positive comments about your appearance. We hope you are as pleased with the response.

We hope you enjoyed the interview. Larry always enjoys speaking with you and is looking forward to having the opportunity again soon.

Creative Leadership. "Commentary" by Thomas Greening, PhD., editor, *Journal of Humanistic Psychology,* Volume 43, No. 2, 2003.

Peter Breggin [is] a creative leader of the critique of psychiatry and psychology. Repeatedly, he has opened my eyes to the dangerous nonsense perpetrated by my own profession and others.

Kudos for *Toxic Psychiatry* (1991)

After the attack on Dr. Breggin's medical license was defeated, he received a contract to write *Toxic Psychiatry* which was published in 1991. Now he was in the middle of that whirlwind time filled with media attention, enjoying his wife and children, seeing a full week of patients, and writing another book.

Like-minded colleagues embraced the message of *Toxic Psychiatry*, media discussed it, and the biopsychiatric field tried and continued to fail to dismiss the book and to dismiss Dr. Breggin. Endorsements for the book poured in, included the following:

The Conscience of American Psychiatry. Bertram P. Karon, PhD, Professor of Psychology, Michigan State University and author of *Psychotherapy of Schizophrenia*.

Dr. Breggin is the conscience of American Psychiatry. The truths he tells are important not only for patients and professionals, but also for the general public. Definitely a 'must read;' even more important, a 'must think about.'

Addressing Pseudoscience Head-On. Loren Mosher, MD, Clinical Professor of Psychiatry, Former Chief of the Center for Studies of Schizophrenia, The National Institute of Mental Health.

Much of today's psychiatric science is based on wish, myth, and politics. Breggin addresses this self-serving pseudoscience head-on.

A Scathing Indictment (1991). "Take Two of These And Call Me When You're Stable," book review of *Toxic Psychiatry* by J. Patrick Gannon, *San Francisco Chronicle*, February 9, 1992.

"*Toxic Psychiatry*," a scathing indictment of biologically oriented treatments of mental illness, should sound an alarm for professionals and consumers alike. Citing the dangers of psychotropic drugs, electroshock therapy and the search for the "magic bullet," psychiatrist Peter Breggin contends that his profession has abandoned its heritage of talking-therapy for biochemical quick fixes that make psychiatrists less healers than lab technicians.

"People suffering from what used to be thought of as 'neuroses' and 'personal problems' are being treated with drugs and shock," says Breggin. "Children with problems that once were handled by remedial education or improved parenting are instead being subjected to medical diagnoses, drugs and hospitals. Old people who used to be cared for by their families are being drugged in nursing homes that find it more cost effective to provide a pill than a caring, stimulating environment."

Modern psychiatry, he implies, is becoming the fast food franchise of the mental health professions, dispensing pills like Big Macs with a hungry eye on the profit margin….

The Leading Voice. Eileen Walkenstein, MD, psychiatrist and author of *Beyond the Couch, Don't Shrink to Fit* and *Your Inner Therapist.*

Peter Breggin is the leading voice in this country exposing psychiatry's betrayal of the most fundamental essence of what it means to be human. In this Drug Age, read this book before your next dose.

An Unholy Split Between the Superego and the ID. "Conformity, Control and Coercion," book review of *Toxic Psychiatry, New Scientist,* 10, April 1993.

Peter Breggin has been described as "the conscience of American psychiatry." In that analogy, the profession is suffering an unholy split between its id and its superego.

Breggin is Professor (Adjunct) of Conflict Analysis and Resolution at George Mason University, Virginia, and former consultant to the US National Institute of Mental Health. He declares that "all of the major psychiatric treatments (surgery, drugs, electroshock) work by producing brain dysfunction." He is sincere, erudite and very, very angry….

Only a biopsychiatric perspective justifies treating people against their will. Breggin neatly turns the liberal argument for keeping "mentally disordered" offenders out of prison on its head, claiming that locking people up should be seen as a police activity and not a therapeutic one. Enforced medication or incarceration is a power that no other medical specialty has; it corrupts, encourages brutal and oppressive treatments and makes psychotherapy or other attempts to help nearly impossible.

"There is no place for the political institution of psychiatry in a free society and it should be abolished," Breggin says. Whether this book will help in the attempt is a moot point. Social change is an ambitious goal, even for the conscience of a nation.

A Tremendous Service. Richard Shulman, PhD, Director of Volunteers in Psychotherapy (www.CTVIP.org), letter to Peter Breggin, 1992.

I have just completed reading *Toxic Psychiatry* and I am writing to express my appreciation. Many times, as I was reading your book, I thought about the effort, dedication and courage it took to face the difficult issues you addressed—to research them so thoroughly, and to speak up so eloquently.

I know that I felt this way when I read two of your other books, but I thought I should add my voice to what I'm sure by now is a wide chorus of thanks and congratulations. This seemed especially important because I know that when you're doing such massive research and preparation, you are often doing it alone. In addition, since we work in professions that can be so dogmatic, intolerant and condemnatory in reaction to differing viewpoints, I felt it was important to tell you how grateful I am that you wrote this book.

We have spoken of our mutual interest regarding "schizophrenia," but I was also greatly heartened to hear you speak out about "hyperactivity." For several years I worked in a children's clinic, where I came to opinions very similar to your own. Regularly I would find that there were un-addressed or submerged familial tensions, where children were so labeled, and that when these issues were discussed more openly, the problems subsided considerably. It seemed to me that these children frequently felt compelled to test out their sense that they were seen as bad or unlovable, or the source of everyone's problems—and that they would test this out by somewhat provocative tactics.

Also, it often occurred that the children felt deprived of parental attention and involvement, or parental authority or firmness would be problematic or inconsistent. At any rate, the pseudo-medical labeling of these problems is a glaring problem; as with so many other issues in "mental health." I am in strong agreement with much of what you wrote about, and I think you have done us all a tremendous service.

Breggin's next medical textbook: *Brain-Disabling Treatments in Psychiatry* (1997) (2008)

Peter Breggin's medical text, *Brain-Disabling Treatments in Psychiatry, (1997, Second Ed. 2008)* was published by Springer Publishing Company. The book broke ground by clearly exposing the adverse reactions and other hazards of the newest classes of psychiatric drugs including the SSRIs and the so-called atypical antipsychotics. Manipulations of scientific and public information by drug companies was also documented and thoroughly referenced.

The Definitive Text. Kevin F. McCready, PhD, Clinical Director, San Joaquin Psychotherapy Center, Clovis, CA.

Peter Breggin has written the definitive text for professionals and the public alike who really want to know the hazards, inadequacies and illusions of psychopharmacology. This book will be a foundation for those who specialize in medication-free treatment."

Breggin and Colleague Write *Your Drug May Be Your Problem* (1999, 2007)

Peter Breggin devoted time between his general psychiatric texts to address the unique issues of children (see Chapter 9).

The first and definitive book written specifically to provide patients and health care providers with detailed information about how to safely come off of psychiatric drugs was written by Dr. Breggin and colleague David Cohen, PhD.

Your Drug May Be Your Problem carefully documented the many adverse effects and dangerous impacts of psychiatric drugs. Then the book provided detailed and clear direction on how to properly taper off the various psychiatric medications.

Suddenly, patients, family members, their counselors and physicians had the information needed to identify drug effects and problems. Further, a clear road map of how to withdraw from psychiatric drugs as well as the information needed to correct the problems caused by drugs was provided.

After the first edition of the book was published in 1999, the two authors were innundated by thank you letters from psychiatric patients around the world and *Your Drug May Be Your Problem* received ringing endorsements. A second edition was published in 2007.

A Great Scientist's Endorsement. Candace Pert, PhD, Research Professor of Physiology and Biophysics, Georgetown University Medical Center, author of *Molecules of the Mind,* Washington, DC .

In non-technical, easy to understand language, Peter Breggin and David Cohen bring an incredibly important and hardly ever recognized message to people who need to understand the dark side of psychiatric drugs and how to stop taking them. I heartily recommend it.

Another Great Scientist's Endorsement. Steven Rose, PhD, Professor of Biology and Director, Brain and Behavior Research Group, Open University, Milton Keynes, England.

The modern medical approach to almost any human problem is to find a drug—a sort of magic bullet—to fix it. But many drugs do more harm than good, and some even cause the problems they are supposed to fix. And once on a drug, coming off may also be dangerous. In this clear and important book, Peter Breggin and David Cohen outline the problems and provide a step-by-step account of how to come off the drug which may be harming you.

A Great Research Psychiatrist's Endorsement. Loren Mosher, MD, Soteria Associates, Former Chief of the Center for Studies in Schizophrenia, NIMH, San Diego, CA.

Confronting current psychiatric drug prescribing practice head-on is a daunting task— we owe Breggin and Cohen a vote of thanks for openly speaking the truth. Despite what the pharmaceutical companies would have us believe, we don't need 'a better life through chemistry.' This book will help debunk this myth and provide practical advice on how to avoid psychiatric drugs and get off them.

A Great Science Writer's endorsement. John Horgan, author of *The End of Science* and *The Undiscovered Mind,* Garrison, NY.

This is a courageous, compassionate book, and a much needed antidote to the pro-drug bias of modern psychiatry and psychology.

Another Great Science Writer's Endorsement. Thomas J. Moore, author of *Prescription for Disaster: The Hidden Dangers in Your Medicine Closet,* Washington, DC.

Your Drug May Be Your Problem is a clear, accurate, and thorough look at the dangers of psychiatric drugs, and a prudent outline of what steps to take for those who want to stop taking them.

A Great Sociologist's Endorsement. Thomas J. Scheff, PhD, Professor Emeritus of Sociology, University of California, Santa Barbara, CA.

I highly recommend this book to persons on psychiatric drugs, and to the physicians who prescribe them. These drugs are very powerful, either for good or for harm. Since the actions for almost all of them are still unknown, the people who use them are being experimented on, mostly without their knowledge.

Drs. Breggin and Cohen are experts on the negative effects of drugs. Their views should be just as widely known as the misleadingly positive advocations of the drug companies.

Growing Cultural Pathology. Fred Bemak, PhD, Professor of Counselor Education and Section Head for Wellness and Human Services, College of Education, Ohio State University, Columbus, OH (Now at George Mason University).

This book leads the way in explaining and redefining the growing pathology of the culture of psychiatric medications. It is a reminder of where we are and a non-medical prescription of where we can go.

A Gold Mine of Information. Tony Stanton, MD, Psychiatric Consultant, Bremerton, Washington.

Working as a consultant, I am constantly looking for ways to help clients achieve a more educated view regarding psychotropic medication. Breggin and Cohen have assembled a gold mine of information to assist in this process. I can think of no other book that has done such a superb job of making such information accessible at any point of decision regarding taking or discontinuing psychotropic medication.

A Book for the Century. Alberto Fergusson, MD, Psychiatrist, Psychoanalyst, and Institute Director, Bogotá, Colombia.

This book is one of the most important things that has happened to psychiatry and especially to so-called 'psychiatric patients' during this century.

Having worked for more than 20 years with so-called schizophrenics— the main victims of the abuse by prescribed psychiatric drugs— I can say that Peter Breggin and David Cohen must be praised for the courage they have had to unmask many pseudoscientific conclusions frequently present in supposedly scientific literature.

A Great Feminist Writer's Endorsement. Kate Millet, PhD, author of *Sexual Politics* and *The Looney Bin Trip*, NY, NY.

I wish I had this book when I was trying to come off psychiatric drugs. How wonderful that you have provided this guide.

Enthusiastic Agreement from a Great Psychiatrist. William Glasser, MD, psychiatrist and author of *Reality Therapy* and *Reality Therapy in Action*, Chatsworth, California.

Nowhere does the false medical thinking—that there is a drug cure for almost all common diseases—do more harm than in the modern psychiatric argument that mental illness is easily diagnosed and then cured by a side-effect-free drug.

Nowhere is the correct psychiatric thinking more evident than in the books by Peter Breggin. In them he explains clearly that patients with mental illnesses are in almost all instances suffering from their inability to connect with important people in their lives and need help making these vital connections.

He supports safe, drug-free counseling as a more effective way to help people, and I enthusiastically agree with this premise.

Struggling with Life's Issues. Al Siebert, PhD, author of *The Survivor Personality*, Portland, Oregon.

Emotional maturity, self-confidence, and life competence come from struggling with stresses, fears, and adversities. When young people become addicted to drugs they remain emotionally immature until they quit and start learning to cope. Breggin and Cohen point out that the same is true of chronic users of psychiatric medications. It is not until they withdraw from the chemical dependency urged on them by psychiatry, that they can develop inner strengths for coping with life's difficulties.

A Turning Point. Douglas C. Smith, MD, Psychiatrist, Juneau, AK.

One hundred years from now, people will read current psychiatric textbooks with the same incredulity we have about bloodletting and snake oil.

Your Drug May Be Your Problem will be remembered as the turning point and as the beacon that showed the way out of these dark days of widespread psychiatric drugging. Breggin and Cohen, like trusted friends, provide us with critical information we need to know in order to make informed decisions about psychiatric drugs, including when and how to stop taking them. They present it all within a coherent philosophy of life and health that makes the routine use of psychiatric drugs obsolete. If you have reached that inevitable point of being disillusioned with your psychiatric drug, this book will be your friend and guide.

A Godsend. Clemmont E. Vontress, PhD, Professor Emeritus of Counseling, George Washington University, recipient of the Counselor Educator of the Year Award (1995) from the American Mental Health Counselors Association, Washington, DC.

This innovative, informative, and easy-to-read book is a godsend for non-medical people such as parents, teachers, counselors, social workers, and psychologists who need to know the potential dangers of referring their children, students, or clients to physicians for psychiatric medication.

Combating Propaganda. Wolf Wolfensberger, PhD, Research Professor of Education, Syracuse University, Director, Training Institute for Human Service Planning, Leadership and Change Agentry, Syracuse, NY.

Your Drug May Be Your Problem provides much useful and very practical information, and is much needed considering that there is such massive propaganda by the pharmaceutical and medical industries about such drugs. This propaganda must be combated, and this book contributes to that effort.

A Counterbalance to False Miracles. Rhoda L. Fisher, PhD, Clinical Psychologist, Syracuse, New York.

Your Drug May Be Your Problem is an honest and straightforward attempt to present a clear picture of drug effects, why we turn to drugs, their role in society, and more. It fills a real need in our current drug culture and in our current complete trust in the drug dispenser himself. The book's main import will be to serve as a counterbalance to the myth of a 'miracle' drug cure. It's a must on everyone's bookshelf!

Say "Yes" to This Book. Thomas Greening, PhD, Professor of Psychology, Saybrook Graduate School, Editor, *Journal of Humanistic Psychology*, Los Angeles, CA.

Anyone considering saying "yes" to psychiatric drugs, or wanting to "just say no" should first say "YES" to buying and reading this essential, informative book. Breggin and Cohen's goal is empowerment of troubled people seeking help, not propaganda, pressure, or profit. This book questions, informs, warns, and leaves the reader far better able to choose wisely.

The Number One Self-Help Guide. Steven Baldwin, PhD, Senior Editor, *Ethical Human Sciences and Services,* Foundation Professor of Psychology, School of Social Sciences, University of Teeside, UK.

I recommend *Your Drug May Be Your Problem* as the number one self-help guide to coming off psychiatric drugs.

"Groundbreaking Book. " David H. Jacobs, PhD, Clinical Psychologist, Resident Faculty, California Institute of Human Science, San Diego, California.

This groundbreaking book provides a comprehensive and honest source of information about adverse and withdrawal effects of commonly-used psychiatric drugs. It should be in the office of all medical and non-medical "mental health" workers. It should also be read by anyone considering the use of psychiatric drugs and those who want to stop.

"A Brave Pioneer." Paula J. Caplan, PhD, author of *They Say You're Crazy* and *The Myths of Women's Masochism* and visiting scholar, Pembroke Center, Brown University, Providence, Rhode Island.

Breggin has been a brave pioneer in not only pointing out but also meticulously documenting the ways that the "Emperor" of traditional mental health treatment is naked. His relentless raising of questions and documentation of false advertising and cover-ups by drug companies and various forms of abuse of patients by a variety of therapists is invaluable and irreplaceable.

A Voice in the Night Now Leads an Orchestra. Jay Haley, United States International University, author of *Leaving Home* and *Learning and Teaching Therapy,* La Jolla, California.

Doctors Peter Breggin and David Cohen take the reader through the risky pathways of psychiatric medication with accurate information as a guide. Dr. Breggin was a voice in the night calling for responsibility with psychiatric medication. Now he leads an orchestra of protest.

The Essence of Peter's Contribution

by Milton F. Shore, PhD

The essence of Peter Breggin's contribution should be seen within the social context of mental health in the United States. The current American approach can best be characterized by: How dare he oppose the underlying current assumption that all mental health problems are totally genetic, neurological and/or chemical in origin and treatable only by biological interventions? The enormous resources brought to bear to discredit him personally and professionally and to fight his carefully documented criticisms comes from many sources:

1. The ideology of the NIMH which has been taken over by the Goodwins and Insels who have transformed the Institute from its broad mandate in mental health (with its unique contribution to community mental health) to the National Institute on Mental Illness focusing on the biological correlates of the severe disorders of schizophrenia, depression, and obsessive-compulsive behavior and their treatment through medication.

2. The pressures of the drug industry whose profits have dramatically increased as they have used the media to stimulate the market for medicinal solutions to a variety of mental health problems (the latest being "social anxiety").

3. The accusations of drug companies who have attempted to brand him as "unscientific" or a handmaiden of the Scientologists (as if stubborn Peter could be a handmaiden of anyone). On the

contrary, so many of his colleagues have been more than willing to accept gifts, stipends, research funding, and other tokens of appreciation from the companies as they push to medicate for ADHD, bipolar disorder (the new fashionable diagnosis), and other newly defined disorders. Colleagues in psychopharmacology have also been snapped up by medical schools as they see patients for 15 minutes at exorbitant rates to monitor their medication as compared to the lower reimbursement for psychotherapy, in that way increasing the school's income.

4. The political pressures of NAMI which has perverted the important consumer movement (as compared to the families of the mentally retarded) by narrowing consumer advocacy in mental health to the very severe disorders and trying to cut off funding for what they label as those with "problems in living" or the so-called "worried well."

Amidst all these forces aligned against him, Peter has stood his ground with confidence (not unlike Peter in "Peter and the Wolf"). Indeed, the efforts of so many to close off debate and criticism and to silence him even to the point of distorting and hiding data or resorting to ad hominem attacks has been wearing thin as we discover more and more the side effects of medications and the empty promises of neurological science "breakthroughs." As Andrew Jackson said, "One man with courage makes a majority." How well that describes Peter.

Milton F. Shore, PhD

Milton is a Maryland psychologist, former editor of the American Journal of Orthopsychiatry, *former president of the American Orthopsychiatry Association, and recipient of the American Psychological Association Award for Outstanding Professional Contributions (1998). He has been a valued Advisory Council member of ICSPP for decades.*

Peter Breggin, the Grand Validator
by Joseph Tarantolo, MD

The good thing about being a skeptic is that I always questioned authority. (Actually I didn't start questioning authority until President Eisenhower lied to us all about the U2 incident). The bad thing about being a skeptic is that I questioned everything, which can be a bit maddening. Before Peter Breggin entered my life I had been in psychiatric practice about 15 years doing individual, group, and family psychotherapy. I dabbled, on occasion, with psychopharmacologic treatments.

I had training in internal medicine in the Harvard Service of the Boston City Hospital and I had been Ward Administrator in one of the Affective Disease units of the NIH. I was not a stranger to the prescription pad. What struck me mostly about psychotropic drugs is that they didn't seem to work and when they did work they seemed to be more trouble than they were worth.

In fact, subliminally I had begun questioning the whole concept of a drug doing its " work" on the central nervous system (CNS). Meanwhile, I wasn't even getting the placebo effect. My negative attitude, if anything, induced a "nocebo" impact.

At any rate, at bottom how could the therapist challenge his patients to face their anxieties while trying to kill them, their anxieties that is, with drugs. There was a disconnect here that, particularly with difficult patients, I did not yet have the courage or coherency to face. I was not much of a student of the psychiatric literature. If anything I tended naively to idealize the randomized placebo controlled trials that were the vogue. Most of my reading was geared toward psychodynamic therapies. Psychoanalysts had not yet completely sold out to biological psychiatry so I was still feeling relatively at ease in their presence. I had read the APA task force on tardive dyskinesia and was well versed in the dangers of benzodiazepine addiction. But still there was a glue missing. I needed validation for that which I could only see darkly. Enter *Toxic Psychiatry!*

I should have marked the date when I first got hold of Peter Breggin's revolutionary tome. For me the term "revolutionary" is not an exaggeration. My reaction to it was visceral. At times I was trembling as I read it. " My God... Yes, yes, of course... That's right... I know that... This is what I really believe." The book's amalgam of humanism, spirituality and scientific documentation shored me up.

The brilliance of Peter's work is that, if you open your mind and heart, he is simply clarifying what we should already have learned before graduating grade school: that, first, we are responsible for our behavior and, second, without love and empathy emotional survival is at risk. He then made clear what we therapists must deduce from these two principles: You cannot drug your problems away. You cannot treat someone against his or her will. You cannot blame biology and genetics for spiritual and psychological overwhelm. The positive message that emanates from this is that the psychotherapist, the psychoanalyst, can have a profound salutary effect through caring, empathy, connection, kindness, and humble counseling and interpretation.

As a private practitioner I had been vulnerable to the glaring distortions of the media's reporting, to the vagaries of drug-company-sponsored research and the seduction of diagnostic manuals. The Center for the Study of Psychiatry and Psychology (ICSPP.org) broke my isolation and gave me courage to stand up to junk science. My skepticism became more coherent; I was no longer flailing blindly.

Certain principles took on flesh:

Severe mental illness often diagnosed as schizophrenia or manic-depression (now called "bipolar") illness was not genetic in origin.

Placebo controlled trials were mostly a sham as evidenced by the reluctance of psych-biologists to use " active placebos" that have side effects, thereby convincing the patient and the doctor that they are "real drugs."

Neuroleptics (now erroneously re-named " anti-psychotics") suppressed all brain function without significantly changing distorted thinking.

The risk of all psychotropics out weighed their benefits.

My practice became more grounded. False hopes promulgated by new drug after new drug were replaced by a more heartfelt hope, that I could assure my patients that they did not have diseases of the brain or irreparable genetic maladies. Very importantly I began learning techniques of how to help patients come off of psychotropic drugs. This was most humbling, and here Peter was of great personal assistance to me. I was gung ho and wanted all my patients off dangerous drugs. Peter's wise council and some bad clinical experiences taught me that this process of weaning/detoxifying took finesse.

More principles to work by:

The patient had to lead the way, I could only guide. I had to be sure that the medical-profession-stimulated qualities of "know it all" arrogance were kept in check. If the patient was not really behind the task, weaning off drugs almost always failed.

Go slowly, be supportive, and mostly be ready for the unmasking of feelings (good and bad) as the chemical control is removed.

Beware of withdrawal reactions!

The theoretical breakthrough for me, however, that Peter has delivered in so penetrating a way is this: the drugs "work" by disabling the normal functioning of the central nervous system, (CNS), including the brain. Indeed, not only is the CNS disabled but also multiple systems feel the toxic effects. The implications of this observation are far reaching. This is not merely a scientific observation. It has deep philosophical/humanistic and spiritual implications. It tells us, practitioners and patients alike, that we must respect the human quest for health. That journey is often painful and circuitous.

The brilliance of Peter's work is that, if you open your mind and heart, he is simply clarifying what we should already have learned before graduating grade school: that, first, we are responsible for our behavior and, second, without love and empathy emotional survival is at risk.

It is so tempting to think that doctor knows best with seductive short cuts and offers of fool's gold. Instead, by respecting that journey, validating it, empathizing with the sojourner, the doctor can bear witness and ease the pain.

Dr. Peter Breggin has eased the pain of this practitioner by giving of his heart and mind. He has helped to allow me to feel proud of my work, as I stay vigilant of my profession.

Thank you, Peter.

Joseph Tarantolo, MD

Joe is a psychiatrist in private practice in Washington, DC and the Chairman of the Board of ICSPP.

Magically Transported

by Toby Tyler Watson, PsyD

In response to hearing that there was a book celebrating the life and work of Peter Breggin, I wanted to write a few brief statements about the man who at first intellectually challenged me and later demonstrated what it meant to be a humanitarian, a teacher, a patriot and hero, and a scholar who could integrate spirituality with psychology and psychiatry.

> I wanted to write a few brief statements about the man who at first intellectually challenged me and later demonstrated what it meant to be a humanitarian, a teacher, a patriot and hero, and a scholar who could integrate spirituality and psychology and psychiatry.

Dr. Breggin and his work were first introduced to me by another gifted man, the late Dr. Kevin McCready. Dr. McCready had told me about the work of Dr. Breggin by giving me his book *Talking Back to Prozac.* As I turned the pages in dismay and frustration, I felt as if I had fallen into the hole from Alice in Wonderland or was magically transported into George Orwell's novel, *1984.*

I read through the book taking notes, highlighting frantically and connecting thoughts from years past. As I tried to hold on to the misinformation I had been told over the years by my poor undergraduate and graduate training, I realized that the seminal work Dr. Breggin had done was far too great of a match for the attempt of my education to make me simply "marketable."

Through the work of other Breggin books, lectures, dinners and personal interactions, Dr. Breggin not only aided my maturation of becoming a critical thinker and more integrated human being, but he aided and has touched thousands of individuals across the planet.

On a weekly basis at my own clinical treatment facility I am reminded of how influential his work has truly become through the consults and patients that call seeking more information about this "God-sent" doctor they call Peter Breggin.

I wish to give thanks to Kevin McCready for helping me meet Peter, and wish to give thanks to Peter Breggin for helping me become a more intelligent, complete and wholly integrated human being.

Toby Tyler Watson, PsyD

Toby is Clinical and Doctorial Training Director at Associated Psychological Health Services in Sheboygan, Wisconsin. He is on the Board of Directors of ICSPP and is the incoming International Director of ICSPP.

I Would Have Gone Crazy

by Stuart Shipko, MD

If it were not for Dr. Breggin and his fine work, perhaps I would, myself, have gone crazy. In the mid 90's as psychiatry became increasingly "biological," and my patients were increasingly referred by medical doctors who had already prescribed two or three drugs, I became increasingly confused.

I felt, as I suspect that most psychiatrists do, that I was a fraud, mostly prescribing drugs for their sedative or activating side effects. Also, it seemed to me that a lot of people were having withdrawal when I tried to change the drugs and the SSRIs generally seemed only to make anxiety worse. My first thought was that I had been out of residency too long and needed to study the literature more closely. This didn't help. When I finally read *Toxic Psychiatry* (1991) it all made sense to me. Without the well documented and well referenced information in this book and Dr. Breggin other publications, I would have no way to formally support my observations or to communicate my own opinions and observations—or to continue to practice.

I consider myself fortunate to be able to stand on the shoulders of this giant.

Stuart Shipko, MD

Stuart is a Diplomate of the American Board of Psychiatry and Neurology. He practices general psychiatry in Pasadena, California and has special interests in panic/anxiety disorders, stress, and issues related to benzodiazepines and antidepressants. It is his observation that most emotional problems are situational, often relating to relationship problems, work or coping with difficult other life circumstances. These circumstances are superimposed on a person's temperaments and memories. Psychotherapy is the first line of treatment for these sorts of problems. The mind has an inherent flexibility and capacity for change that is best facilitated through an empathic psychotherapy.

Dr. Shipko is the author of Surviving Panic Disorder.

Reflections on the Life and Times of Peter Breggin

by Lawrence A. Plumlee, MD

Peter and I were both born in 1936. We were educated at a time when psychiatry in the United States was influenced by psychoanalysis. In the 1950's, the country was excited by technical changes that were making life easier for the majority as machines replaced human labor.

It was inevitable that many would succumb to the notion that technology would also simplify the treatment of emotional distress originating from problems in human relationships.

Four years before I met Peter, I became active in peer counseling as a way of healing through catharsis outside the medical system. In co-counseling, we all learned to listen to one another in kind, and to promote cathartic discharge of old hurts as a way of empowering ourselves and thinking more clearly. Even in medical school in the late '50's, I had been taught at Johns Hopkins that wise elders were being used successfully as psychotherapists in the kibbutzim. Among cocounselors, Janet Foner began to develop and teach those whose experiences with psychiatry had failed to bring us healing. In 1987, Janet Foner played a tape of a talk by Peter for her group of mental health system survivors. For me, it was an "Aha! moment."

I was thrilled to learn that there was a psychiatrist who shared so many of my views on psychiatry, and furthermore, one who lived in Bethesda, Maryland, where I was living while seeking help for my toxic encephalopathy at the National Institutes of Health. I was so excited by this tape that I obtained a copy of it and tapes of some radio interviews which Peter had done. I contacted Peter through his office telephone listing and soon met him. His Center for the Study of Psychiatry in Bethesda then consisted of Peter, Ginger and a part time helper. I was amazed to learn that he had already published a book called *Psychiatric*

Drugs: Hazards to the Brain in 1983, and other books and articles about electroshock damage and psychosurgery going back into the '70's.

When Janet told me that Peter was speaking at a NARPA meeting in Austin, Texas, I flew there to hear him and learn more of his thinking. I was not disappointed, for Peter's 1-2 hour talk was crammed with new insights about how psychiatric drugs were injuring persons seeking help from psychiatrists. Peter was not just a psychiatrist who was helping drug victims get off of prescribed drugs and reclaim their natural abilities to think and heal. He was also a brilliant and original scholar who was searching the scientific literature for peer-reviewed papers, and compiling the first books and scientific papers to document the history of the promotion of toxic treatments to replace healing with psychotherapy. But Peter was not just a brilliant psychiatrist and scholarly researcher. He was an activist who, unlike almost all of the psychiatric scholars of his day, was accepting opportunities to debate his views on television, radio, and in the press. Like Ockham's Razor, Peter was deconstructing the shallow biochemical theories which the drug industry had devised to shore up their toxic, soul-destroying creations.

Like Ockham's Razor, Peter was deconstructing the shallow biochemical theories which the drug industry had devised to shore up their toxic, soul-destroying creations.

But Peter was not just a psychiatrist and a brilliant scholar and a successful activist. He was also an expert witness who was reconstructing the law of toxic torts by helping those damaged by drugs receive financial compensation from those who had poisoned them without prior informed consent. This was a very high-risk situation in which hundreds of thousands of dollars were risked by patients and lawyers to seek millions of dollars to compensate for lives ruined by psychiatric procedures and drugs.

Multibillion dollar chemical companies had seemingly unlimited money to spend to avoid court precedents that could cost them billions of dollars in sales. But such stakes were literally the price of justice, which was what Peter cared most about, and he did not shy away from them. He showed that he was up to the intellectual task of fighting with the brightest lawyers as he successfully collaborated with the best of plaintiff lawyers.

I could only watch in amazement these battles, which intellectually exceeded any that might be seen in the movies. As the SSRI antidepressants came on the scene, Peter showed his continued mental agility by learning a new scientific literature and debunking the pseudoscience of many new chemical entities. And amidst it all, he continued to write important new books and make media appearances.

And as his media exposure brought in professional allies, he was assembling them into the board of directors and advisory council for his Center for the Study of Psychiatry, which he initially called his support group. (Later it would become our mutual support group.) I was excited by his invitation to join this originally small and impressive group of colleagues, which began to assemble annually in his living room.

I was very impressed by Kevin McCready, PhD who was bravely and successfully treating without drugs, persons as outpatients whom psychiatrists would have hospitalized in the twinkling of an eye. And Loren Mosher, MD, whose Soteria studies showing that amateurs simply listening to hallucinating and delusional persons produced more permanent recovery from these symptoms than did antipsychotic drugs. These were exhilarating evenings which kept growing bigger each year.

When NIMH attempted to build a program to force powerful, toxic drugs into distressed inner city children to "protect" them from becoming violent years later, Peter found black members of Congress to stop it. Soon black counselors and professors appeared in Peter's living room. Within a few years, the group grew to such a crowd that the Center needed to rent a conference room in the hotel a block away so that we might have several days to hear more details of each other's work and ask questions.

The expansion of the Center for the Study of Psychiatry led to an expanded name that recognized an international concern about psychiatric drugs that went beyond psychiatry into psychology, social work, and other forms of therapy—the International Center for the Study of Psychiatry and Psychology. The growth has continued.

How many of us get to know a reformer of such importance who so generously shares his successes with his friends, and to whom all colleagues who seek truth and justice are his friends?

Just because I was entertained and astounded by Peter's productivity does not mean that I agreed with him without reservations. Early on, we disagreed about the origins of the exquisite increase in susceptibility to toxic chemicals, which is seen in a portion of persons who have been overexposed to toxic chemicals. This has come to be known since as "toxicant-induced loss of tolerance." As the years have passed, evidence has amassed that differences in detoxification metabolism among persons accounts for some persons developing much more severe side effects from drugs. Tests for such susceptibility are still not generally part of prescribing routines in doctors offices, and Peter has been rightly adamant that all patients who are at risk of serious, disabling effects of psychiatric drugs must be warned about these risks.

What a joy it has been to share these past two decades with Peter and all who have been involved in his saga of psychiatric reform! He has undertaken his life's work at great risk. How many of us get to know a reformer of such importance who so generously shares his successes with his friends, and to whom all colleagues who seek truth and justice are friends? There seem to be no limits to the numbers of persons who may bask in the light of Peter's successes.

Lawrence A. Plumlee, MD

Larry is a graduate of Princeton University and the Johns Hopkins University School of Medicine. After an internship in internal medicine and a fellowship in physiology at Johns Hopkins, he was a research investigator in psychophysiology at the Walter Reed Army Institute of Research, Division of Neuropsychiatry and published several research papers. Subsequently, he became medical science adviser in the Office of Research of the U.S. Public Health Service's Consumer Protection and Environmental Health Service, and later at the U.S. Environmental Protection Agency. Part time, he was Assistant Professor of Behavioral Biology at Johns Hopkins. Presently he is editor of The Environmental Physician *at the American Academy of Environmental Medicine, and President of the Chemical Sensitivity Disorders Association. He also serves on the boards of directors of the New Hope Foundation, Inc., the International Center for the Study of Psychiatry and Psychology (ICSPP), and the Maryland Pesticide Network.*

Peter Breggin: A Personal Note
by Sharon Presley, PhD

I first met Peter Breggin when I was finishing graduate school in psychology back in the 1970s. I invited him to give a talk for Laissez Faire Books in New York City (I was co-proprietor at the time). He was a "troublemaker" then, just as he is now. I loved it. We became friends and actually spoke about psychological issues on the same bill several years later at another venue. The many occasions on which I have seen Peter over the years have been delightful and stimulating. What fun it is to hear him at a psychology convention, ripping up the opposition!

When I began my teaching career in the early 1980s, Peter's ideas were useful and continue to be useful today. Whenever the subject of psychiatric drugs comes up, I share with my classes the concerns expressed by Peter, mentioning the ICSPP web site and his books and suggesting that critical consumers need to read both sides of the drug debate. I tell them about the side effects of psychiatric drugs, how the majority of users quit because of the side effects, and how the long—term effects have not been tested. When the chapter on abnormal psychology comes in my Introductory Psychology class, I often mention that even schizophrenia can be treated by nondrug means, using the examples that Peter has talked about. When the subject of Ritalin comes up, I share Peter's concerns as well as the concerns of other psychologists.

I now use the A&E video "Generation Rx: Reading, Writing and Ritalin" (in which Peter is interviewed) in my Developmental Psychology class. As someone who also teaches Critical Thinking, I try to encourage critical thinking about many psychological issues in all of my classes. I have found his ideas to be invaluable tools for increasing critical thinking about psychiatric drugs. His ideas have also added enormously to the discussions in these classes and I think students have really benefited from hearing this information. They don't get too much of it elsewhere!

This last year I had the occasion to invite Peter to speak again at a conference I arranged on "Autonomy in the Family." His talk, based on his book, *Reclaiming Our Children*, was extremely well received and added enormously to the theme of the conference.

Peter's early book, *The Psychology of Freedom* (1980), was a stimulus to thinking about what contributions psychology can make to the promotion of liberty. I have continued thinking about this concept over the years. I am now planning to write a book on how psychological research supports the idea that freedom is psychologically healthy, that individuality and autonomy are efficacious, and that resistance to unjust authority is both psychologically and socially desirable. Peter will certainly be noted in the acknowledgements of this book.

On a personal note, Peter is not only a thoughtful person whose ideas have influenced me and been useful to my classroom efforts and activities, he has always been a sweet and supportive friend. He's a terrific guy and my life is richer for knowing him.

Sharon Presley, PhD

Sharon has a doctorate in social psychology from the City University of New York Graduate Center. Her PhD dissertation was a study of political resisters to authority. She now teaches psychology and critical thinking courses at California State University, East Bay in Hayward. Her research specialties are obedience and resistance to authority, women resisters to authority, and gender issues. She is the co-editor of Exquisite Rebel: The Essays of Voltairine de Cleyre *published in 2005 by SUNY Press. This book won an American Library Association Choice award for Outstanding Academic Title 2005. She is a speaker and consultant in addition to teaching and writing.*

Peter Breggin: Guardian of the Gateway to Good Science

by Diane Kern, MFT

For more than thirty years now Peter Breggin has been calling for nothing less than good science in psychiatry. He has demanded thoughtful inquiry, restraint and accountability. It would appear today that his labors are bearing rich fruit. Developments in quantum theory have profound implications for psychology; one by one, sciences have had to acknowledge complexity and the limits of knowledge and the knowable. These developments coupled with heightened public concern about the trustworthiness of research in psychiatry are forcing change.

It's a very big universe folks and sad to say, I did not hear of the work of Peter Breggin during the course of 20 years of clinical practice.

I have practiced in the purportedly progressive clinical context of Berkeley, California; I have practiced in San Francisco, California, home to no less than four psychoanalytic institutes. I have witnessed the evolution of an uneasy partnership between neuroscientists, psychologists and technology. Many pathways for professional development have presented themselves to me. I have ventured a short distance down each only to find piecemeal attempts to scientize the business of helping people.

I'm all for science and medical science in particular. However, as we all know, no scientific development emerges in a vacuum. The science that drives mental health care today is constrained by its own history. Western science, empowered with technical devices enabling exploration of the innermost recesses of the body, has suffered from an, albeit necessary, tunnel vision. This has given us the blessing of phenomenal understanding of our physical systems as well as technology to save and enhance the lives of millions of people.

Fortunately, in Peter Breggin we have had a thoughtful witness to the impact of these events upon psychiatry in particular. I came upon his work a scant five years ago attending a professional training seminar offered by Ty Colbert. I was immediately taken with Peter's bold stance in favor of critical examination of issues. His books, *Toxic Psychiatry, The War against Children of Color* (with Ginger Breggin) and *Talking Back to Ritalin,* really pack a wallop. I cannot overstate the importance of his work upon my own professional development.

It is difficult to sustain a view of one's work that runs counter to "prevailing wisdom." I have to thank my clients for helping me to maintain my perspective. With them I have continued to explore the business of "being." Discovering Peter's work and the organization created by Peter and then run with the help of his wife Ginger has provided the collegial network I very much needed.

Peter Breggin has consistently brought a higher standard of science to bear upon mental health care theory and practice. He has directed our attention to the unfortunate consequences of unquestioned philosophical assumptions. He has questioned the materialist bias predisposing researchers to over-emphasis upon the material form and processes of the brain. He has questioned the wisdom of failure to scrutinize financial policy and practice supporting research. He has questioned the application of technology with limited understanding.

Peter has consistently argued for a systems approach that gives weight to the context of our lives at every level. He has pointed to the relationship between the individual and family, social institutions and culture. Fortunately, the best of contemporary science demands that we abandon reductionist methods (or at the very least, qualify the results). Any understanding of the part is enriched with understanding of the whole.

The systems approach, advocated by Peter, also provided a platform for the emergence of whole schools of thought in the nineteen-fifties (e.g. family systems theory). Historical constraints hampered the development of this rich theoretical work; we did not have the mathematical tools to analyze systems. Well, now we do.

Quantum mechanics permits analysis of social systems in ways not previously possible. All material things are connected and multilayered levels of "reality" and "potential reality" (the quantum domain) have causal relations. This is increasingly demonstrable.

Application of new research methodologies is providing a new scientific foundation for much of what we have known to be true. Hopefully psychiatry will soon more fully integrate a holistic psychosocial approach to "treatment" of folks experiencing mental and emotional difficulty.

Peter's work parallels that of the scientific revolution brought about by quantum theory. Experiments can only be understood as results derived from experimentation, constrained by the underlying processes informing the experiment. This includes the psychology of the experimenter, the worldview that leads her/him to imagine the form of the universe and the form of "things" (processes) that are to be the subject of study. This awareness integral to quantum theory, is a given in good science today.

Peter's work parallels that of the scientific revolution brought about by quantum theory.

Quantum theory also asserts that the material world (that includes us, folks) emerges from a non-material "realm." Subjectivity appears to be a process of continuous creativity informed by "active information" derived from this non-material "realm." We have new views of just what is in play when we allude to an "unconscious." Hopefully in the coming decade, better science will prevail and these developments will cross-fertilize psychiatry.

It is tempting to romanticize Peter's efforts as "tireless," "pioneering" and "courageous." However, his efforts cannot have been "tireless." They have no doubt been frequently exhausting. No doubt the efforts to dismiss or minimize the value of Peter's work have stung. I am grateful to Peter for finding the fortitude to continue. Peter has benefited from a tradition of the extraordinary insight of theorists who preceded him but he is among few who have continued to assert the merits of their work.

Courageous? Absolutely. Peter has called upon inner resources far beyond any I have been able to muster. I am happy to have this opportunity to thank Peter for his labors.

Peter has consistently engaged his peers, the public and legislators. He has become a strategist picking his battles well. He is very much an unrecognized leader in the worldwide movement to ensure social and environmental justice.

Peter would protect the integrity of diverse self-organizing social systems (cultures), he would protect the integrity of intimate family groups, he would protect our bodies from unnecessary and/or ill informed harm, and he would protect the integrity of our right to be individuals; no small task. His efforts have born rich fruit.

Diane Kern, MFT

Diane is the founder of Insight Center in Walnut Creek and San Francisco, California. She provides educational and clinical services. She is working to refresh psychological theory with the benefit of our growing understanding of quantum processes. Quantum processes give rise to the patterns of thought we characterize as personality. Helping strategies for all of us may be derived from understanding of these dynamics. For further information see www.insightcenter.net.

Providing the People All the Truth

by Kelly O'Meara

I first came to know Dr. Breggin in 1999 while I was an investigative reporter with the *Washington Times' Insight Magazine.* I was conducting interviews for an article I was preparing to write about the connection between school shooters and psychiatric drugs.

Over and over again, Dr. Breggin was recommended to me as a source on the issue and he proved to be a wealth of information and was kind enough to walk a cub reporter through the maze of misinformation and disinformation permeating the arena of mental health.

Dr. Breggin, a man I consider a pioneer in exposing the truth about the alleged benefits and known adverse reactions to psychotropic drugs, has spent his life in the service of others, often at peril to his professional career. Through his numerous books and scientific papers, he has made it his mission to fully inform the public.

My respect for Dr. Breggin only grew when I became aware of the personal risk and responsibility he was assuming when I realized he was greatly at odds with the vast majority of experts in his field who preferred to spout the psychiatric community's biochemical mental disease line. Despite the perils of taking an opposing view, Dr. Breggin has never wavered in his efforts and continues today, through his writings, to thoughtfully and compassionately make people aware of the truths and fictions of mental health. It is his compassion, though, that is most striking.

While Dr. Breggin certainly has the educational or technical background to confound and confuse the masses with the best of psychiatrists and psychopharmacologists, it is his underlying understanding and compassion for those suffering from emotional and spiritual trauma that sets him apart from his peers. Rather than go with the establishment and settle for, and support, unproven mental health diagnoses, Dr. Breggin has taken the high road—putting his patients and the public's well being first.

As a reporter, it is my duty to provide the truth about the issue. Dr. Breggin was a diamond in the rough and over a period of seven years and writing more than two dozen articles about the psycho/pharma debate, I came to depend on his insight and honesty.

Although my articles were highly critical and exposed the myth of mental health's alleged biochemical brain abnormality, it is to Dr. Breggin's credit of what is medically known that the psychiatric community never questioned or attacked the information I presented in any of those articles.

Dr. Breggin has been on the front-lines of exposing the truth about what is known and not known about mental illness for decades and the progress being made today in alerting the public to the known adverse reactions to psychotropic drugs is largely due to his efforts.

It is an honor to know Dr. Breggin and I am thankful for his personal and professional courage to provide the People all the truth.

Kelly Patricia O'Meara

Kelly is a former investigative reporter with the Washington Times' Insight Magazine *and the author of* Psyched Out: How Psychiatry Sells Mental Illness and Pushes Pills That Kill.

For Everyone in the Medical and Mental Health Field

by Bart P. Billings, PhD, U. S. Army COL (Ret.)

I am very impressed by Peter R. Breggin's book, *Medication Madness*. It was released in July 2008 and is a must read for just about everyone in the medical and mental health field. For that matter, for anyone taking medication.

Dr. Breggin is a Harvard-trained (former full-time consultant at the National Institute of Mental Health) psychiatrist and an expert in clinical psychopharmacology. He has written numerous books on the subject of psychopharmacology etc. and his latest book, *Medication Madness*, is very impressive.

Based on my 34 years of experience in the military (Founder and Director of International Combat Stress Conference for 16 yrs.), I feel *Medication Madness* is especially important for anyone in the military, including family members.

It is his understanding and compassion for those suffering from emotional and spiritual trauma that sets him apart from his peers.

Bart P. Billings, PhD, U. S. Army COL (Ret.)

Dr. Billings is a psychologist and the Founder and Director of the International Combat Stress Conference.

Chapter Eight

Testifying in Court

Introduction

In the early 1990s, Dr. Breggin was asked to be the medical and scientific expert for the nearly 200 combined Prozac product liability suits that charged Eli Lilly with negligence in the development and marketing of Prozac, especially in regard to the drug's capacity to cause suicide and violence.

The suits were brought by many different attorneys but the court combined them for the purpose of developing their scientific and legal basis. All the suits in which Dr. Breggin was involved were settled and Dr. Breggin has gone on to consult and testify in dozens of product liability suits involving every class of psychiatric drug, including antidepressants, antipsychotic drugs, stimulants, tranquilizers and mood stabilizers.

In these lawsuits, judges empowered Dr. Breggin to go inside the secret files of pharmaceutical companies to determine if the companies had committed negligence. This opportunity has provided him unprecedented expertise about the inner workings of the drug companies and the FDA, as well as the overall flaws of the drug approval process.

Tardive dyskinesia caused by "antipsychotic" drugs continues to be a main concern for Dr. Breggin. Tens of millions of patients are suffering from this persistent, untreatable disorder that can vary from disfiguring to wholly disabling and agonizing. Dr. Breggin has testified and consulted in dozens of successful tardive dyskinesia cases in the US and Canada. Among the many adult cases that have gone to trial with him as a medical expert, the injured patients have won all but one, and the exception was a hung jury. Many others have been settled, sometimes for millions of dollars.

Dr. Breggin was the medical expert in the only malpractice suit to be won against a psychosurgeon and the only suit to be won against a doctor involved in electroshock treatment.

Dr. Breggin was the main medical expert in the famous Kaimowitz case in the early 1970s in which a three-judge panel stopped an experimental psychosurgery project in the Michigan State Hospitals. The judicial opinion, which drew heavily on Dr. Breggin's testimony, helped put a stop to all lobotomy and psychosurgery in America's state mental hospitals and other public institutions such as the Veterans Administration.

Dr. Breggin has been the medical expert in the only malpractice suit to be won against a psychosurgeon and the only suit to be won against a doctor involved in electroshock treatment.

Dr. Breggin has evaluated many cases of medication-induced criminal behavior, including bizarre robberies, violence and suicide. The most detailed information about several of these cases can be found in his recent book, *Medication Madness: A Psychiatrist Exposes the Dangers of Mood-Altering Drugs* (2008).

In attempting to exonerate individuals who have committed crimes under the influence of psychiatric medications, most states allow for a plea of involuntary intoxication on the grounds that the individual did not knowingly take a drug that could change his behavior for the worse. Dr. Breggin describes the application of this legal principle and illustrates it with numerous cases in *Medication Madness.* He also introduces the concept of medication spellbinding—how psychoactive drugs mask their mental and behavioral effects, sometimes making people feel that they are doing better than ever when they are doing worse than ever.

Dr. Breggin is by far the world's most experienced medical expert concerning the adverse effects of drugs, electroshock and psychosurgery.

Dr. Breggin's medical expert reports have resulted in reduced sentences without going to trial. In one of Dr. Breggin's cases, a Virginia trial judge found a man not guilty of assaulting a police officer because of involuntary intoxication with multiple psychiatric drugs. This was the first such case in Virginia.

In other hearings and trials, the judge or jury has reduced the sentence without exonerating the individual. For example, in Connecticut a judge agreed to a plea of involuntary intoxication for a man accused of robbing banks, on the grounds that he was involuntarily intoxicated by Xanax and Prozac.

Dr. Breggin is by far the world's most experienced medical expert concerning the adverse effects of drugs, electroshock and psychosurgery. His website, www.breggin.com and his book, *Medication Madness,* contain a great deal more information about his medical-legal work.

Like Barry Bonds

by Donald J. Farber, JD

As a second career lawyer following a U.S. Navy career and additional Department of State employment, I entered the law in 1993. Virtually by accident, I happened on to a personal injury suit, a Paxil double murder and suicide. Entering a previously unexplored world for me, I immediately became interested in antidepressant cases. Since 1999, over 90% of my cases have involved antidepressants, and I continue to practice in the arena. "Biology 101" was never so interesting.

The above is a quick introduction into how I met Dr. Peter Breggin. Attorneys get brochures in the mail all the time on "experts" pushing their credentials. Experts are more than merely important in complex litigation cases. They are vital. Their vitality, however, is beyond pure "expertise." Technical correctness is never self-evident. It must be laid out in plain language and simple logic so that laypersons, i.e. judges, jurors; and certainly lawyers, too, can understand and follow. That is how I "discovered" Peter Breggin. I found him, literally, in a court opinion in which the judge spoke in detail about what "Dr. Breggin testified to." Anytime a judge talks positively about an expert witness, that's the expert to grab. So chalk one up to good research. I found my "expert." Peter and I have worked on several cases since.

I found Peter in a court opinion in which the judge spoke in detail about what "Dr. Breggin testified to." Anytime a judge talks positively about an expert witness, that's the expert to grab.

My first observation of Dr. Breggin in litigation discovery, going through pharmaceutical documents in the "Paxil" library inside SmithKline Beecham (now GlaxoSmithKline) outside Philadelphia in February 2000, was like a baseball fan seeing Barry Bonds pick out a bat at the dugout bat rack. Suffice to say the fan is impressed by his first look at how the "pro" goes about his business. Not only did Peter proceed with haste to go through the large Paxil library but he taught me throughout this process what he was looking for, and why. It actually was fun as I caught the hang of it. Peter Breggin was an exercise in speed and efficiency looking at pharmaceutical clinical trial records. He filled up whole yellow legal pads with the fastest scribbling I've ever seen. Going through thousands of documents without a "card catalog" or "table of contents" to guide one, and to try to look for "smoking guns" along the way is not a simple task. Finding the "needles in the haystack" is the critical task of lawyers and medical experts going through a pharmaceutical library. My three days spent with Dr. Breggin and his assistant Ian Goddard sifting through Paxil documents was an instrumental learning experience in my legal career far beyond the relatively short calendar period involved. The many technical "tricks" he taught me in those three days I have been able to build upon, and serve additional clients over the years with the Breggin insight.

Rush Limbaugh, the radio talk show host, calls himself the "truth detector." I use the same term to describe Peter Breggin in his reporting of the facts—and myths—about psychotropic medications. I'm also old enough to remember Harry Truman, and apply Truman's line to Breggin. I thought of this Truman line when I heard an industry psychiatrist or two over the years call Breggin's views on antidepressants "alarmist." When Truman was asked why he always gave the Republicans hell, he replied, "I don't give them hell. I just tell the truth, and they think it's hell."

Highlighting Dr. Breggin's technical and testimonial skills is to state the obvious. Many psychiatrists and medical experts—and other professionals of course—possess similar attributes of high competence. What separates Dr. Breggin is his tenacity of principle for truth. I've never seen a tougher guy than Peter Breggin, but his toughness was not meanness. It was a stalwart sense of confidence that what he was espousing was true. As the "Truman" quip suggests, I have seen Dr. Breggin castigated at times for his opinions and writings, and surely that was never pleasant.

But that might have been expected in what a medical historian told the New York Times was a "religious war" over the issue of antidepressant suicide. History does persist in righting itself, and for Peter Breggin it has to be of considerable satisfaction that antidepressant suicide warnings were initiated by the FDA in 2004.

Most interesting in this lawyer's eyes was the reaction of mainline psychiatry when the FDA finally changed course on antidepressants. First, the general suicide warning was issued in March 2004. The "black box" warning for the pediatric community followed in October 2004. "Young adults" were added to the "black box" in May 2007. Based purely on staked out positions in this "war" over the years, one would have expected from mainline psychiatry a total and unrelenting uprising against the FDA. But they followed like lambs. While there was considerable vocal opposition to the "black box," some going so far as alleging that it had caused a rise in youth suicides, the bulk of mainline psychiatry effectively admitted, though not loudly, that the FDA's revised labeling guidelines to monitor patients for suicide after commencing an antidepressant was "sound medical practice." In short, these tumultuous events and their after effects indicated to me the entire psychiatric community was listening to Peter Breggin all along, and believing him. It was only their convention that would not allow them

What separates Dr. Breggin is his tenacity of principle for truth.

to openly acknowledge the rebellious nature of Breggin's truth. Such is group-think, and why individuals like Peter Breggin are necessary for our survival as a critically thinking society.

These events and their after effects indicated to me the entire psychiatric community was listening to Peter Breggin all along, and believing him.

Suicide testing for antidepressants is finally underway at the direction of the National Institute for Mental Health (NIMH). It is starting 16 years late because of the FDA's intransigence on the Prozac issue going back to 1991. Better late than never one has to conclude—a reality, no doubt, that now calls for Dr. Breggin to examine those NIMH trials and results with the same scrutiny as that given Eli Lilly and GlaxoSmithKline over the years.

The battle never ends. Thank you Peter Breggin for your courage and leadership.

Donald J. Farber, JD

Don was in the U.S. Navy for many years, retiring with the rank of commander, following which he worked for four years as a diplomat with the U.S. Department of State in Taiwan administering arms sales to the Taiwan Navy. Don does litigation in the areas of product liability, personal injury, medical malpractice, commercial law, military law, employment law, immigration law, real estate and landlord-tenant law. His first product liability antidepressant case in 1999 involved a man who drowned himself and his two children in a bathtub soon after starting Paxil, and since then Don has developed extensive experience in the arena of antidepressant product liability.

Peter Breggin—The Truthseeker

by Derek Braslow, JD

I have only known Peter Breggin for a couple years, although it seems as if I have known him my entire legal career. He has been an invaluable resource for my law firm and a most valuable ally for my firm's clients, all of whom have suffered from the horrible and deadly side effects of psychotropic medications.

When I first met him, I was in awe of his intelligence and great insight. But, the more time I spent with him, the more I realized that his greatest characteristic is not his intellect but his integrity – a characteristic which is evidenced by his unparalleled determination to seek the truth in psychiatry.

Before anyone was warning about the true dangers of psychotropic medications, Peter courageously warned our government and the medical community. I am certain that Peter has saved countless of lives by informing the public about the risks of these drugs. And he has done this in the face of what I believe to be enormous pressure from other mental health professionals, the majority of whom unknowingly spew big pharma's deceit. I cannot think of many men or women who have meant more to their profession than Peter. He is truly the conscience of psychiatry.

I cannot think of many men or women who have meant more to their profession than Peter. He is truly the conscience of psychiatry.

On a more personal note, while I consider Peter a critical advisor to my legal cases and one who can explain the most complex issue in terms that I can understand, I enjoy working with him even more because he is wonderfully charismatic and compassionate.

It takes a special person to be able to comfort those who have lost a loved one to suicide – and Peter, whether he agrees to take on the case or not, is always honest and sympathetic to my clients. He is an expert who truly cares.

It is an honor to have been asked to write something on Peter's behalf. I know that my words cannot do him justice but I hope he knows how much I, and so many others, appreciate his commitment to the cause of justice.

Derek Braslow, JD

Derek is a founding partner of Pogust & Braslow and has dedicated his practice to fighting for victims of pharmaceutical drugs. He has been a determined advocate for children, adolescents and adults who have become suicidal as a result of ingesting psychotropic medication. He has been a featured speaker on clinical trials, bioethics and pharmaceutical litigation and policy. He has testified before the FDA's Psychopharmacologic Drug Advisory Committee regarding the risk of suicide and antidepressants and has been counsel to numerous clients who have testified before the FDA's Subcommittees regarding the deadly risks of ADHD drugs and antidepressants for children and adolescents.

Law, Medicines and the Wisdom of Peter Breggin with Observation from the Courtroom

By Graham Dukes, MD
Oslo, Norway

The minds of the Ancient Greeks, it is said, were the first to be much exercised by the question as to what would happen if an irresistible force were to encounter an immovable object. Anyone who is still troubled by this venerable conundrum might do well to spend a little while in a Court of Law, and more especially in one that is seeking to come to grips with a medico-legal dispute. For there it is that such collisions can occur - both within and between two learned professions - and there it is that conflicts between supposed certainties tend to dominate the scene.

That late, great British humorist Paul Jennings once set out, with his tongue only partly in his cheek, to delineate the medical profession as he had come to know it. What intrigued him most was the cloak of superior authority with which many a doctor was automatically endowed on qualifying; his self-confidence demanded it; his senior clinical years bolstered it ("He goes round like a bishop in procession, headed by acolytes") and many a patient would humbly accept it ("Doctors are men like himself, only better.").

With some doctors the air of infallibility came to extend beyond the consulting room; I myself have indeed encountered certain medical men who, when one appeared to question their taste in jackets or the quality of their piano-playing would react with a glare that implied accusations of insolent insubordination. Goodness knows, not all doctors are like that, but there are a certain number of them around.

As to the man of law, he can at his worst be equally dreadful, for the silken gown may be as potent a symbol of infallibility as the stethoscope. He will strive with the greatest conviction to convince a jury of the rectitude of the view that he has been retained to adopt, while his equally authoritative opponent across the courtroom will with equal conviction present precisely the opposite view. Both will claim an unequalled degree of personal authority derived from a vast comprehension of the law and its proper interpretation, leaving an honest juryman in mind of the legendary Dr. Benjamin Jowett of Oxford, of whom it was written:

> I am Jowett
> All that is known, I know it;
> I am Master of this College
> And what I don't know isn't knowledge.

At this point, a hapless judge and jury may well be prepared to let their conclusions depend very much upon the promised contribution of the expert witnesses who are to be paraded before them. How helpful and convincing these can be depends in part on their field of expertise. I have seen how one court, dealing with a stark electrical disaster, was swayed entirely and in an instant by an engineer waving a piece of fused wire, pointing visibly to a crucial short circuit. In matters of medicine it may be rather less straightforward, for example:

"Tell me, Dr. G, in view of your twenty years of unrivalled experience in this field, was the injury to this patient directly attributable to his having been prescribed a potent tranquillizer, such as would render him incapable under the given circumstances of driving a motor vehicle?"

I recall the very case in which that question was put. Dr. G, a practitioner who clearly had very little prior experience in court, eyed the attorney who no doubt had rehearsed his part with him for the best part of the previous day. He glanced nervously across the courtroom at Dr. F., already glaring at him and ready to pounce upon him as soon as the defence was called. He no doubt wished to high heaven that he was back in his surgery, where one did not have to answer such convoluted questions. Then he mumbled acquiescence and was invited to step down. The next half hour, during which Dr. F. set out to reverse indignantly everything that had so far been said and sworn, appeared to leave the jury utterly bewildered.

None of the above is at all removed from reality; indeed it is as close to some real-life events as one can come without direct citation. Medical-legal disputes brought before a court or an arbitration tribunal are not always so clear-cut that the diagnosis which one felt justified in making in one's office will be suited to the rough-and-tumble of the courtroom. The diagnosis may not remain convincing after vicious cross-examination or be readily explained in an understandable fashion to a lay jury. Indeed, the very reason why such matters reach a court is likely to be that they are genuinely subject to disagreement. The black and white cases presented by plaintiff on the one hand and defendant on the other are an inevitable component of the process of seeking justice, but they are relatively coarse tools, representing the irresistible force and the immovable object colliding, to the confusion of all concerned.

Whether in the end justice is truly done can then indeed depend to a large extent on the expert witnesses. One encounters some superb experts in this field; one meets others who one might—if one may be permitted a euphemism—term regrettable, merely accentuating the force of the collision with their air of impregnable authority. And in between there are those experts who are well intentioned but inept.

It is at this point in my story that I can at last—in recognition and gratitude—turn to the contribution that my friend Peter Breggin has made to this field where litigation has concerned psychopharmacology. For Peter is the very antithesis of the impregnably self-opinated physician; he tells the truth as he sees it, yet he is always open to the possibility of other truths beyond. One recognizes that approach in so much of his work, and particularly in his untiring quest to uncover simple human traits that have too long been overlaid with rash pathological assertions.

In the vexed controversy about Attention Deficit Hyperactivity Disorder that has so disfigured American psychiatry, the one voice may rant against Ritalin while the other raves at the risks of under-diagnosing this supposedly fearful ailment; but in books like *Talking Back to Ritalin* (revised, 2001) and *Brain-Disabling Treatments in Psychiatry* (second edition, 2008), Peter chooses to dig more deeply and more wisely, recognizing in many instances of so-called ADHD the natural need for a child to daydream, for little girls to fidget and little boys to climb big trees. With that, the ADHD bubble bursts and we begin to understand.

Many of the situations in which medicinal disputes end up in court call for just such compassionate comprehension as Dr. Breggin can offer, precisely because they are subtle. Harm attributed to psychotropic medicines has been so often associated not with agents as monumentally vicious as methylphenidate but with substances that have a broad and entirely valid role to play in society; a jury will have no difficulty with a case of poisoning with opium, but it may wrestle mightily with a cases where an apparently innocuous minor tranquilizer is in the middle of the picture.

What in fact went wrong and why? How many parties were truly at fault—if indeed there was fault at all? An unconscionable advertiser, a slip made in haste by a regulator, a mix-up in a pharmacy or unclear instructions given by a nurse may all play a role, to say nothing of misconceptions that may for a host of reasons have taken root among physicians, patients and the public at large.

These things may be difficult enough for the experts to untangle, and they may prove well-nigh incomprehensible for a well-meaning jury.

And then it is that many a conscientious attorney has succeeded in calling Peter Breggin to his aid. I do not know how many shadowy invitations Dr. Breggin has set aside, but I do know that he has accepted to assist only in those instances where he had good reason to believe that he could serve the best of all causes, that of justice.

In court, Dr. Breggin's answers from the witness box are calm, qualified, and above all abundantly clear. They are patently honest and impartial. They bear the stamp of reasoned authority and brave conviction. They reflect a broad and deep knowledge; but, even more important than that, they display the understanding that comes with wisdom and a deep respect for one's fellow men.

M. N. G. (Graham) Dukes, MD

Graham is a physician and a lawyer, trained at Cambridge University in Britain and Leiden in the Netherlands. He has worked in drug research, national drug regulation and the World Health Organization. Awarded a professorship in Drug Policy at the University of Groningen, he now lectures at the University of Oslo in Norway. He is the long-time editor of Meyler's Side Effects of Drugs *and the author of many books on drug policy including* Responsibility for Drug-Induced Injury: A Reference Book for Lawyers, the Health Professions and Manufacturers, *and* The Law and Ethics of the Pharmaceutical Industry. *He is a senior consultant on drug policy to the World Bank and has frequently served as an expert witness in medical-legal disputes.*

Kermit Green Meets the Expert

by Pam Clay, JD

In 1984, if I had a pound of gold for every time I had searched the trenches for a capable expert, I wouldn't have a penny to my name. I had been an attorney for less than two years, representing people labeled developmentally disabled at treatment team meetings, in administrative hearings, and occasional guardianship hearings. I was green—Kermit green.

I had spent most of my time fighting with a regional comprehensive care center that had been granted a Medicaid waiver to serve these individuals in their own communities rather than being locked away in an institution. The problem was this particular center decided that their community would be better off if there was still a lock and key method of treatment. Wanting to appear "progressive," they decided to create invisible prisons (or at least only visible to only a few) using the latest and greatest psychotropics. My efforts focused on four young adults, all graduates of the state institutions, who had been given so many drugs in such high doses that they had lost many of their functional abilities. One man couldn't even walk anymore because of the contractions and involuntary movements (tardive dyskinesia) created by these "behavior management treatments."

Finally, I had enough, or maybe I had finally gotten up the nerve, and my first major lawsuit was ready to be filed in the U.S. District Court for the Western District of Kentucky. It was drafted as a major civil rights action and would be litigated under the rules of complex litigation. (To paint a more complete picture; later, as the case was scheduled for trial, 30 days were set aside for the jury to hear the evidence.) A companion case with the same four plaintiffs was to be filed in state court as a medical malpractice case. The problem was, before I could do anything, I had to have an expert. I didn't have a clue.

Almost on cue a co-worker mentioned a special report done by Dan Rather on the CBS Evening News. It was an expose` on the harmful effects of psychotropic drugs. I was told they cited a national expert, but my co-worker didn't catch the name.

I wrote CBS for the transcript. There, in the form of a script written for a movie, was Peter Breggin, a leading authority on the misuse of the same medications my clients had been put on. Next questions, "How did one find this national authority, Dr. Breggin, and how would I get him to talk to a public interest lawyer that had very little money for expert witnesses?" Answer: Buy the book mentioned in the newscast, check out the "about the author" section, and call directory assistance!

Much to my amazement this guy who had been on national TV (a big deal in the circles I traveled in) answered his own phone and was on the other end of the line! I explained to him that I was a public interest lawyer (actually, I worked for the state) that we had no money, that I was representing four young adults who had been gravely harmed by being overmedicated, that the document review alone supporting our claims took up two full file cabinets, that there would be oh, 20 or 30 depositions to review before it was all over, and would he please, please be willing to serve as our vastly underpaid and incredibly overworked expert. And, "Oh, this was my first big case so I really didn't know what I was doing, so could he guide me through that too?" Answer: Sure, no problem, but could I wait on a review because he was getting married the next weekend?" Well, that was easy.

Throughout the course of this particular case, so tediously long that I became certain it would be inherited by whichever nephew or niece was willing to pick up the gauntlet, Peter, Ginger, and I maintained a relationship by phone. We did this for three years. I can recall, after arriving at the office at 6:30 a.m. so I could get a head start on the workday, and getting home around 10:30 p.m. (I told you it was a monster case), getting a call from Peter around

11:00 p.m. We would review what I had learned during the day and walk through what needed to be done next. I asked myself many times, "Do these people ever rest?" Later I came to learn, and as we all know now, the answer is "No, they don't, not when there is a wrong to be righted."

Sometime during this 3-year interval I recall Peter being distracted. Following a dramatic and convincing appearance by Peter on the Oprah Winfrey show, the Maryland medical licensing board had been convinced that they should withdraw Peter's license to practice medicine. Big mistake. Not only did they have Peter to contend with, but now they had roused Ginger's ire. I can personally attest, at any time necessary, that indeed one or two people can change the world. I have seen it in my lifetime. Ginger Breggin is a 20-person office. Needless to say the licensing issue went away.

Finally in 1988 the National Association of Rights Protection and Advocacy (NARPA), a patient advocacy group, was having a conference in Detroit. I had been asked to be a presenter, and Peter would be there as well. We were to meet for the first time and Ginger would be there, too. My life would never be the same again. The three of us became friends for the first time. We were up most of the night talking, about our work, about our passions, about our hopes and dreams. Our values and views were so similar that it was as if we had been childhood neighbors and had shared a lifetime of memories. I felt like Ginger was my sister. That time was magical and I will always cherish the memory.

Later that year, Peter and Ginger invited me to drop by their lake house in Virginia on my annual pilgrimage to the beach. The world they would introduce me to was so enchanting that it was hard to take in. It was full of noble battles, of befriending strays, both human and canine, of love that I could only take in doses. I have always been guarded, it was my nature.

Peter and Ginger innately knew this and coaxed me out of

myself, much like a kind person will do with a stray animal. It was, and is, the gentleness of their friendship that warms my heart to this very day. I have never been so keenly aware of the deliberateness with which they cared for me as their friend. There have been many trips to the lake house, and I hope many more to their new Eden in Central New York.

I now look back with satisfaction on my time as an advocate for people with disabilities. I have turned to new dragons, but always with the support and insight of my old friends.

I remain in awe of the impact the Breggins have had on the treatment of injured souls. Our suit ended in settlement, each of the plaintiffs getting a sum of money in trust, a guaranteed array of community services, and policies about drugging that have hopefully helped many, many more people with disabilities not become further disabled by the lazy use of chemical restraints.

Peter and Ginger have grown a whole crop of compassionate people willing to allow their clients the dignity of being different. But the true legacy of Peter and Ginger Breggin is their unconditional love, for each other and for their friends.

What a gift!

Pam Clay, JD

When she began working with Peter Breggin, Pam was on the staff of the Kentucky Department of Public Advocacy, Protection and Advocacy. Pam lives in Lexington and works for another government agency where she continues to protect the rights of citizens.

A Letter to Peter Breggin
by Stuart Shipko, MD

Dear Peter:

I just loved *Medication Madness.* What a great book on so many levels. It gives insight into your personal professional development, lots of clinical pearls, and is sort of a textbook on involuntary intoxication. I am referring it to all the attorneys that I have been working with. I read the book really slowly and was sorry when it was over.

With my similar experiences in travel for testimony, the hotel scene and preparation—the Wesbecker case was an incredible heartbreaker. It is to your credit that you were able to carry on after that. Incidentally, I gave an educational lecture to a group of attorneys and mentioned the Wesbecker case, and there were some in the audience who shouted me down and said that this could not have happened in our legal system. I can appreciate how difficult your path has been.

Spellbinding is a missing link in the issue of adverse drug reactions.

Spellbinding is such an important concept. There needs to be an axiom that a person quickly loses sight of the changes in himself that a drug might make. This is so true. Spellbinding is a missing link in the issue of adverse drug reactions. After just a short period of time people will forget that the drug is affecting them. Next time I testify, I can invoke spellbinding and reference your book.

A guidebook and a reference book; a real gift.

Peter, your entire body of work has had a lot of influence on my thinking, but *Medication Madness* is the first really good book on the horrible things that can happen because of psychiatric drugs. It is really well written and I enjoyed the more personal flavor. Most of all, I really needed your book as it is so closely related to the work I do. Now that you have identified and defined spellbinding and have published so many clinical issues related to it, I can reference it when I provide testimony.

Thanks again, you are a hero.

Stuart Shipko, MD

Stuart is a Diplomate of the American Board of Psychiatry and Neurology. He practices general psychiatry and has special interests in panic/anxiety disorders, stress, and issues related to benzodiazepines and antidepressants. He is the author of Surviving Panic Disorder.

Chapter Nine

Advocating for Children

Introduction

Dr. Breggin has devoted himself to trying to stop the psychiatric onslaught against the world's children. His discovery that little children were having their brains mutilated by psychosurgery in Mississippi was one of the driving motivations behind his anti-psychosurgery campaign (chapter 3).

Dr. Breggin was often a lone voice among professionals in the early years when he began his criticism of diagnosing children with ADHD and medicating them with stimulants, but now there is a chorus of mental health practitioners who want to meet the real needs of children for improved parenting and schooling.

Dr. Breggin has written many books and articles, as well as blogs, on the hazards of diagnosing children and treating them with psychiatric drugs. He often gives seminars on family and educational approaches to helping children. In addition, he consults and testifies in legal cases aimed at preventing the medicating of children. And he continues to see individual children and their parents providing both psychotherapy and psychopharmacology expertise on how to help children come off of their damaging psychiatric drugs.

Finally, he continues to write about better approaches to helping children in many of his books including *Medication Madness* (2008), *Brain-Disabling Treatments in Psychiatry* (2008), *Reclaiming Our Children* (2000), *The Ritalin Fact Book* (2002), *Talking Back to Ritalin* (Revised, 2001) and *The Heart of Being Helpful* (1997).

Defending Institutionalized Children in Kentucky. "Children Kept Illegally at Psychiatric Hospital, State Investigation Finds," ***Courier Journal,*** **Kentucky, November 3, 1987.**

An investigation of a state psychiatric hospital concludes that children have been kept there illegally, and that other treatment programs that would be less expensive and more appropriate are urgently needed....

Peter R. Breggin, a Maryland psychiatrist and consultant to the National Institute of Mental Health who has evaluated institutions in Kentucky, says in a letter included in the report that there is "great potential for harm." Even under ideal circumstances, longer stays expose children to "stigmatization and humiliation," he said....

Sticking to the Facts. "Dyslexia Label Not Supported by Science" by John Rosemond, May 2, 1992.

[Since reversals of letters or words] are common in young children, and virtually non-existent in all but barely literate adults, it's a safe bet we're talking about a maturation process, one that proceeds at a faster rate in some children than in others.

There is, furthermore, no conclusive proof of neurological malfunction in the brains of so-called dyslexic kids. In his book, *Toxic Psychiatry*...Dr. Peter Breggin maintains the terms learning disabled and dyslexia spring not from science but from a parent movement born of frustration....

Dyslexia is a theoretical disorder. No one will ever be able to prove that Thomas Edison, or any other historical figure, had dyslexia, whatever dyslexia is.

Until someone demonstrates conclusive, concrete proof of a neurological malfunction in the way the brains of so-called dyslexic children process perceptual information, I propose nothing more radical than that we stick to the facts.

Outraged. **"Lock Therapy—More children are being committed to private psychiatric institutions than ever before. But who's really benefiting—the patients or the hospitals?" by Rob Waters, *Parenting,* May 1992.**

...Problems [are] now surfacing in the growing industry of private psychiatric hospitals for children. Though recent studies are few, even dated statistics on the rising numbers of children being placed in psychiatric wards are foreboding. In 1986 (the last year for which National Institute of Mental Health figures are available), 38,682 children ages 10 to 14 were hospitalized in public and private settings, a 69 percent increase over 1980. And in...California, admissions of children under 12 doubled between 1984 and 1988, according to the state health department.

Mental health experts say that this dramatic increase in admissions reflects the serious problems faced by America's children. They point to the growing numbers of kids who are neglected, abused or who use drugs....

...Doctors are starting to prescribe such drugs to younger and younger patients. "I have put two-year-old children on anti-depressant medications," one doctor says.

Psychiatrist and author Peter Breggin of Bethesda, Maryland is outraged at the notion of giving antidepressants to young children. "It's unethical," he says. "It's highly experimental, and it's not justified by the literature or by the Food and Drug Administration...."

Attending to the Child's Needs. **"Use of Ritalin for Children Is on the Rise—The drug is given to children diagnosed with attention deficit disorder. But some critics say it is overprescribed" by Kathy Boccella, *The Philadelphia Inquirer,* April 14, 1996.**

[F]ifteen years ago, almost no one had heard of attention deficit disorder (ADD), but today experts say it afflicts as many as 3.5 million children in the United States or up to 5 percent [of children] up to the age of 18. The most common treatment has been Ritalin, a stimulant whose production soared more than 500 percent in the last five years, according to the Drug Enforcement Administration.

But even as more and more frustrated parents embrace the drug as a panacea, some researchers estimate that from 30 percent to 50 percent of those taking it may not even have the disorder....

"Basically, you are taking children who are in conflict with adults and drugging them," said Dr. Peter R. Breggin, a Bethesda, Md. psychiatrist and leading opponent of the drug. "You have a child who is depressed, who can't concentrate, who is having trouble in school and you're drugging him instead of saying what can we do to attend to the child's needs."

Often a phone call from the teacher and a brief doctor's office visit are all that's needed to get a prescription, according to Breggin and others, even though most experts say Ritalin should never be given without a psychological and physical evaluation, and teaching children how to control their behavior....

Teachers Pushing Pills. "The Pill That Teachers Push" by Jeanie Russell, *Good Housekeeping*, December 1997.

....Hundreds of thousands of American children....have been affected by the rush to Ritalin. The drug's use to treat ADD has become so rampant that at the slightest sign of trouble...parents are circled by the school's teachers, psychologists, and even principal, all pushing Ritalin....

Peter R. Breggin, M.D., a psychiatrist in Bethesda, Md., and author of the upcoming *Talking Back to Ritalin*, agrees. "There are so many stresses on kids today—divorces, step-parent families, kids not brought up to respect authority—so they bring more problems to school," he says. "Plus, classrooms have gotten increasingly out of touch with children. It's commonplace that a child everyone labels ADD can focus perfectly well on a computer, but has to be drugged to sit in class. We're demanding that kids raised on TV, videos, and computers sit in classes with boring material from the 1940s. On top of that, you have teachers who have more training in identifying ADD than in figuring out how to invigorate their classrooms."

A Disaster for Children. "A Culture of Pills" by Kristen Bellstrom, *SmartMoney*, September 2005.

Pop quiz: What prescriptions are you most likely to find in a college student's medicine cabinet—allergy meds, acne fighters, or antidepressants? If you answered antidepressants, give yourself an A.....

But some critics say that college-age students using these medications need more monitoring than adults, both because their bodies and environments are changing so much and because they may be more sensitive to some drugs. Some antidepressants, for example, have been linked to suicidal behavior among adolescents. "It's a disaster that during a critical period of their development so many of our young people are being taught that drugs are the answer," says Peter Breggin, psychiatrist and author of *Talking Back to Prozac*....

An Invitation to Abuse Drugs. "High school's little helper, by Jaimal Yogis, *San Francisco Magazine,* February 2006.

....Sometimes these kids aren't acting on their own; parents are putting on the pressure, subtly or directly. "Parents are literally taking their kids to doctors because they want their grades to be better," says Dr. Peter Breggin, founder of the International Center for the Study of Psychiatry and Psychology...."That's an invitation for kids to abuse these drugs." Breggin frequently gets calls from parents who need help with a child who has been hurt in some way from ADHD drugs, which they initially encouraged....

No Doubt About Prozac-Induced Violence. "Guns, Drugs And Kids: What's Wrong With This Picture?" by Arianna Huffington, *Arianna Online*, July 9, 1998.

"I have no doubt that Prozac can cause or contribute to violence and suicide," Dr. Peter Breggin, the psychiatrist and author of "*Talking Back to Prozac*" told me. "I've seen many cases. In a recent clinical trial, 6 percent of the children became psychotic on Prozac. And manic psychosis can lead to violence."

Record Numbers of Antidepressant Prescriptions. "More Kids are Given Antidepressants" by Greg Barrett *Detroit News and Free Press*, March 7, 2004.

[M]ore than 1 million American kids [are] taking psychotropic drugs for major depression, anxiety or attention deficit disorders.

The Food and Drug Administration estimates that doctors wrote a record number of antidepressant prescriptions for children—about 11 million—in 2002. About 2.7 million of those prescriptions were for children 11 and under....

New York psychiatrist Peter Breggin blames ubiquitous TV advertising by drug companies like Zoloft-maker Pfizer, Inc. that "push antidepressants" into the mainstream....

Breggin, a psychiatrist for more than 30 years and the author of "*The Anti-Depressant Fact Book*" said children suffer significant bouts of anxiety and depression, but there's very little science to support drug treatment.

A decrease in serotonin, a neurotransmitter with a hand in everything from sleep to appetite, is implicated in depression. But drug company studies on children and the medicines that attempt to regulate serotonin have produced questionable results.

About half the studies showed the antidepressant tested was no more effective on children than a placebo.

"If it was only about serotonin, then therapy alone would never work," Breggin said. "The child might be depressed because of something at home or at school or whatever, but it takes time—sometimes lots of time—to find out exactly what the problem is and work through it."

The Scapegoating of American Children. "The Scapegoating of American Children" by Peter R. Breggin, *The Wall Street Journal*, November 7, 1989.

The widespread use of psychiatric diagnosis, drugs and mental hospitalization raises serious questions about how we should deal with emotional stresses among children. Does psychiatry provide us answers—or an escape from our own problems at the expense of our children? …

As a psychiatrist, I am especially concerned about how the mental health professions play into blaming the child for the problems of parents, families, schools, and society. Increasingly, schools and parents find it comforting to accept the new biological psychiatry approach that declares the youngster to be genetically and biologically defective, and suitable for psychiatric treatment, including drugs and hospitalization. Parents forsake responsibility for raising their own children, not only injuring their offspring but depriving themselves of the satisfaction of being good parents. The children are stigmatized and feel to blame for problems that are almost wholly beyond their control.

We need a dramatic turnabout in which we, as responsible adults, retake responsibility for our children.

Talking Back to Ritalin

Talking Back to Ritalin (1998, revised 2001) was written by Dr. Breggin in response to the burgeoning psychiatric trend of diagnosing and medicating children with dangerous psychoactive drugs. Hundreds of parents and other concerned adults wrote to Dr. Breggin over the years, thanking him for the assistance his book provided when their children were caught in the psychiatric net. The book also received many formal endorsements from professionals:

The Most Valuable Book. Kevin McCready, PhD, Director, San Joaquin Psychotherapy Center, Clovis, CA.

If nothing is more important than the spirit and well-being of our children, this book may be the most valuable one you will ever need.

Daring to Tell the Truth. Douglas C. Smith, MD, psychiatrist, Juneau, Alaska.

I used to prescribe Ritalin until I read this book. I thought the occasional dramatic "cures" (I now know what's really going on here) and the sheer desperation of some parents outweighed the risks (I now have a better idea just what the risks are).

But it wasn't just new knowledge that changed my mind— it was inspiration.

Peter Breggin views children as having wonderfully complex brains that cannot be improved with foreign chemicals, and with precious souls that can be understood and valued. This view rises with warmth out of every page. Breggin offers better solutions that are practical but not simplistic, and he dares to tell the truth— not to make us feel guilty, but to make us wiser.

Every Child Needs a Hero. Jeffrey Moussaieff Masson, Ph. D., Former Projects Director of the Freud Archives, New Zealand

Every child needs a hero—a champion who will speak truth to power. That hero is Peter Breggin. When he writes on behalf of children and caring parents, the world should stand up and take notice. This book is packed with information needed by anyone who is considering prescribing psychiatric drugs to children.

A Clarion Call. Eileen Walkenstein, MD, psychiatrist, Philadelphia, PA.

This book is a clarion call for parents, teachers, and yes, physicians to start using their critical intelligence and wake up to the massive harm being done to our children under the guise of treatment.

Reclaiming Our Children

Peter was inspired to write *Reclaiming Our Children* (2000) after watching the horror of the Columbine school shootings unfold on national television. This book is a plea for more effective, humane and genuine relationships with our children and teenagers. Enthusiastic endorsements followed its publication:

A Dark Secret. Fred Bemak, EdD, Professor of Counselor Education, Ohio State University.

Psychiatrist Peter Breggin once again captures the heartbeat of a nation's struggle and brings to light one of our darker secrets-that we are sacrificing our children on the altar of our own adult-based needs and values. Anyone concerned with the lives of our children should read this book.

Destined to Be a Classic. Clemmont E. Vontress, PhD, Professor Emeritus of Counseling, George Washington University.

This very engaging and well-documented book is destined to be a classic and a boon to parents, psychologists, psychiatrists, counselors, social workers, teachers and others interested in getting a handle on a problem that threatens our whole society.

Stop the Scapegoating. Kevin McCready, PhD, Director, San Joaquin Psychotherapy Center, Clovis, CA.

A bold and insightful work that could only come from the man hailed as "The Conscience of American Psychiatry."

Instead of quick fixes Breggin offers realistic, long-term solutions based on spiritual virtues of love, charity, and nurturing discipline. He both challenges and inspires us to stop scapegoating our children and to face and overcome the fatal flaws in ourselves and our society.

Courage and Compassion. John Horgan, author of *The End of Science* and *The Undiscovered Mind.*

Peter Breggin's courageous, compassionate writings serve as a much-needed antidote to the genetic determinism and pro-drug bias of modern psychiatry and psychology.

Peter Challenges the Biocentric ADHD Model

by Brian Kean, PhD

It is more than I can do to detail every event in which I have witnessed my friend Peter Breggin's advocating for the rights of children against the psychopharmaceutical complex. I will focus on two relatively early events that were very significant in challenging the biopsychiatric ADHD model.

The National Institutes of Health (NIH) Consensus Conference

The closest approximation of the ideal speech situation in evaluating truth and validity claims concerning ADHD occurred in the consensus conference held in the U.S. by the National Institutes of Health; the NIH Consensus Conference (1998) Diagnosis and Treatment of Attention Deficit Hyperactivity Disorder (ADHD). The NIH Consensus Statement (1998b) indicated that the conference was "...convened to evaluate available scientific information and resolve safety and efficacy issues related to biomedical technology" (p. i).

The NIH Consensus Statements are developed:

> By nonadvocate non-Federal panels of experts, based on (1) presentations by investigators working in areas relevant to the consensus questions during a 2-day public session, (2) questions and statements from conference attendees during open discussion periods that are part of the public session, and (3) closed deliberations by the panel during the remainder of the second day and morning of the third. This statement is an independent report of the consensus panel and is not a policy statement by the NIH or the Federal Government (p.i)

I was staying with Peter and Ginger when the NIH Consensus Conference concerning ADHD was announced. It would take place on the NIH campus, a short walk from Peter's home and office.

The conference's organizing panel consisted of staff from the National Institute of Mental Health (NIMH) and also the president of Children and Adults with Attention Deficit Disorder (CHADD). Like many previous inquiries in the United States, the initial announcement and selection of the presenters appeared to be structured to effectively exclude any critical perspectives on the diagnosis and treatment. Peter sent his new book, *Talking Back to Ritalin*, and some of his papers, to the director of the National Institutes of Health (NIH), the organization with the final say about the contents of the conference. The Director's Office of NIH decided that the conference needed Dr. Breggin and appointed him the scientific presenter on adverse drug effects in children.

After hearing all the evidence, the Consensus Panel released an initial statement for the purpose of obtaining feedback from the public and professionals. This met sufficient criticism from the ADHD/stimulant drug advocates that the panel was forced to release a final revised statement more favorable to these advocates that was made available on the Internet (NIH, 1998a, p. 2). This final revised statement continued to raise somewhat more muted concerns about the diagnosis and treatment of ADHD, some of them reflecting Dr. Breggin's scientific testimony. After the Consensus Panel finished its work and went home, the government issued yet another version of the Consensus Panel statement within a few weeks after the conference (NIH, 1998b, p. 2).

Table 1 details a few of the multiple changes that ADHD/stimulant drug advocates at NIMH made in the documents between the original statement (NIH, 1998a) and the later version (NIH, 1998b) that the government distributed, allegedly as the findings of the panel. NIMH made significant modifications that promoted the use of drugs for ADHD, claimed validity of the diagnosis, and downplayed potentially negative information that concerned the diagnosis and drug treatment. It systematically undermined the stated conclusions of the more objective Consensus Panel.

Final Revised Consensus Panel Statement	**Government Revised Version**	**Section of Document**	**Comment by Author**
There are no data to indicate that ADHD is due to brain malfunction. Further research to establish the validity of the disorder continues to be a problem.	Although research has suggested a central nervous system basis for ADHD, further research is necessary to firmly establish ADHD as a brain disorder.	What is the scientific evidence for the disorder?	Dramatically different statements. Talking up of the credibility and trustworthiness of the positivistic scientific research. Second part of the statement has been changed in terms of known scientific information.
However, stimulant treatments do not "normalize" the entire range of behavior problems, and children under treatment still manifest a higher level of some behavior problems than normal children.	However, stimulant treatments may not "normalize" the entire range of behavior problems, and children under treatment still manifest a higher level of some behavior problems than normal children.	What is the impact of ADHD on Individuals, Families and Society?	Change from "do not" to "may not" implies improved effectiveness of drug therapy beyond assessments made by the Consensus Panel.
Intensive direct interventions in children with ADHD, such as summer camp programs, have produced improvements in key areas of functioning.	Intensive direct interventions in children with ADHD have produced improvements in key areas of functioning.		Elimination of the findings of the effectiveness of behavioral interventions in the MTA (1999) study.

Table1: Comparison of a few of the alterations to the NIH Consensus Statement (1998) following initial release.

At the time of release of the original statement, CHADD made significant criticism of the Consensus Panel findings. Sheila Anderson, the President of CHADD at the time, was one of the organizing committee members for the Consensus Conference and probably helped to rework the document. Breggin (2001), as a scientific speaker at the conference, noted the motives and the process behind the changes to the consensus statement:

> The consensus conference panel raised so many doubts about the concept of ADHD and its treatment with drugs that the conference planners had to rewrite much of it themselves after the panel had gone home. This, of course, was highly misleading and unethical. The consensus statement that has been published and that appears on NIMH's web site is a gross distortion of the actual conclusions of the panel at the conference (p. 16).

Without Peter Breggin's advocacy no attention whatsoever would have been given to risks associated with stimulant treatment and very little critical review of the ADHD diagnosis would have been made.

The only existing significant independent scientific analysis concerning the ADHD phenomenon was subjected to alteration resulting in a selective transmission of knowledge to the wider society. The modifications to the Consensus Panel initial statement illustrated the power of the ADHD/stimulant drug lobby in the United States. Without Peter Breggin's advocacy no attention whatsoever would have been given to risks associated with stimulant treatment and very little critical review of the ADHD diagnosis would have been made. Peter's critiques of stimulant mediation and his medical deconstruction of the ADHD diagnosis at the consensus conference, in his books, journal articles, media appearances and legal cases, have been the most effective counter to the ADHD lobby to date.

Ritalin Litigation Conference

After lengthy consultations with Peter, on November 17, 2000 the Dallas law firm Waters and Kraus launched a class action lawsuit in Texas against Novartis (the manufacturer of Ritalin), the American Psychiatric Association (APA) and Children and Adults with Attention-Deficit/Hyperactivity Disorder (CHADD). The allegations claimed that:

> Novartis, in combination with the American Psychiatric Association (APA), planned, conspired, and colluded to create, develop, promote, and confirm the diagnoses of Attention Deficit Disorder (ADD) and Attention Deficit Hyperactivity Disorder (ADHD), by vastly and needlessly overbroad diagnostic criteria, in a highly successful effort to increase the market for its product Ritalin. Due to the concerted efforts of these two parties, Attention Deficit Disorder was first listed in the *Diagnostic and Statistical Manual of Mental Disorders (DSM)* in 1980. (Waters & Krauss, 2000, p. 8).

Following the first action, civil lawsuits were filed in California and New Jersey making similar allegations. Although Dr. Breggin did not participate in these additional suits, his initial work on the first suit provided much of their basis.

In March 2001 I traveled to New York City to attend the American Conference Institute "Ritalin Litigation" conference.

The opening session entitled "Ritalin and ADHD Primer: Diagnosis, Treatment and Strategies for Ritalin Lawsuits" involved pro-biopsychiatric presentations by Andrew Adesman and by Lawrence Diller. Adesman detailed the APA guidelines for diagnosis and evaluation of ADHD, emphasized the seriousness of the disorder, and claimed, "safe and effective treatment is available and the benefits of treatment outweigh the risk" (Adesman, p. 18). Diller followed by continuing to minimize the issues and risks, claiming that Ritalin "works," although he also mentioned the importance of "better parenting and schools for children" (Diller, 2001, p. 14).

In the opening session I was sitting next to Peter as he made notes on palm cards during Adesman's and Diller's presentations. Both initial presenters made use of PowerPoint slides to support their presentations. Following morning coffee break Peter presented "A Plaintiffs' Medical Consultant's Perspective on Ritalin." As always, he spoke with a few jotted notes and no visual aids. Peter's ability to analyze and deconstruct their arguments was highlighted by his enthusiasm for the topic and his charm, beginning with a personal greeting as he chided Diller with a gentle "Larry, Larry, Larry…" and then went on to shred his presentation.

Many of us who attended the Ritalin Litigation conference believed that this could be the potential turning point in addressing the ADHD epidemic. Peter's view, however, was far more cautious and conservative, perhaps influenced by his lengthy experience in the legal system. He pointed out that the main strategy by the pharmaceutical companies involved keeping the cases out of court and that the class action suits might not get approved by the courts. Although he had been the primary consultant to the first model suit brought by attorney Andy Waters, he thought that a great deal more research was required before the lawsuits could fly. Instead, he favored individual product liability suits aimed at developing more research and discovery materials. He also had concerns that class action suits too often benefit the lawyers more than the injured patients, who often end up with relatively small monetary awards. He was right in his doubts about the suits succeeding and the courts rejected them in the following years.

I believe that in time these suits will resurface with greater intensity. Perhaps the key issue that will bring the class actions back before the legal system is the research by the late Nadine Lambert detailing the significantly increased risk of the development of cocaine abuse in young adults as a result of early childhood treatment with methylphenidate or dexamphetamine (Lambert, 1998, 2002, 2005; Lambert, McLeod & Schenk, 2006). If they do resurface in the near future one thing is certain, Peter Breggin—who has long warned about stimulant treatment leading to later addiction to street drugs—will be there as an expert legal witness.

Peter Breggin and Child Rights

As I described earlier in the book when talking more about the development of my friendship with Peter, his fight for child rights against biopsychiatry has spanned over thirty years. He stands alone in this world in terms of his advocacy for children in a society now driven for a quick fix to the problems of children. Peter's overall view of the flaws in biopsychiatry can best be summarized by his statement (Breggin and Breggin, 1998) that:

> The reduction of human experience to an expression of DNA or a wholly biological event shows an underlying bias and ideology-even though it is presented as objective research. (p. xiv.)

Peter Breggin, in conjunction with Ginger Breggin, has been the most significant advocate in the fight for human rights against psychiatric abuses. They stand alone in terms of their influence in the formation of ICSPP, the establishment of the journal *Ethical Human Psychology and Psychiatry*, and the support network of worldwide professionals. My personal observations of Peter indicate that he has lived a life congruent with his philosophy. Through his intellect and integrity, he has been strong enough to stand as a man alone to fight what many would believe are unassailable forces. In *Beyond Conflict* (1992), Peter concluded:

> At some point, a sufficient number of people must refuse to participate in the destructiveness that tortures human society, nature and our earth. In the long run, nothing can substitute for the actions of individuals dedicated to both the preservation of liberty and the furtherance of love. Above all, we need without embarrassment to embrace love as our best approach to resolving conflict and, beyond that, as our way of life. (Breggin, 1992, p. 259)

Bibliography

Adesman, A. (2001). Diagnosis and treatment of ADHD in children and adolescents. *Ritalin Litigation.* American Conference Institute, March 29-30, 2001, New York City.

Breggin, P. R. (1995). Speed for Breakfast. Four Corners. Sydney: Transcript of Swanson, N. ABC Broadcasting documentary, 12 February.

Diller, L. H. (2001). Ritalin: Facts and controversy. *Ritalin Litigation.* American Conference Institute, March 29-30, 2001, New York City.

Lambert, N. M. (1998). Stimulant treatment as a risk factor for nicotine use and substance abuse. *NIH Consensus Development Conference on Diagnosis and Treatment of Attention Deficit Hyperactivity Disorder*, pp. 191-200, National Institutes of Health, Bethesda, Maryland, November 16-18.

Lambert, N. M. (2002). Stimulant treatment as a risk factor for nicotine use and substance abuse, In P.S. Jensen & J. Cooper, eds. *Diagnosis and Treatment of Attention-Deficit Hyperactivity Disorder: an Evidence-Based Approach*, chapter 18, pp.11-20, Kingston, NJ: Civic Research Institute.

Lambert, N. M. (2005). The contribution of childhood ADHD, conduct problems, and stimulant treatment to adolescent and adult tobacco and psychoactive substance abuse. *Ethical Human Psychology and Psychiatry*, 7, 197-221.

Lambert, N. M., McLeod, M. & Schenk, S. (2006) Subjective responses to initial experience with cocaine: an exploration of the incentive-sensitization theory of drug abuse, *Addiction*, 101(5):713-725.

National Institutes of Health [NIH]. (1998a). Diagnosis and Treatment of Attention Deficit Hyperactivity Disorder. *NIH Consensus Statement 1998 (draft)*. Rockville, Maryland: Author. Retrieved 21/11/98 from http://odp.od.nih.gov/consensus/cons/110/110_statement.

National Institutes of Health[NIH]. (1998b). Diagnosis and treatment of Attention Deficit Hyperactivity Disorder (ADHD). *NIH Consensus Statement, 16(2)*. November 16-18. William H. Natcher Conference Center: National Institutes of Health. Bethesda, Maryland.

Waters, C. A. & Kraus, P. A. (2000). Class action in the United States District Court for the Southern District of Texas Brownsville Division. No. B-00-82. Received M. N. Milby, Clerk of Court, 17 November.

Brian Kean, PhD

Please see Brian's biography after his presentation in Chapter One.

A Tribute to Dr. Peter Breggin

by Karen R. Effrem, MD

Dr. Peter Breggin has been very influential in my understanding of children's psychiatric issues, as well as in informing my writing, speaking, and activism in this area. Through reading just some of his well-documented books and then meeting him in November of 2000, he confirmed what had begun as intuitive concerns about the dangers of prescribing psychiatric drugs to children.

By 2004, this concern had blossomed into intense concern and opposition to the psychiatric screening, labeling, and drugging of children, starting with prenatal psychotropic drug exposure after the screening of pregnant women, and continuing from infancy onward through many state and federal education and health programs.

As a newly practicing pediatrician in the early 1990's, the use of psychotropic drugs in children had always concerned me. At that time, I was aware that the psychostimulant drugs, like Ritalin, caused loss of appetite, weight loss, and sleep difficulties. Because of just those concerns, when meeting patients with attention and behavior difficulties, I always did my best to steer the families away from the stimulants and had them try to focus on diet, family issues, amount of television watched, and the learning environment at home and at school. When needing to renew Ritalin prescriptions for my colleagues, I always tried to have families reconsider these ideas and work to reduce the amount of medication or eliminate it altogether.

I was also vaguely aware that there were side effects with the antidepressant medications, but because I did not directly deal with these patients, but generally referred them to psychiatry, I did not know the extent of the problems with them.

It was not until I had read two of Dr. Breggin's books—*Talk-*

ing Back to Ritalin (1998, revised in 2001) and *The War Against Children* (with Ginger Breggin, 1998)—that the full extent of both the ineffectiveness and the severe, if not fatal, side effects of these compounds that are clearly dangerous to children's normal physical and mental development were made obvious to me. Dr. Breggin's painstaking and scholarly research, as well as his willingness to take the slings and arrows of the psychopharmaceutical complex that is clearly interested in preserving its financial and power interests, played an enormous role in bringing the dangers of these agents, especially for children, to light for both professionals, like myself, as well as parents who are too frequently and too strongly urged to put their children on these dangerous and ineffective compounds.

Dr. Breggin's important work and being one of the most influential voices in making clear the dangers of SSRI antidepressant induced suicide and violence due to the drug induced akathisia has also been very influential on me and my advocacy work. The solid information clarified by Peter's research and legal work has been helpful in showing the dangers of the overuse of these medications.

The many examples of patients, particularly children and adolescents, about whom he has testified and consulted and who have been involved in mass shootings, heinous crimes, and drug induced psychosis have been very important to bring forward not only medically, but also legally and on the education and health policy fronts.

These legal and policy implications have been particularly important and helpful during my congressional and state legislative testimony concerning bills that are meant to prevent coercive psychiatric drugging and screening.

I have greatly appreciated being involved with the International Center for the Study of Psychiatry and Psychology (ICSPP.org) founded by Dr. Breggin and his wife Ginger, both for its academic work and for the camaraderie of professionals and lay people who share the Breggins' passion for truth and justice in the psychiatric field.

In conclusion, Dr. Peter Breggin has contributed greatly to the clinical, as well as the legal and policy understanding of the dangers of psychiatric drugs.

It is with great gratitude for his dedicated work to the field of psychiatry and the protection of human liberty and dignity that I submit this offering to this well-deserved appreciation of his work and life.

Karen Effrem, MD

Dr. Karen Effrem is a pediatrician, researcher, and conference speaker. Dr. Effrem's undergraduate degree is in pharmacy from Purdue University, her medical degree is from Johns Hopkins University and her pediatric training from the University of Minnesota. She has provided testimony for Congress, as well as in-depth analysis of numerous pieces of major federal education, health, and early childhood legislation for congressional staff and many organizations. Besides the International Center for the Study of Psychiatry and Psychology, Dr. Effrem serves on the boards of three other national organizations – EdWatch, The Alliance for Human Research Protection, and the National Physicians Center. She has spoken at numerous state and national conferences. She has been interviewed by the Fox News Channel, the British Medical Journal, the Wall Street Journal, WorldNetDaily, NewsMax, newspapers, and radio and television stations across the country. Dr. Karen Effrem and her husband, Paul, have three children and live in the Minneapolis metro area.

A Giant Influence

by Nora Porter, MD

Like so many members of ICSPP, I came as a rebel, specifically a whistleblower. When I began working in children's disability in the early 90's, it didn't take long to see how many people at so many different levels had a vested interest in labeling more and more children ADHD or bipolar to justify putting them on drugs. Like most whistleblowers, I didn't realize at the time just what a behemoth I had taken on—the pharmaceutical industry, the government, political factions, legal organizations, and more. Fools rush in where angels fear to tread...

In the inexplicable and fortuitous way these things have of happening, I met educator Mike Valentine, who told me I might find some kindred spirits at this organization he belonged to. Kindred spirits? Yes, and far more. Like so many who come to ICSPP, at the first annual conference I attended I felt I had finally found a home. What a relief it was to know I wasn't crazy because I didn't believe the pharmaceutical/mental health industry's fantasies of brain disorders and chemical imbalances. There I was in a room with not one, not ten, but hundreds of professionals all agreeing, The Emperor Has No Clothes!

And heading those professionals was Peter Breggin, a man small in physical stature but larger than life in so many other ways. By that time it was clear to anyone of discernment that Peter, who had for so long toiled alone, now was part of a winning team—Ginger, his help-mate and soul-mate, had herself become an additional catalyst, inviting like-minded people to become more involved in the work of ICSPP.

What work Peter has been involved in! Each quarter when I re-read the "Three Decades of ICSPP Accomplishments" in the center's newsletter, I am awed again—discrediting ECT and stopping the resurgence of lobotomies in the 1970s; stopping the racist search for "the genetics of violence" by the federal government in the 1990s; exposing the risks of tardive dyskinesia in children and adults caused by the "antipsychotic" drugs; breaking the news in *Toxic Psychiatry* in 1991 that the SSRI antidepressants cause suicide and violence; and exploding the myth of ADHD and outlining the dangers of stimulants for children. And to the question, "If not drugs or psychosurgery, what?" Peter's answer and those of his colleagues has always been, "Rational, compassionate care."

Peter has a lethal combination of talents: the shrewdness of the politician, the agility of the salesman, the precision of the marksman, and a laser-like analytic ability, resulting in an irrefutable logical persuasion which is, I suppose, why so many advocates of biological psychiatry hate him. Despite this, Peter's compassion and empathy permeate his work.

What comes to mind when I think of Peter? Character in spades; brilliance; determination; courage; tenacity; eloquence; warmth; compassion; empathy; humor; shrewdness; magnetism; humanity; common sense; and boundless energy.

I love hearing Peter speak. He often starts with a story, told with the appropriate humor, or pathos, or righteous anger, which immediately engages us, so we want to hear more. And I love reading what he writes, because it's so lucid and refreshingly down to earth compared with the dry, lifeless academic nonsense we usually encounter.

Peter has a lethal combination of talents—the shrewdness of the politician, the agility of the salesman, the precision of the marksman, and a laser-like analytic ability, resulting in an irrefutable logical persuasion which is, I suppose, why so many advocates of biological psychiatry hate him. Despite this, Peter's compassion and empathy permeate his work. When we become crusaders, it's easy to turn into cynics or bitter, blind zealots. He remains profoundly caring.

Peter cultivated diversity before the word entered our culture. Just look at the composition of ICSPP! He embraced African-Americans long before it was "cool" to do so. There's no question what he thinks of women. He honored Ginger by making her co-author of two of his books and co-founding editor of *EHPP*, and women have always had full rank and status in the organization.

Look at the range of religions, nationalities, and callings represented—physicians, psychiatrists, academic professors, psychologists, counselors, researchers, physical and occupational therapists, sociologists, writers, lawyers, educators, administrators, consumers/sufferers/survivors, and even U.S. Congressmen and Senators when he was still running the organization. People from all walks of life are members. This broad, multi-layered cast of characters attests to Peter's inclusiveness from so early on.

Like some giant sun, over the years he gradually attracted a wonderful constellation of circling planets, all of us united by the gravitational pull of our rebellion against what Jefferson called "any form of tyranny over the mind of man" as it has manifested in each of our individual lives.

There is no way to express my profound gratitude for Peter's work and especially for his founding of ICSPP, which clearly saved my sanity and gave me the courage and confidence to speak out when I needed to against the madness of drugging.

I'm no longer in the reformer/rabble-rouser category. As clearly as I was called to be a whistleblower fifteen years ago, the understanding came years later that this was no longer my path. How good it is to know that the firebrands Peter and Ginger attracted to their organization have grown in number, strength, and clarity of voice.

I continue to support ICSPP in spirit always, in funds annually, and occasionally, when priorities allow, in presence.

It remains an exceptional privilege to have become a friend and colleague of this visionary, Peter Breggin. He remains for us all the consummate role model of the Principled Professional, who has not tired of being the conscience of psychiatry and who in so many ways has inspired us all to speak truth to power, even in the face of danger.

Nora C. Porter, MD

Nora is a graduate of Cornell University Medical College and Harvard's Mind/Body Medical Institute. She has a practice in Mind/Body Medicine in Central Pennsylvania where she helps people find ways of reducing stress and treating medical conditions without drugs.

In Honor of Peter Breggin

by Michael Valentine, PhD

For years I have been challenging the medical model's assumption that ADHD was some type of biochemical imbalance and/or a genetically caused disorder. In the late 70's and early 80's, from my ethnocentric point of view and my limited awareness of the bigger picture, I thought I was one of a few in the field questioning the reality of this supposed condition.

In those early days I was operating on what I considered the tried and true beliefs and assumptions that through education, good parenting, love, involvement and structured guidance, children could learn manners and learn to control their behavior. Initially when challenging the concept of ADHD, I relied more on educational research that investigated various parenting and teaching styles and/or educational environments in relation to various outcome measures (i.e., academic performance, persistence, locus of control, various personality characteristics, etc.).

I believed that this research supported the obvious—the social environment and milieu a child grew up in had profound impact on the child socially, academically, behaviorally and emotionally. As a corollary to this, I believed if a child's family or school environments were significantly changed in positive ways, then the child's behavior would also change and that this could be accomplished without the use of medications.

As the epidemic of the medical model beliefs about ADHD began to take over school systems, traditional beliefs in education and social psychology, the capability of parents and teachers to be responsible for the behavior of their students and children was more and more called into question and conceptualized as "old fashioned, out dated and non-empirical." This biochemical, genetically determined medical model research was heralded as "cutting edge," and parents, teachers and children were told it wasn't their fault—ADHD was a disease, a disorder that couldn't be cured but could be controlled with proper medication.

Over the years ADHD went through a metamorphosis of various possible causes, definitions, redefinitions and attempts to "properly" diagnose the condition. Meanwhile, I stuck to, as some of my critics would say, a "simplistic" approach of asking questions and having people explain to me how a particular behavior—that was supposedly caused by the biochemistry, genetics, or sugar levels—sometimes instantly changed under various conditions (i.e., father walks in the room and the child's behavior calms down; the child runs around the corner at school and sees the principal and stops his inappropriate behavior immediately; the child can't sit still for two minutes but will sit for two hours doing a task he likes).

> His presentation was inspiring, exhilarating, and intellectually stimulating; and the amazing thing was that this information was coming from a psychiatrist.

I would ask, "Do these children have two biochemical systems—one to turn on the behavior and one to turn it off?" "How did he learn to turn it off initially?" "How does the learning override his chemistry or genes?" "Does the boy ever control his behavior in other situations?" "What makes the difference between the times he can and the times he can't control his behavior?" And, "If he can control the behavior, how is that translated into changes in neurotransmitters, biochemistry, genetics, etc.?"

I taught adults to look for the obvious "evidence" that the child was capable of controlling his behavior by observing the child turn his behavior on and off under various situations. I would show them that when they believed in the child's capabilities to behave well and they interacted with him in ways that were consistent with that belief, they had different results than when they believed he couldn't control himself.

During this time, I was primarily interested in helping individual students or families and was not as aware of how wide spread this booming ADHD problem was; the science or lack of science of the medical model's perspective; and the broad underlying influence of the pharmaceutical companies and the long-term political and economic ramifications. Even though I was confident in what I was doing to help families and even though I had very good success with difficult cases, I would never directly challenge anyone in the medical field. Primarily, I felt I wasn't very knowledgeable about their research and how to critically analyze it. To be honest, in those days I still trusted the medical field and believed their representatives and leaders were ethical, truthful, scientific and had the public's best interests at heart.

In the late 80's just by chance, I heard Dr. Peter Breggin speaking on a radio show in Los Angeles. Instantly I realized that I had to meet him. At the end of the show he announced he would be giving an all day workshop in Westwood the next day. I spent that day listening to Peter talking about the problems in psychiatry, psychology, the drugging of our children, the pharmaceutical companies widespread influence on political, social, racial and economic issues and how all these things converged to impact our children. His presentation was inspiring, exhilarating, and intellectually stimulating; and the amazing thing was that this information was coming from a psychiatrist. No offense, but I had begun to generalize that most psychiatrists, especially those I had dealt with recently, were all slightly "nuts" (even though I am against labeling, this could become a highly sophisticated DSM diagnostic term in the near future), had no clue how to work with children and didn't do anything else but hand out drugs.

Meeting Peter was an enlightening, refreshing experience. He helped change the direction of my professional career. He had a wealth of information and filled in the blanks of the partial picture I had of what I felt was going wrong in the helping profession. I talked to Peter every chance I could during that day. He inspired me to learn more, do more and join in the good fight for kids. Since our first meeting more than 15 years ago, I have read Peter's books; networked with other like-minded professionals across the country; researched most of the medical model's information on ADHD; kept track of the use of methylphenidate by zip code, state, and country; followed the research money and funding for various university and NIMH ADHD projects across the country; debated or tried to debate some of the leading "experts" on ADHD; appeared on many TV and radio programs; made numerous videotapes; wrote books and journal articles questioning the validity of the concept of ADHD; and gave hundreds of seminars and workshops where helpful information, references and websites were handed out so that edu-

> Peter helped me gain a global picture of what was happening, not only in terms of ADHD specifically, but in the mental health field generally. He gave me a better understanding of the enormous economic forces and vested interest groups vying to control public perceptions and policies.

cators, psychologists, social workers, ministers and parents could have an alternative view of ADHD and interventions to help children without having to drug them.

Most of what I just described probably would not have happened if Peter Breggin hadn't crystallized and galvanized my thinking and exposed me to some of the leading minds challenging the medical model. Peter helped me gain a global picture of what was happening, not only in terms of ADHD specifically, but in the mental health field generally. He gave me a better understanding of the enormous economic forces and vested interest groups vying to control public perceptions and policies. He helped demystify the mystique of the medical model's and the pharmaceutical companies' rhetoric and helped me develop the skills necessary to better evaluate their research and challenge them. Peter has been a friend, mentor, colleague and a positive role model for me. He is an energetic, intelligent, committed, passionate person with dignity, courage and integrity. He is a champion in the fight for children and others who have been harmed by the mental health system. Peter, I thank you, deeply, appreciate you and honor you. You have made the world a better place.

Michael Valentine, PhD

Michael is an educator, school psychologist, family therapist, and national and international educational and behavioral consultant to schools. He has helped turn around many out of control inner-city schools. He is the author of How to Deal with Discipline Problems in the Schools: A Practical Guide for Educators *and* How to Deal with Difficult Discipline Problems: A Family-Systems Approach. *Michael lives in Coto de Caza, California.*

Dr. Peter Breggin Saves Lives!
by Nadine De Santo, EdS

As a school psychologist since 1979, I have collected my own observations about children's behavior. In the 1980's I read the "symptoms" of Attention Deficit Disorder and Attention Deficit Hyperactivity Disorder in the DSM and wondered why there were so many characteristics common to creative people. (I knew many artists, and my husband was one!) Additionally, when a child was referred for evaluation for ADD/ADHD, much more was going on in his life than some "disorder" that caused distractibility, impulsivity and hyperactivity. Usually there was a parent split and/or chaotic family life, the child was fairly bright and imaginative, often had allergies and asthma, was taking an asthma medication known to cause hyperactivity and was undisciplined. I saw the same profile repeatedly.

In the 1990's a colleague brought to our staff meeting some published excerpts from a new book, *Toxic Psychiatry*. The information he shared was from Dr. Breggin's chapter on the many disabilities being "discovered" or actually created by mental health professionals and educators. I was surprised to learn that someone "out there" was speaking against the disabling attitudes and methods, voicing opinions that I was beginning to share, too. What a wonderfully courageous person.

Some time later, my husband Steve excitedly told me he had heard Dr. Peter Breggin interviewed on the radio. A couple years after that we learned through Steve's uncle, a pastor, that Dr. Breggin's in-laws attended his church. Suddenly, an impersonal medical authority was not so impersonal. Would we be able to meet him some time? Yes, when he spoke at the public library during a visit to Ginger's wonderful parents, only 45 minutes away.

What a privilege it was to meet Dr. Breggin and his gracious and remarkable wife Ginger. When she asked if I would like to be a part of the ICSPP listserv, since I was so "isolated" philosophically on my job, I said, "Of course!"

Over the next two years I sought out Dr. Breggin's latest books, learning specifics about the dangers of medications I was seeing listed in the histories of children referred for evaluation, and so much more! I also read great articles and entries on the ICSPP listserv and found camaraderie in the heart-felt postings. On the job I was trying to reason with parents who were drugging their children at the teacher's suggestion and/or out of their own feelings of inadequacy and frustration. Colleagues and special education supervisors were pushing the drugs as well! It was heartening to know I was not alone in this battle against drugging children.

When news came about the ICSPP conference in Newark, NJ, I had to go. My anticipation of the conference was great, and when I arrived I learned that the "family" was just like any other; drawn together with one common bond, but with some great differences in personality, politics and religion. As Dr. Breggin has striven for the application of "social and spiritual solutions to social and spiritual problems," so we were united with him. I basked in his words and spirit as he addressed his "family" and I felt like I had "come home" professionally. I appreciated and valued the other presenters' offerings and went back to Indiana with more life-saving facts, warm memories, energized hope and encouragement to carry on.

I have shared many copies of Dr. Breggin's articles, loaned his books, and given away many copies of *The Antidepressant Fact Book*. I even won over my direct supervisor; now when he describes the negative side effects of Abilify, I can sit back, needing to say little or nothing about these dangerous drugs. In the school conferences he attends, many parents have changed the course of their children's lives and even their own by putting drug-free strategies to work in their families.

Now I want to offer two examples to illustrate how Dr. Breggin is saving lives in Indiana; the first describes a "wild" six-year old girl and the second, a teacher who was repeatedly suicidal.

A little background: for several years I've had the responsibility of evaluating all the most behaviorally disordered children in the district. Usually I don't find a severe emotional "disorder" or "disability" but rather a strong-willed, bright, creative, dramatic, and very manipulative child who has been underdisciplined and overindulged. Where teachers, school administrators, counselors and parents see disability, I see "gifts out of control." Over the decades I've conducted many impromptu trainings and unloaded reams of handouts in an effort to equip the adults to understand and handle more effectively the children's intense temperamental characteristics, which can be strengths when expressed appropriately. Some adults "get it" and the child, as well as everyone concerned, benefits.

After reading one girl's history, I thought, "This might be the first truly disturbed child I meet." The kindergartener had some important early health issues and also was medicated from age three with Trileptal. Risperdal was added later in a continuing but inadequate attempt to manage her "bipolar disorder." This six-year old's behavior was very challenging but "manageable" by her 30-year veteran teacher, until her parents mentioned to the psychiatrist that the behavior seemed to be getting worse at home. Of course, the psychiatrist obliged by increasing the medication dosage.

Things went downhill from there. The child became even more aggressive and violent, and was excluded from public school until the doctors at an esteemed children's hospital could figure out what was "wrong." Absolutely no medical tests were completed (!), and—you will not be surprised—she received a prescription for Abilify (an adult antipsychotic drug), with a recommendation to work with a behavior specialist on "anger management." The child was accepted back at school for a couple weeks, until her violent behavioral episodes escalated even further. The teacher nearly had a nervous breakdown over the whole situation, the child was referred to me for an evaluation for emotional disability, and then expelled from kindergarten!

Over the course of my evaluation, I learned that this girl was one of the most wildly creative, dramatic and undisciplined children I'd ever met. She wasn't emotionally disabled, but the parents needed to get her off the drugs and they needed some effective strategies to use with this unusual child. I sent these capable and caring, formally-educated-but-naïve parents home with some strong recommendations and a copy of Dr. Breggin's book (with David Cohen), *Your Drug May Be Your Problem.*

A few months later the girl was completely drug-free and learning to behave like a civilized human being. After talking with the mother about their initial parenting successes, I sent her an email that went something like this:

Congratulations!! You have begun to save your child from a lifetime of psychiatric labeling as "disordered," a lifetime of drugging with powerful medications, and a lifetime of disability thinking. You are effectively combining love, understanding of temperament, and discipline, which is training your daughter to be respectful and in control of herself. Keep it up, and you're going to raise her to be a wonderfully unique, capable and responsible contributor to her family, her community and her world!

A year later the child finished first grade in the same school with the same teacher, who witnessed her transformation. I can only pray that the child's previous forced drugging at such a tender age will have no permanent effects. Her parents are convinced that the psychoactive drugs pushed their child over the edge emotionally and behaviorally.

Dr. Breggin's writings persuaded them that the drugs were not the way to handle their child's strong temperament, and gave them the determination to get her completely drug free.

My second example of how Dr. Peter Breggin saves lives is through my opportunity to share information with school personnel. A few years ago a school administrator wanted to get my take on a teacher whose voice one day turned high-pitched and robotic; very strange! The teacher described how her eyes did not seem to follow in sync with her head movements, she heard sirens and whistles and of course she felt emotionally unstable.

> Dr. Breggin's writings persuaded them that the drugs were not the way to handle their child's strong temperament, and gave them the determination to get her completely drug free.

Through my questioning she remembered that she missed taking her antidepressant for a day. I asked her to call her doctor's office to confirm my suspicions and to get instructions. She did so and I was right.

I learned that this teacher had experienced many challenges: caring for a child with life-threatening illnesses, the molestation of her other children, and being a single mother following a divorce. She started taking Prozac. A few years later, during a lengthy period of her son's illness, she continued teaching fulltime but spent nights at the hospital grading papers and trying to get a little sleep. She eventually collapsed in complete exhaustion in a fetal position…and was taken to the "behavioral hospital."

She was given more prescriptions for psychoactive medications, was in and out of the psychiatric hospital several more times, and at one time she was shackled and transported from the

ER at her local hospital to a psychiatric facility. Ultimately she lost custody of her children because of the hospitalizations for her so-called "mental illness."

Later she came to realize that every hospitalization occurred after prescribed medication changes. To think of all she endured, and that she even lost her children by following "doctor's orders." When I first met this teacher she was starting to take a fourth medication, this one for panic attacks. She was in danger of losing her job due to missed work, and in prior years had been on "suicide watch" during parent-teacher conferences.

After several conversations I finally was able to convince her that she was a good teacher and loving mother who had needed respite and rest, not the treatment she was receiving from psychiatry. I gave her some suggestions for renewing her mind with the facts, which included Dr. Breggin's writings. Over the next couple of months she was in survival mode but suffered no breakdowns.

On a Monday she was doing quite well but by Thursday she called me and said, "I'm spiraling down!" I asked her, "What happened since Monday??" She said, "Let's see. On Tuesday I visited my psychiatrist and suggested I start withdrawing from some of my medications. My psychiatrist said I was in my 'manic phase,' opened the *DSM*, read to me (again) the description of bipolar disorder, gave me a copy of it and reminded me that I would have to take the medicines for the rest of my life. On Wednesday I went to my counselor and she discussed my bipolar disorder again."

I asked the teacher, "Can you figure out what's happening here?" After the same sequence of events happened a second time, she began to understand why she "spiraled down," when other aspects of her life were actually improving.

Over the next year she carefully cut her antidepressant down and stopped taking a couple of the add-on drugs. Her psychiatrist was impressed and wanted to document her "discontinuation" schedule, since it might work for some of her other patients!

My teacher-friend had many challenging days, partly because she was still paying for earlier decisions, but she worked hard at her job, which she loved, began rebuilding her reputation, and even regained custody of her children! She is a wonderful mother and teacher. This woman went from being oppressed by her "inexplicable depression," suicidal thoughts, "bipolar disorder" and psychoactive drugs to living victoriously on love, hope and truth—thereby reclaiming her spirit, her job, her children, her life!!

I thank God that people are alive today and have a bright future because they have learned the truth about brain-disabling drugs and about life-giving alternatives through Dr. Peter Breggin's work and influence.

It is a privilege for me to know this great man!

Nadine S. De Santo, EdS

Nadine is a school psychologist in Indiana. She also teaches classes incorporating personality, learning style, challenging temperments, and drug-free discipline, at schools, churches and the women's division of the local rescue mission.

Saving My Professional Life
by Bob Jacobs, PhD, JD

I started my clinical practice in 1981, having been trained by an early pioneer in biological psychiatry. I was gung-ho about all the new "diseases" and "medications" being developed. But as I started working with children and families, like so many other practitioners, I started to question what I had been taught. How could children who were "unable to sit still and focus" sit for hours fixated on their Nintendo systems? How could we say children were "sick" in the absence of any evidence, and if they truly were "sick," how come they so often got "well" simply because others (teachers, parents) made changes? The clincher was meeting and getting to know the children, and hearing them describe seeing the world in a fog because of the drugs they were taking.

How could children who were "unable to sit still and focus" sit for hours fixated on their Nintendo systems? How could we say children were "sick" in the absence of any evidence, and if they truly were "sick," how come they so often got "well" simply because others (teachers, parents) made changes?

I started to do research, and was shocked to learn these children were being given amphetamines and other dangerous drugs, simply because their behavior was displeasing to adults. The more

I saw the more radical I became, and by the mid-1980's I was speaking out in local venues about the dangers of psychiatry, especially for children.

Pretty quickly I found myself ostracized by the medical community. Pediatricians had been my primary referral source, but that dried up when they knew my position. I refused to work with psychiatrists because they were drugging children. I felt like an outcast and wondered if I was losing my mind, or maybe just too stupid to understand why these children needed to be drugged.

I was about to give up on the profession, when I picked up a book called *Toxic Psychiatry*. It was the first time a professional book made me cry. This amazing writer was saying all the things that I had thought and felt so strongly for years, but thought I was alone on the planet in believing. And he went further, to help me understand things I had not even considered before. Peter Breggin saved my professional life and he validated me in a way that empowered me to spread the word about the dangers of psychiatry to thousands of others around the world over the last 20 years.

This amazing writer was saying all the things that I had thought and felt so strongly for years, but thought I was alone on the planet in believing.

In 1993 I had the pleasure of meeting Peter for the first time when he agreed to come to Jackson, Wyoming to spend a day training my staff (at the community mental health center, which I had renamed the community counseling center). The staff was moved by this brilliant and compassionate man, but the Board of Directors, several of whom were staunch advocates of biological psychiatry, were not. I kept fighting them, and it ultimately cost me my job.

I moved to Florida with my two children and, in 1999, wound up losing another job after I was attacked for writing a book review strongly endorsing Peter's book *Talking Back to Ritalin*. The ensuing 11 months of unemployment were terrifying, as I didn't know how I was going to support my children. Both Peter and Ginger were wonderfully supportive during this period, talking with me often and always being there for me. I will never forget their enormous kindness.

Every time I speak out on this subject I know in my heart I would not be able to do so if it were not for Peter. I am sure there are hundreds of others like me who are "out there" being brave only because we were emboldened and validated by Peter's work. Peter has protected countless children and adults through his groundbreaking work, and it has been a tremendous honor to have the privilege of knowing him.

Congratulations, Peter!

Bob Jacobs, PhD, JD

Bob is an attorney and manager of the Education Team for The Advocacy Center for Persons with Disabilities, Inc. Bob is also a psychologist and spent 20 years working with children as a teacher, coach, therapist and clinical administrator before enrolling in law school in 2000. Bob graduated from the University of Florida Levin College of Law in May of 2003 and was admitted to the Florida Bar in September of that year. He has a doctorate in psychology and two masters degrees in addition to the J.D. During the late 1990's he was host of the government-access television show "Parenting with Dr. Bob" which won a National Association of Counties award for "Innovation in County Government." Bob has written and spoken extensively in the U.S. and in Australia on the issue of the overuse of psychiatric diagnoses and prescription drugs with children.

Re-Energized and Renewed

by Michael C. Gilbert, PsyD

In the late 1990's, I first learned of Dr. Breggin's work from a segment on NPR regarding his book, *Talking Back to Ritalin.* At the time, I was completing graduate school and getting ready to start a new career as a psychologist. Previously, I had worked with children as a counselor in various settings, such as foster care, group homes, and a psychiatric hospital. In fact, one of my positions required that I receive training so that I could dispense the psychiatric medications to the children in the group home. These experiences left me uneasy about the labeling and medicating of children, especially those that had been neglected or abused by the adults in their lives. I immediately ordered the book.

Talking Back to Ritalin validated many of my personal beliefs, such as the misuse of DSM diagnoses and medication with our youth. This initial exposure to a credible source of scientific information led me to further research and investigate the facts related to these issues. Dr. Breggin's writings were especially enlightening and helped me form a foundation of knowledge and understanding to build upon.

In October 2000, I attended my first ICSPP Conference in New York City and immediately felt a connection. Thanks to Dr. Breggin's vision and dedication, I had been introduced to a group of professionals seeking to educate parents, professionals, and the public about the facts surrounding the potential dangers of medical model theories and psychiatric drugs. After listening to the presentations of Dr. Breggin and others, I was inspired to attempt and deliver this message through my work with children and families in Central New York.

To my happy surprise, Ginger and Peter Breggin ended up moving to Central New York in late 2002. During the past couple of years, Dr. Breggin has graciously accepted my invitations to speak to parents and professionals in the area. I also contacted

Dr. Breggin for guidance after my credibility was attacked by a variety of professionals due to my challenging their diagnosis and medication of a young girl with whom I had worked. Without hesitation, he wrote a letter supporting my position in the case. He later followed-up to check on the outcome as well as to ask if there was anything else he could do. I am grateful for his unselfish and genuinely caring response to my situation.

Dr. Breggin's remarkable career and writings have been an inspiration throughout the world. There have been numerous times when I have questioned whether or not to continue in my attempts to challenge and change the current treatment of our youth. However, each time I listen to Dr. Breggin give a lecture or read his publications, I am re-energized and have renewed hope that I can help make a difference to some of the children and families in my area. The impact of Dr. Breggin's work is immeasurable and will be felt for generations to come. As a result of his compassion and perseverance, there are many around the world who will continue to promote the ideals needed to strengthen families and communities and in the process reclaim our youth and provide them an opportunity for childhood as it should be.

Michael C. Gilbert, PsyD

Michael Gilbert has worked in the mental health field for over 15 years, including the past 9 years as a psychologist with the Syracuse City Schools. In 2000 he founded It's About Childhood & Family, Inc. as a not-for-profit clinical and resource center. One of the main missions of the organization is to educate parents regarding issues related to diagnostic labels and use of psychiatric medication with children. Dr. Gilbert has presented to parents and professionals throughout Central New York, makes TV appearances, and is conducting research evaluating a medication-free approach for children exhibiting ADHD-like behaviors.

A Fishing Companion
by Scott Davis, MA

I found myself at odds, quite early in my career as a public school teacher, with the practice of labeling rambunctious or otherwise bothersome boys as "hyperactive" and then giving them Ritalin. I suspected that the "science" behind the "hyperactive" label (which morphed to ADD which morphed to ADHD), was probably as phony as the racially biased intelligence studies from the nineteenth century.

Clearly, there was a story around each youngster: this one was bored to tears by a pedantic teacher, that one was dying to spend time with a dad who was not there, this one loved to work with his hands but school rarely allowed it, that one wanted to just be outside - away from a disintegrating family or a school full of rules. It seemed to me both facile and a kind of group denial and, well…arrogant to place the locus of dysfunction in the child's neurobiology.

This stance, of course, put me at odds with many parents and teachers who had a vested interest in having the student medicated. Word got to the docs in town and one "reported" me to my boss for questioning the establishment.

Then, about fifteen years ago, I heard a person on the radio making the same arguments I had been making in my school and supporting them with good science. And this person was a doctor—a psychiatrist, no less! I went to the library that very afternoon and began my acquaintance with Dr. Breggin's books. Later, I became a member of ICSPP.

It is the most encouraging thing to have a group of outstanding professionals lend legitimacy to parents and teachers who are bucking entrenched interests on behalf of kids. I was able to engage in discussions at work with deeper conviction in the soundness of my perspectives. Here and there, I think that conviction was what carried the day and a young person's life took a different path than it might otherwise have.

Peter, Ginger and those involved with the Center cannot know how many they have encouraged with their work, but they can be sure that my situation is representative of thousands who work in the schools. I remember thinking that Peter Breggin must be a remarkable and serious person to have the independence of mind and the courage to go against the flow of a whole profession and a massive industry.

Through the strangest of geographical coincidences, I was able, many years later, to actually come to know Peter and his lovely wife Ginger personally as a friend and sometimes fishing companion. Rather than the stolid, august personna that I would have expected—which would have been OK—I found a person who loves our small town, takes delight in its people, and casts his fly rod with the enthusiasm and gusto of an eleven year old. I've come to realize that these life-affirming qualities fit nicely with the trajectory of his life.

The life work of Peter Breggin was not an act of defiance, it was an act of love for life. And where does one's love of life manifest itself more deeply than in advocating for kids?

Scott Davis, MA

Scott received his BA from Hobart College, his MA from University of Wisconsin and studied many additional hours at Cornell. He has authored math software and taught high school math, social studies, and science in Lansing, NY for 35 years, and acted as math coordinator. He also served as an adjunct in the School of Education at SUNY Binghamton.

A Kinder, Gentler Way

by Betsy Root, MSW

I am very fortunate to have made the acquaintance of Peter and Ginger since they relocated in the Finger Lakes Region of New York, where I live. I will share how knowing them has had special meaning and how finding Peter's voluminous works changed my life. First, a brief autobiographical sketch elucidates why I was so impacted by the discovery of Peter rather late in my career.

Soon after commencing my first clinical appointment I became disillusioned with traditional medical model practice. I articulated my concerns at meetings. Eventually I gained the reputation of being one who "makes waves," a characteristic generally frowned upon in typical community mental health centers where I spent my entire professional career.

It puzzled me that I repeatedly ended up crosswise with my colleagues, especially my superiors. I couldn't figure out why I was so hard to get along with! In each successive job, I simply believed the traditional way consumers were treated was ineffective at best and often harmful. One middle aged man sticks in my mind especially. He was an employee assistance referral. He practiced rituals and read books about witchcraft. This worried his co-workers. He explained to me that he was a Pagan who did indeed partake of seasonal rituals and believed in "good" witchcraft. He was an eccentric little man to be sure, but harmless and actually quite intelligent. The agency psychiatrist labeled

I simply believed the traditional way consumers were treated was ineffective at best and often harmful.

him "paranoid schizophrenic" and prescribed antipsychotics. The workplace was informed of this diagnosis. I asked the psychiatrist what criteria led her to this conclusion. Incensed, she responded that he was delusional on account of his rituals, and she added insult to injury by asserting that he was slightly retarded as well as schizophrenic. I knew better. But my audacity was topical at the next staff meeting and my days at that clinic were numbered. This became a familiar pattern.

With my reservations about mental health treatment now legitimized and then some, I felt free to promote radical change in the field within the constraints of my employment.

By 2001 I'd been specializing in children and was even more horrified by the way children were being treated with drugs than by what I had observed in adults. A workshop introduced me to Howard Glasser, author of *Transforming the Difficult Child: the Nurtured Heart Approach.* Very taken by Glasser's alternative to medication and his unique approach to parent/child interaction, I attended advanced training with him in Tucson, AZ. He mentioned that he had been reading a lot of Peter Breggin's books.

Following Glasser's lead, I frequented the library to borrow all of Peter's books (and some co-authored with Ginger) that were available and bought many of them. I devoured them, one by one, starting with *Toxic Psychiatry* and have not been the same since. With my reservations about mental health treatment now legitimized and then some, I felt free to promote radical change in the field within the constraints of my employment. I will say more about that later.

Having familiarized myself with the Breggins' work, I wanted to meet them. I sent off a letter inviting them to a dinner party at my home with other therapists and a state legislator. I was thrilled when Peter left a phone message, "even though we don't ordinarily accept such invitations—yours was so sweet." We agreed to meet ahead of time for lunch to get acquainted. We met at his Ithaca office where Peter immediately put me at ease with a warm greeting and tour of his beautiful suite of rooms that he shares with Ginger. On display were some of Ginger's breathtaking photographs. Peter absolutely disarmed me during lunch and I felt we had known each other already a long time. I was impressed by his gracious remarks about Ginger whom he obviously adored and respected as full partner in his work. I detected in his manner an extraordinary ability to connect with others in short order.

> I was delighted with *The Heart of Being Helpful*—it was a wonderful choice, containing as it does the essential solution to the dominant psychiatric miasma.

The eve of the party arrived. We gathered a nice group and enjoyed an informal meal on my deck. Again, I felt the gentle relating to as Peter invited me to sit next to him, insisting that my hostess duties not exclude me from conversation. For her part, Ginger looked after my blind poodle so he wasn't stepped on by all the shuffling of feet. I was delighted with the gift of Peter's book, *The Heart of Being Helpful*, replete with a personalized message. The book was a wonderful choice, containing as it does the essential solution to the dominant psychiatric miasma.

Now about effecting change in my workplace. As a public union employee, I was protected from easy termination, as previous employers were wont to practice on me. Moreover, in this county mental health clinic it was my good fortune to have as my boss a psychologist named Charlie Capanzano who actually encouraged debate! He cheered me on as I went head to head with the staff psychiatrist. He did so out of respect for my breadth of experience and literary research.

One day at staff meeting, Charlie reported that he had accidentally bumped into Peter and Ginger Breggin as they were leaving their office.

He indicated he would like to have Dr. Breggin come speak to us. Of course, I spoke right up to announce I had already made the acquaintance of Peter and Ginger. Charlie assigned me the task of inviting them to our clinic. I did and they accepted.

I had the honor of introducing Peter and Ginger to the staff. I applauded their decades of good work citing some of the books I brought along for display. Peter delivered an uplifting message. He talked about the importance of the therapeutic relationship and mostly of the preeminence of love within professional boundaries. The simplicity of his message probably surprised the staff. They liked him. Too bad our psychiatrist only stuck his head in for an instant. He deprived himself of Peter's wisdom.

Peter and Ginger's visit to our clinic was some years ago. Buoyed up by Charlie's support, I became ever more bold in protecting my child clients from our clinic's traditional methods. I steered their parents and guardians away from the psychiatrist by providing information they needed to make sound treatment decisions.

During the Individual Educational Plan (IEP) meetings at local schools I stood up resolutely to special education directors, nurses, teachers and anyone else who tried pressuring parents to drug their kids. In addition I voluntarily facilitated numerous well-attended inservice trainings for colleagues to expose the truth about the psycho-pharmaceutical complex and to promote drug-free treatment approaches for both children and adults.

When the drug representatives spread their sumptuous food before us, I countered their misinformation with facts gleaned from Peter's literature and that of others affiliated with ICSPP. To my satisfaction, I became their pariah. I reported to the clinic and county administrator when I witnessed one salesperson from Astra Zeneca illegally promoting Seroquel for children (our child psychiatrist repeatedly invited this salesman into his office).

I retired this spring. My reward was having several colleagues tell me how much they appreciated hearing my point of view. Some said, under my influence, they radically changed their perspective and once enlightened there was no turning back. So it goes that the circle of illumination, lit by Peter and friends of ICSPP, expands as each of us takes up the torch in our own dominion.

I set out to portray Peter's influence on me as a therapist. But he has influenced me in other ways too. At the conclusion of the 9th Annual ICSPP Conference, it came across loud and clear that what we are really about is learning and teaching the art of loving one another. When so much is said and done—and indeed heroic feats have been accomplished through Peter's contributions and ICSPP these past decades—still it comes down to improving the human condition and that begins with kindness and loving care.

Thanks, Peter, for expressing this so eloquently through your writings and by your example.

Elizabeth Root, MSW, ACSW-R, MSEd

Betsy, a clinical social worker for 14 years, treated children and families in a clinic where she encouraged skillful parenting as an alternative to medication. Also a long-time thriving survivor of the biomedical psychiatric establishment, Betsy promotes normalization through collaborative, strength-based, psychosocial approaches. She is continuing her work in retirement now as a writer.

A Personal Tribute to Peter and Ginger Breggin

by Dorothy A. Cassidy, MEd

In writing a tribute to Peter, the image of Ginger keeps tumbling in and cannot be unattached. In Hindu ontology, Radha-Krishna and Sita-Ram, the spouse's role is recognized as crucial and thus the female is mentioned first. I mention this not to hint at anything more divine than for the rest of us, it just stumbled in again as I tried to write what is probably going to be a kind of autobiographical/biographical tale of how not one but two key people have played a pivotal place in what has turned out to be, surprisingly, my life's mission—trying to stop or limit the chemical abuse of children under the guise of help and to subscribe to the search for real ethical solutions.

How does one begin to describe the many life events that lead one to search out and connect with people such as Ginger and Peter? Was it my father's electric shock treatments that left him unable to do certain tasks he once knew and put holes in his memory? Was it several of my relatives who were treated for "mental illness?" Was it the pills beside my stepmother's bed, some of which may have been prescribed by her psychiatrist, which I suspect left her illogical and may have contributed to her violent nature? Years later, teachers and certain friends and relatives hinted that maybe something was wrong with my son and some Ritalin would be in order. He turned out just fine without it and is a son to be proud of. Was it that nagging doubt placed in my head by relatives who warned me that, because so many of my kin were "crazy," I was next in line? Certainly, as one of the many former polio children, having a number of orthopedic surgeries that left me a bit worse off each time than before was a sobering reminder that modern medicine did not have all the right answers.

The real prod came from years of teaching students (32 years now), mostly in special education, observing that, where it was once rare to have a student on any medicine other than occasionally anti-seizure medication, now I was watching more and more of them on psychoactive drugs and seeing the changes in their little bodies and minds. Despite the rhetoric, I could not bring myself to see what limited "good" came of it. Children were having all sorts of adverse events that I had not witnessed before: What? He went to the hospital because he "suddenly" developed a heart condition! Oh, he is in the psychiatric hospital and they have changed his medications and he still is having lots of problems! I saw little bodies twisting in varied ways and noted when those began after a "dose."

> She advised the audience to be cautious and to read a book by a controversial psychiatrist named Peter Breggin; the book, was *Toxic Psychiatry.*

Although many parents were all too happy to take their child off the stuff, be it Ritalin or Adderall or some other drug, there were still some parents who thought that it was their only recourse; besides, other educators seemed to approve and recommend it and their doctor or psychiatrist was well trained and knew more than any of us. Needless to say, not to be able to help children who were being chemically tortured, was a torture to me. I felt pretty much alone. We are not to question doctors, are we? What to do?

I first heard the name Peter Breggin in November of 1996 at the Orton Dyslexia Society conference in Boston, Massachusetts. ADD was a hot topic and sessions filled up so fast that I had to settle for audiotapes of the speakers. All but one was in favor of the diagnosis and the medications for it. Her name escapes me, but she advised the audience to be cautious and to read a book by a controversial psychiatrist named Peter Breggin; the book, *Toxic Psychiatry.* At this time too, I had a dear roommate who was labeled bipolar and she was on Lithium and Klonopin. I felt very strongly that part of her problems were those meds. They really did not work that well if they weren't actually causing the symptoms. *Toxic Psychiatry* seemed to be describing her adverse drug reactions and those of my students quite succinctly.

Soon I was approaching the individual members of the Horry County School Board (in the Myrtle Beach, SC area) about my concerns over Ritalin and its kin. I discovered that one, Chappell Dew, the local Ace Hardware man as well as being on the School Board, shared my same passion and mission.

I told him about Peter Breggin and his book *Toxic Psychiatry,* which he immediately purchased. Chappell did some of his own research about the numbers of children on these drugs at schools in our District and contacted Peter. At this time Peter was writing his first edition of *Talking Back to Ritalin.* Our then superintendent of schools, Gerrita Postlewait, Ph.D., issued a directive to all educators within the District to no longer bring up and promote medication. Both Chappell Dew and Dr. Postlewait are mentioned in the original *Talking Back to Ritalin.*

After finally getting my tail out from between my legs (I was very nervous about the whole thing), I actually spoke at the School Board's public forum for five minutes concerning issues involving psychiatric drugs in the schools. A lawyer who was listening later asked me to serve as an expert witness in a custody battle that involved a parent who did not want his five year old daughter medicated for "ADD." He could not find any medical doctor who would dare to testify against the diagnosis or drug.

Finally, after *Talking Back to Ritalin* came out and I had read it thoroughly, taken notes, and gone to Chapin Public Library, which assisted me in getting some of the articles that were cited, the case was more or less decided out of court. The other parent basically gave in.

The plaintiff, his lawyer and the guardian ad litem, also a lawyer, also had Peter's book and had obviously devoured it because there were notes throughout their copies. The child was taken off Ritalin and now resides with her dad, the plaintiff.

During the summer of 1998, I wrote to Ginger Breggin and explained a little about who I was and the relationship I had with Chappell Dew. Soon Ginger was writing to ask me to be on the Advisory Board of the ICSPP! That was the real beginning of my activism. I was no longer mostly alone without a "scientific" leg to stand on. I had something more to go on than "just my feelings."

On January 4, 1999, I met the Breggins for the first time at their home in Bethesda, Maryland for tea. They invited me to meet them after a quick call from me to say I was visiting my son in the area. Peter was working on a manuscript that was being mailed to David Cohen, *Your Drug May be Your Problem.* I shall never forget how they made me feel so welcomed and I sensed that I had met my friends.

I began in February 1999 to do a number of public seminars a year. In the beginning, it was not difficult to get invited to do presentations at state conferences for the Council for Exceptional

Many times Ginger, Peter, and many others of ICSPP, have given me needed information, advice, and encouragement for situations that I might be faced with, usually involving a child or even an adult.

Children and The South Carolina Education Association. Ginger had sent me some excellent articles by Peter and I had articles from others of the ICSPP that I could distribute. These pieces gave credence to my reform work. The seminars have variously been called "ADD/ADHD, Depression, Bipolar, etc.: First Do No Harm to Kids: Solutions." Presently, I hold several seminars a year and occasionally I may present at a church or club or for a chiropractor's Kids Day America (a day that promotes healthy living habits).

Throughout these years, many times Ginger, Peter, and many others of ICSPP have given me needed information, advice, and encouragement for situations that I might be faced with, usually involving a child or even an adult. Locally, I could have lost my job over my stance, but the Horry County Education Association and some unknown ones have stuck their necks out for me and I am still employed as a special educator, having taught all grades and, now adult education. I was never the Lone Ranger.

Thank you Peter and thank you Ginger for your unselfish devotion to those called "mentally ill" and for those of us who wish to contribute to their better causes. You have made it a little safer for the rest of us, while you were willing to take on so much of the risks, time, effort, and myriad costs. The order of your names does not matter: They go together.

Dorothy Cassidy, MEd, SpEd

Dorothy, a graduate of the University of Virginia, is a Special Education Teacher in Horry County Schools in the Myrtle Beach area of South Carolina. Dorothy is a member of the Board of Directors of ICSPP.

Courageous Trailblazer

by Sharon A. Collins, MD

I am a pediatrician who practices in the Midwest. I have been in practice 26 years. When I started my practice, I was horrified at the number of children I began to see who were diagnosed with ADD and casually placed on Ritalin for their "disorder." I expressed my dissatisfaction against the use of stimulant, mind-altering medications in our children without first considering other methods of helping them.

However, I was criticized for not understanding the medical realities of the behaviors I was seeing. It caused me to feel ashamed for daring to go against the current wisdom of our days—against the research of prominent scientists and physicians of our time. These feelings came out of my own issues of fear which I had not yet dealt with.

I nevertheless stood against the current practice, but soon found myself overwhelmed with calls from teachers and counselors who bombarded me with their worries concerning the futures of these children whose behaviors were out of control. If I would only help them by starting medication, their futures could and definitely would be brighter. I reviewed the medications and their potential effects and I was horrified.

When I moved from the first community and began practicing in another state 7 years later, I was even more shocked to find that in the second community, the problems were worse. Not only did I see more and more patients whose parents came to me demanding that I begin their children on Ritalin, but they now came with behavior checklists (lists of personal observations) regarding a child's behaviors that certainly needed to be dealt with, but not with drugs.

Many parents and teachers became very angry with me. The parents who listened to me and did what I said were bombarded with threats of failure for their children. Most caved in and got someone else to put their children on drugs. Several of them had to remove their children from the schools and either put them into private schools at great personal expense or home schooled them, which came with its own challenges. There were few alternatives for them at that time. I could find only one counselor in the community who agreed philosophically with me. Of course, he was limited in the number of patients he could take on. He quickly became overwhelmed with my referrals. Some patients literally screamed at me and slammed the door as they left my office because I tried to give them something to try with their child before they made the decision to begin Ritalin.

> Not only did I see more and more patients whose parents came to me demanding that I begin their children on Ritalin, but they now came with behavior checklists regarding a child's behaviors that certainly needed to be dealt with, but not with drugs.

One father told me he did not come to my office for behavior therapy and counsel on discipline. He said he already knew what his son needed—and it was Ritalin. He told me he wasted a day from work for this "foolishness" and he refused to pay for what he felt was a total waste of his time. The reaction towards anyone who disagreed with the medical opinions toward ADD and ADHD in the 1980s and 1990s was extremely noxious and intimidating.

When I discovered Dr. Peter Breggin and read about his stance on drugging children for these behaviors, I was shocked and relieved to find that there was another MD who believed as I did. After devouring a lot of his material, I finally invited him to speak in my community. I approached the psychiatrists in town to let them know of my plans. They tried to discourage me from having Dr. Breggin come. They gave me the names of several other “more acceptable” speakers. However, I wanted Dr. Breggin because of his strong stance and no-nonsense approach. I arranged for the physicians who attended to get continuing medical education (CME) credits. However, only one physician besides me attended. She did not have a positive response toward what Dr. Breggin said, but was gracious to me. However, what happened next was interesting. The backlash from teachers, counselors, and physicians was painful to me.

Dr. Breggin impressed me very much. He was clinically astute and well researched. I also saw in him a man whose heart was tenderly directed toward the children—the most vulnerable of us.

I was told that I would never be able to request that a physician visit our community for CME credits ever again without undergoing very careful scrutiny to make sure all the other physicians agreed on his or her validity.

Despite all that, Dr. Breggin impressed me very much. He was clinically astute and well researched. I also saw in him a man whose heart was tenderly directed toward the children—the most vulnerable of us. He wanted to prevent what he saw as the beginning of the destruction of the brains of our children.

I have had the chance to get to know him personally since then. He continues to be a champion for all who are medicinally abused by the current methods of psychiatric medicine—multiple drug therapy for all emotional and mental diagnoses.

A lot of time has passed since I first met Dr. Breggin. The pharmaceutical answers to these problems have swelled and the number of drugs used to deal with behavior problems have increased dramatically. Dr. Breggin is more relevant today than he was 25 years ago. It is because of him that others are waking up.

Others now feel empowered to speak out against the atrocities perpetrated against children in this country. Non-drug solutions in medicine are not progressing as fast as I hoped they would. However, I shudder to think what the future would have been like had not Dr. Breggin taken such a passionate stance and spoken out against this when he did.

I thank you, Peter, for being there for the children of this country. And I personally thank you for being there for me when I needed support. I continue to hold you in the highest regard and as you are in your retirement years, rest in the knowledge that you have made a huge difference in my life and in the lives of many people.

Sharon Collins, MD

Sharon is in practice in Cedar Rapids, Iowa, where she is a general pediatrician with an interest in behavioral problems. Her passion is helping children maximize their physical and emotional health so they can realize their dreams; and empowering parents to help their children reach their highest potential without the use of force, manipulation, intimidation, or abuse.

Changing Beliefs and Attitudes: From the Professional to Personal

by Thomas Cushman, PhD

I vividly remember where I was in 1993 when I was browsing the bookstore shelves and had a provocative sounding title jump out at me. How could one ignore the title *Toxic Psychiatry* given biological psychiatry's ever-increasing stranglehold on the thinking of mental health professionals? As a psychologist, the research and the science were so clear and compelling that psychosocial forces such as school failure led to motivational problems and progressed to learned helplessness where children would become anxious, inattentive, passive and depressed. Research-based evidence indicated that abused and neglected children vigilantly focused on their context, but not on their schoolwork. Depression and anxiety were not illnesses but symptoms of trauma or chronically stressful circumstances such as poverty, broken relationships and the death or loss of loved ones. So often, psychosocial stressors had psychosocial solutions or interventions.

As a psychologist the research and the science were so clear and compelling that psychosocial forces such as school failure led to motivational problems and progressed to learned helplessness.

Despite the overwhelming evidence, biological psychiatry would have us believe that inattention, depression and even "poor conduct" were due to deficiencies of specific neurochemical transmitters—especially dopamine and serotonin. Progressively more often, graduate students in our training programs, from strong undergraduate universities, would exclaim that we "know" that "ADHD" is from a dopamine imbalance and "depression" is from an imbalance in serotonin. Students were, and still are, shocked when challenged with a request for evidence—and by the suggestion that there is none. In their psychopharmacology courses, the dopamine and serotonin hypotheses are taught as facts, not as hypotheses. Is there a credible voice that can speak to the issue and consequently save (not too strongly worded) children from the oppression inherent in the prescription of mind-altering drugs that subdue the passion and crush the spirit?

One Legacy of Dr. Peter Breggin

Peter Breggin, M.D. is, of course, a credible voice for professionals throughout the world, who have learned through his many works that psychiatric medications are not just over-used, but a form of oppression and biologically dangerous. Can science overcome the power of marketing and the barrage of sound bites on the network news every evening? Dr. Breggin has had the credibility, and perhaps more importantly, the courage, to challenge biological psychiatry and the pharmaceutical industry. However, given the resources and money put into indoctrinating the public, can beliefs and attitudes really be changed by new information from a credible source?

Information and Attitude Change: Serving Tens of Thousands of Children; One Child at a Time

We had the good fortune of having Dr. Breggin address our professional community recently. Many of our program's graduate students were in attendance, which gave us the opportunity to ask them, through the use of a brief survey and informal, unstructured discussions, what impact he had on their thinking. While our methodology was informal (as a pilot for more research), we did collect some information systematically. The questions we were asking: Can a single, hour-long presentation by Dr. Breggin, change the knowledge base and attitudes in a manner that will affect professional practice in the schools where most "ADHD" diagnoses are initiated and/or made?

The short answer is "yes." We asked a small sample of school psychology trainees to respond to a number of questions related to Dr. Breggin's presentation. Questions were asked on a Likert Scale of 1 to 5 with 1 being "strongly believed" to 5 being "strongly did/do not believe." The first question was: "How much did you believe ADHD to be a valid diagnosis" before and after Dr. Breggin's presentation? The mean score changed from 2.5 to 3.5 suggesting movement from a belief that can be fairly deeply entrenched, even among trainees.

The next question asked, "How much did you believe the various psychotropic drugs to be safe?" Beliefs before the presentation had a mean value of 3 and after the presentation the mean value was 4.4. That suggests Dr. Breggin's impact was very influential in terms of drug safety. Similarly, school psychology trainees clearly indicated they thought psychotropic drugs were effective (X=2.5) before the presentation and did not believe they were effective (X=3.9) after the discussion. Students also indicated they would take a medication, or give it to their children before the talk (X=3) but not after (X=4.1). The graduate students in school psychology also moved from their belief that "ADHD" and depression are "biologically based disorders" (X=2.25) to believing they are not biologically based (X=3.5).

While this is just a small sample of those in attendance, it does suggest Dr. Breggin can have a profound impact on the views of graduate students who will soon be in the forefront of making diagnostic decisions and hearing the question: "Does this child have ADHD?" One graduate student commented, "I have always been directed to the work of Russell Barkley (who is heavily funded by the pharmaceutical companies) for information on ADD." Another student commented, "I feel Dr. Breggin made a lot of compelling points I can take with me into my career." It is important to keep in mind that these students heard Dr. Breggin for a single one hour presentation, producing considerable change in the beliefs and attitudes that drive professional practice. By this one talk, how many children may avoid the devastating negative effects of psychotropic drugs?

From Beliefs to Professional Practice

In a very recent paper, one of our graduate students indicated she was working with a child who was taking a newly prescribed, time-released version of methylphenidate. Once she learned of the medication, she went to the school nurse to follow up. The nurse indicated the child had a very new complaint of chest pain. The trainee then approached the child's teacher who said she was seeing tics for the first time. The school psychology trainee immediately contacted the child's mother who made an emergency appointment with the prescribing physician, who, presumably, stopped the medication (follow-up information was not available). Yet another graduate student has had her adolescent's medication terminated. Dr. Breggin has had a significant impact on one community as a result of a single, short presentation—the same effect is surely taking place wherever he visits. It is likely there are thousands of children who would otherwise be drugged, if not for Dr. Breggin's work.

Personal Practice

As a result of Dr. Breggin's scholarship, I train students differently than I would if I had not had the benefit of his books such as *Toxic Psychiatry, Reclaiming Our Children* and *Talking Back to Ritalin*. In our training program students learn to ask "Why is this child inattentive" rather than "Does this child have ADHD?"

In my practice and that of so many students that leave SUNY Oswego, sources of inattention can invariably be traced to difficulties or just differences ranging from early childhood trauma to varieties of temperament. Then, interventions can be developed that relate directly to the source of the problem. In the absence of Dr. Breggin's influence, many, many more children would be subjected to the negative and often devastating side effects of psychotropic drugs.

Courage

Dr. Breggin has courageously challenged an empire that is well-funded and works hard to protect its hold on a practice that is such a disservice to so many children. Peter, my personal and heartfelt thanks for being there for so many professionals, and so many children, adolescents and parents. I know of no one who has been the kind of advocate you have been for so many who had no real voice.

Thomas Cushman, PhD

Tom recently retired as professor and past chair of the Department of Counseling and Psychological Services at SUNY Oswego. He is a licensed psychologist and certified school psychologist. In 2007-2008 he invited Dr. Breggin to teach as a Visiting Scholar in his department.

Chapter 10

Working with Psychiatric Survivors

Introduction

Beginning with the anti-psychosurgery campaign in the early 1970's, Dr. Breggin has worked very closely with psychiatric survivors—individuals who became activists against psychiatric abuse—including Leonard Frank, Judi Chamberlin, David Oaks, Rae Unzicker before her untimely death, and many others. Their joint efforts included opposition to psychosurgery, electroshock and involuntary treatment. In later years, with the formation of the International Center for the Study of Psychiatry and Psychology (ICSPP), more of Dr. Breggin's efforts have been directed toward research and writing, working with fellow professionals, and participating as an expert in the legal system. However, he has remained forever grateful for the past and continuing support of the psychiatric survivor activists.

Dr. Breggin continues to believe that psychiatric survivors are key to achieving psychiatric reform. He supports them in his publications and has worked with the reform movement on numerous occasions, such as their joint efforts to draw attention to the tragic death of Esmin Green, an involuntary patient who died in July 2008 while sitting unattended and ignored on a bench for 24 hours in the admitting area of a psychiatric facility.

Rae Unzicker was a remarkable woman who surmounted psychiatric abuse to become a leader in the psychiatric survivor movement and an international advocate for disability civil rights.

She was a presidential appointment to the National Council on Disability.

Rae and Peter met the night before the 1987 Oprah Winfrey show on which they both appeared with other patient advocates to document psychiatric abuses. This was the show whose stunning success led the psychiatric establishment to attack of Dr. Breggin's medical license (chapter 5). Peter and Rae almost instantly became close friends.

Rae liked to create her own extended family and, although younger than Peter, she chose him to be her "son." She died after a painful illness at age 52 in 2001. Rae wrote this letter to Peter by hand on hotel stationery shortly after they met:

Remember the Angel
by Rae Unzicker

Peter, you are not alone. You've never been alone. Remember the angel and the elves who guard and protect you. Listen, when you feel lonely, listen to the flutter of their wings. Know they're standing in for the millions of people whose lives you have affected in a profoundly important way. The human heart is the essential element for effective social action. Continue to trust your heart. Believe me, I've experienced it and it's eminently trustworthy. In the meantime, as the "official" spokes person for thousands of ex-inmates: thank you.

I want to be in touch with you more often. I want to call you and tell you how special you are, how happy I am that you survived those times and waited for Ginger. And I will.

Much, much love to both of you. Mom.

Thank You, Dr. Peter Breggin

by Jim Gottstein, JD

Like many people, my first exposure to your work was reading *Toxic Psychiatry*. In *Toxic Psychiatry* you validated my own sense that psychiatry is harmful to one's physical and mental health. However, I must admit I hadn't previously understood the vast scope of the harm being inflicted by current psychiatric practices.

I have since purchased all of your books. *Brain Disabling Treatments* is an astonishingly brilliant, and very accessible distillation of *Toxic Psychiatry*. I also found *Your Drug May Be Your Problem* (with David Cohen) to be a particularly terrific, practical, day-to-day reference offering detailed descriptions of (1) the reasons each of the covered drugs is prescribed and what they do (or don't do), (2) the negative effects, and (3) the withdrawal effects.

Psychiatric survivors around the world—those who, as I did briefly, have experienced psychiatry from the wrong side of the locks and needles—have been validated and buoyed by your work. Psychiatry tells us we are crazy when we say there is nothing wrong with our brains, and they insist the drugs cannot possibly be causing any of the problems we are experiencing. You validate our experiences with the truth that there was likely nothing wrong with our brain before the introduction of Psychiatry's brain and body damaging "treatment."

You counter the "Abandon All Hope Ye Who Enter Here" mantra of the system with the truth that we can get off the drugs, overcome our difficulties and resume or even surpass the quality of our previous lives.

Instead of the lie the system tells us that the psychiatric symptoms we experience when coming off the drugs is proof we are mentally ill, you tell us the truth that these withdrawal effects have nothing to do with any "underlying mental illness." This information reduces the fear associated with the symptoms and strengthens our ability to weather the storm.

By telling the truth about these things, you have been and continue to be the inspiration for thousands of people around the globe, giving hope and catalyzing recovery.

While I believe most everyone knows right from wrong, there are few who will absolutely follow their moral compass in the face of substantial negative consequences for doing so. You are such a person. By courageously facing down the Psychiatric/Pharmaceutical Hegemony with its immense power, you have also been an inspiration to me in my professional life. Your courage gives me courage—if you can do it, I can do it.

You have also helped inflict meaningful blows with your work as an expert witness. I can only hope to accomplish a fraction of what you have and are continuing to accomplish. And to do that I have to stand on your shoulders. Your scholarly publications show the way to prove in court that, as Leonard Roy Frank points out, "Psychiatry is to medicine what astrology is to astronomy."

I can see why Big Pharma is afraid of you. You have success as an expert witness because juries trust you to tell the truth, just as your patients do. You will tell the good and bad. You have the credibility of scholarly, truthful, research in your writings. I know I can rely on what you say in my own work. And I do.

Your leveraging your personal work by nurturing of the International Center for the Study of Psychiatry and Psychology (ICSPP) has been important to me and, frankly, to the world. ICSPP serves as a haven to me and its other members in our battles against the horrors perpetrated by current psychiatric practice. Like a good parent, you nurture, encourage and let ICSPP blossom on its own, yet are also there to be helpful when needed.

By launching ICSPP's journal, *Ethical Human Psychology and Psychiatry* and keeping it alive, you have also leveraged your own leading scholarly writings with those of others. I am finding, more and more, that I am using these articles in my legal cases and other advocacy work, which is focused on mounting a strategic litigation campaign against forced psychiatric drugging.

To me, though, even more important than all of this is your kindness; you are caring. It emanates from you. You will be truthful, direct and firm when you see someone going in the wrong direction, but you are always kind. I remember the first time I met you when you didn't know me from Adam. You took the time to talk with me, learn about me, and to relate to me. My observation is you do that with everyone. Most people of your stature get a big head. You don't. That is what makes you a truly big man.

Thank you, Dr. Peter Breggin. It is an honor for me to be able to join my voice with the others here in documenting your life and work. You are a beacon to me and to legions of others, giving us courage and lighting the way. The world is a far better place for you being in it. I have no doubt the impact of your positive presence will grow far larger as the broader populace comes to realize, "Dr. Breggin is right; he's always been right." Most importantly, thank you for being you. We love you.

James B. Gottstein, JD

Jim Gottstein grew up in Anchorage, Alaska. He attended the University of Oregon and graduated with honors (BS, Finance) in 1974. Subsequently enrolling in Harvard Law School, Jim completed his formal legal studies in 1978, graduating with a J.D. degree. In addition to over 25 years of private practice, Jim has been an attorney advocate for people diagnosed with serious mental illness. He co-founded the Law Project for Psychiatric Rights (PsychRights) and is currently president. Jim is on the Board of Directors of ICSPP. Much of his time is devoted to defending and promoting the well being of those whose lives have been placed in jeopardy by involuntary treatment and biological psychiatry.

Testimonial for Peter

by Al Siebert, PhD

Peter Breggin is the first psychiatrist who gave me hope that perhaps one day our society will free itself from the illusion of "mental illness." He is the first professional who spoke and wrote about a fundamental issue that I couldn't get published anywhere—that psychiatry is not a successful mental health profession, it is an ineffective mental illness profession. By speaking out as he did, Peter helped me feel validated and less isolated.

I was embarrassingly naïve about psychiatry and clinical psychology during all my years in graduate school. Throughout my entire program in clinical psychology I actually believed that psychiatrists and psychologists wanted to eliminate mental illness. It never occurred to me that they were so co-dependent on being surrounded by people with invisible diseases, they were creating and sustaining the so-called "mental illnesses" they claimed they wanted to cure.

I was so naïve that when I discovered that the perception of mental illness in others was mostly a stress reaction in the mind of the beholder, I assumed that the staff at the Menninger Clinic, where I was starting a two-year NIMH post-doctoral fellowship, would be delighted and immediately start to work on their own minds.

Instead, they proved that my hypothesis was valid. The Menninger people were so distressed by what they heard me tell them they cancelled my fellowship. I accepted that, but they were so disturbed by my ideas they had me locked up on the back ward of the local VA hospital (I'm a veteran), diagnosed me as having acute paranoid schizophrenia, and declared that I needed very long-term treatment. I laughed at them. I waited until they wrote up my case for the VA records, then signed out "Against Medical Advice" thirty days later.

That was in 1965. I had many cognitively lonely years until I heard about Peter Breggin and read his books. I appreciate Peter's courage. I know that by speaking out as he has that he must have been subjected to many efforts to silence him. His persistence and the kindred spirits that he and Ginger attracted lifted my optimism and strengthened my belief that one day the ineffective mental illness professions will dissolve and be replaced by competent, effective, true mental health experts.

> I had many cognitively lonely years until I heard about Peter Breggin and read his books. I appreciate Peter's courage. His persistence and the kindred spirits that he and Ginger attracted lifted my optimism and strengthened my belief that one day the ineffective mental illness professions will dissolve and be replaced by competent, effective, true mental health experts.

What I went through closely matches Maslow's description of self-actualizing peak experiences. It felt joyous to feel my mind break free from what Buddhists call "consensus realities."

I returned to my family home in Portland, Oregon, and found that with my PhD and teaching credentials it was easy to obtain teaching positions at local colleges, where I soon received outstanding evaluations.

I discovered that with my mind free from professional and social consensus realities I developed a reliable talent for "pattern empathy." This is an ability to discern patterns of thoughts, feelings and actions—and their probable consequences—that I enjoy teaching to others.

In my spare time I conducted intensive research into the inner nature of life's best survivors—people transformed for the better by extreme adversity. My book *The Survivor Personality: Why Some People Are Stronger, Smarter, and More Skillful at Handling Life's Difficulties...and How You Can Be, Too (1996)*, is now in its 17th printing and is published in six languages.

In recent years I've gained recognition as one of the leading professionals in the emerging new field of resiliency psychology and enjoy speaking at conferences and meetings of many groups. My disillusioning, transformational experience was the best thing that ever happened to me, and I'm committed to showing others how life-changing experiences can be for them, too.

Al Siebert, PhD

With great sadness, we wish to report the death of long-time survivor personality and resiliency research pioneer Dr. Al Siebert. He died peacefully at his home overlooking the river on June 25, 2009, surrounded by family. Al Siebert (1934-2009) received his PhD in clinical psychology from the University of Michigan. He was a life-member of the American Psychology Association. He was Director of The Resiliency Center in Portland, Oregon, and author of The Resiliency Advantage: Master Change, Thrive Under Pressure, and Bounce Back From Setbacks (2005), winner of the Independent Publishers 2006 Best Self-Help Book award.

Harm at the Hands of Psychiatrists

by Libby

I've suffered a lot of unintentional harm at the hands of psychiatrists and Dr. Breggin's beautiful, courageous books have reconvinced me of everything I firmly believe in, and in the hope that sanity and empathy will prevail. I was diagnosed years ago with major depression, bipolar disorder and PTSD but no longer suffer from any psychological or psychiatric symptoms whatsoever, having changed and grown in my own personal, limited capacity. I'm far from perfect, and far from being an entirely happy human being. But my psychological "toolbox" has grown a hundredfold in the last six years, in ways that it never grew when I was in psychiatric treatment, quite the contrary. And, thinking of all the psychiatric patients in the world, this leaves me sad and terrified to my stomach.

I started going to psychologists, and quite quickly got sent to psychiatrists too, in my early twenties. I was soon diagnosed with Major Depression and Bipolar Disorder as well as PTSD, and treated with everything and anything from Xanax to every kind of antidepressant my doctors could think of. Apart from becoming entirely addicted to my meds, I'm not sure the years of treatment did much good. My psychiatrists gave me more and more prescriptions, knew I was hoarding up on meds and taking dangerous amounts, and were quite happy to let the situation continue as it was. As a result, a few years of my life—the years I took Xanax—are largely wiped from my memory and the memories that I do have are contradictory, such as events that ought to have happened in a certain year seemingly happening a year later, and vice versa.

I've given up trying to make sense of this mess; I've accepted the fact that a few years of my life will probably be confused or wiped from my memory for life and that I will have to simply move on. The urge to use Xanax remained for three years after I stopped, but probably because I didn't touch the stuff again, it has dwindled down to nothing and disappeared completely. I have recently had to take Xanax before an operation, and to my surprise, I didn't find it attractive or disturbing. It didn't recreate any urge to take it. It was gone.

I distinctly remember the last conversation I had six years ago with my psychiatrist, a kind man against whom I really cannot and would not say a harsh word on a personal basis. It's just that I believe his education and experience included all the wrong things and none of the right ones. I was about to leave, planning to move to another country and start an entirely different and new life. I had asked him for a letter that I could give my new doctor and told him I planned to go to university and study a rather difficult profession. He responded by saying, "But you do realize that people like you can't do that, don't you? You will always be sick; it's like diabetes, you'll never get better. Why don't you do something easier in life, something that you won't fail at this time?" I was too distressed and too shy to think of an appropriate response, and left his office in shock. When I wrote him an email the next day expressing my disbelief at what he had said, he responded by pointing out my destructive and illogical rage. Needless to say, I never went to see a psychiatrist again.

But I did leave, move abroad, stop all my meds gradually (having stopped abruptly a few times before and knowing how painful the withdrawal symptoms can be, I was wiser this time), and started studying Buddhist philosophy and meditation. The first two or three years were really rough. I still suffered from depression, and at times was terrified the feeling would never leave me no matter how much effort I put into changing. But I persisted, even if I dragged myself out of bed in the morning and fell back into bed as soon as my daily duties were done. I did get up, though, and function, and kept learning to meditate, and refused to give up. I started developing a close relationship with a Buddhist teacher, who in his empathy, compassion and wisdom was the direct opposite of the psychiatrists I had met before.

Six years later I now have absolutely no symptoms of depression left, and no symptoms of Bipolar Disorder. I still have some minor symptoms of PTSD, for example, if I hear a loud surprising noise I'll jump higher than others and be more agitated; but I no longer need ten meters of personal space around me in order to feel safe and unthreatened.

Before my recovery I was hospitalized twice for depression and Bipolar Disorder, for a couple of months each time. There was no doubt I fit the criteria; I underwent a large number of psychological tests and was given an official diagnosis, along with an explanation that I'll never recover and will always need to take meds. I agreed I was sick; I felt sick; but I deeply refused to agree with the theory that said I would be like this for life. I felt terrible; my personal skills, emotionally and socially, were appalling. And I was undoubtedly in a deep depression, self-injuring, and at times not getting out of bed for days, and didn't talk to a single soul for months. So, does that mean I must still have mental problems now? But I don't have a trace left. In that case, are they as permanent as they are believed to be? Are we truly as unchanging, as solidly locked into our present state of being as we think, so much so that there is no hope for change, no hope for personal growth, for a transformation?

I'm not a doctor, not a psychologist. I know nothing of the mind. The little that I know comes from limited personal experience. But I feel that Dr. Breggin is the kind of psychiatrist all psychiatrists should be; the real psychiatrist, the one who truly thinks of the human mind in all of its complexity and doesn't limit it to biological theories that haven't proven themselves as much more helpful than placebos. I know from personal experience that working on my emotions can entirely cure depression and other mental problems. It requires time, and effort – and courage, and more faith in myself than I often felt I would ever have, and far more optimism than I had ever learned to feel.

But I found out that not giving up and persisting brings unbelievable results. And I refuse to believe my case is an isolated extreme, or that others are doomed to a life of mental anguish as well as chemical harm. I refuse to believe that anything is fixed and unchanging, or that the human spirit has no need for empathy.

I personally respect Dr. Breggin a great deal for the deep empathy and compassion that arises from his writing.

I want to share with you the meditation that I do every day, the meditation that has helped me to get rid of Major Depression and Bipolar Disorder completely. Of course, not everyone in the world likes meditation, and quite obviously not everyone is Buddhist, so I'm fully aware that it won't necessarily work for everyone.

I believe there are 6 billion different types of "medicine" for depression out there in the world, each suited for a different individual. A hallmark of Buddhism is that there is a large array of teachings on every topic, each one presented at a slightly different angle or in a slightly different way. It's our personal responsibility to choose the ones that move us the most, and to make use of them. They say that Buddha taught 84,000 different Dharmas, and if I understand it correctly, out of these 84,000 presentations we can each find the ones that work the best for us and apply it to our daily lives. This is the one that helps me the best, and if writing it down will help just one more person, I'll feel great gratitude.

This meditation is called "Giving and Receiving," and is a meditation on love and compassion. Its strength lies in its simplicity: it is said to "ride" in the breath, and it doesn't require belief in any specific religion or philosophy. All that is necessary is to be human, and to breathe in and out. This meditation is a complete 180-degree turn from what we ordinarily feel; instead of avoiding pain, we embrace it out of a growing feeling of empathy.

What we receive from others is everything that is undesirable—all the suffering, pain and dissatisfaction in their lives, in the form of dark light that we breathe in. We breathe all of this pain into our heart, drawing it into our nostrils and down to our heart, and we imagine that when it reaches the heart and touches the seat of our selfishness at the heart, our ego, there's a big explosion and nothing remains of either pain or our ego. And as we breathe out, we visualize that we send out in the form of white light, all the happiness, great things and small joys alike, that we have—anything that might make others happy, and satisfy all their needs and desires.

I find this meditation intensely beautiful, and I personally respect Dr. Breggin a great deal for the deep empathy and compassion that arises from his writing. His books remind me often of this favorite meditation of mine. For this reason, I would like to thank him from the bottom of my heart for these long years of kindness, and for offering all of us a sane and ethical alternative to present day psychiatry.

Libby

Libby studied music and was a cellist for many years. When she was 26, she became a Buddhist nun. Since then she's been practicing and studying Tibetan Buddhism in Europe, the U.S. and India.

Peter Breggin Tribute

by David W. Oaks

The first time I remember meeting Peter was at a legal rights conference in Portland, Oregon where he was a keynote speaker. With some psychiatric survivors I had just formed a new small organization that, while open to the public, was led by psychiatric survivors. After Peter spoke I approached him in the hallway and I was blunt, "Because we're organizing psychiatric survivors, who are mainly poor, we need to focus on getting money for this new group."

I could tell Peter was surprised, as anyone would be. But being Peter he didn't dismiss me. Peter talked with me and brainstormed with me. When his book *Toxic Psychiatry* came out he personally fronted our organization a "loan" of his books so we could fundraise.

It was only years later that I understood why. Over the next nearly two decades of friendship, whenever I have heard Peter asked that inevitable and mournful question, "The oppression from the mental health industry is so big, what are we to do?" Peter would answer, in so many words, that he felt a key was supporting the organized voice of psychiatric survivors.

I distinctly remember the first experience I had of helping to get out what would eventually become boxes and boxes of the book *Toxic Psychiatry* and other titles to the public. *Toxic Psychiatry* broke so much silence on so many key topics, such as neuroleptic drugs, which I had been forced to take. I told Peter in so many words, "So this, finally, is what it is like to experience significant healing from a psychiatrist!" Since then I have said many times that Peter is one of those few psychiatrists who offers hope for his profession, because he is a true soul healer.

I need to emphasize that though Peter has written so many helpful books, when I reflect upon his effectiveness I always hone in on one specific quality: Peter is willing to nonviolently face off directly with power. Isn't this what activists like Martin Luther King, Jr. did? Isn't this ferment necessary for healing in our troubled world?

I know dozens of wonderful mental health professionals with helpful books, or who do good work behind closed doors. But for me, what helps make Peter, Peter, is that community organizing instinct, the willingness to go in front of Oprah, or the FDA, or a judge, or a radio host and, in an articulate and often witty way confront oppression. Peter is no closed-door ally. In the field of mental health professionals, Peter's name must be found in the definition of the word chutzpah.

I take a deep satisfaction that it was Harvard volunteer programs that pointed both of us onto our respective career tracks. Not to slight thousands of conventional investment brokers and lawyers, but isn't a career like Peter's closest to the intellectual and moral humanist ideals that Harvard embraces?

I've taken advice Peter has offered over the years. I distinctly remember the moment Peter addressed some questions during a question and answer period at a conference from psychiatric survivors about the fees he charged for testifying in court. Peter spoke from the heart about how difficult this work is, how important it is for us to all sustain ourselves and enjoy a satisfying quality of life, and how his fees have helped fund his activist work. I'm sure many others like Peter and myself who count their mental health activism by the decades will agree.

We all know that in a field where so many people are hurt so deeply, it can be difficult for mental health professionals to build bridges to those who have personally experienced trauma at the hands of the mental health system. I appreciate that Peter has continued to build those bridges. I know that literally thousands of psychiatric survivors have a warm place in their hearts for Peter, and appreciate his work.

I do have one significant difference with something Peter says. I respect an individual's right to define himself. However, so often I hear Peter describe himself as a "reformer" of the mental health system. Perhaps this modesty is just a clever strategic play. Because clearly Peter is a nonviolent revolutionary, through and through, in the true American tradition going back to writer activists such as Thomas Paine.

I remember Peter has brought waves of laughter to a crowd when he recounts the dismay some establishment psychiatrists have displayed toward him, and he says quizzically, "But I'm just one Jewish psychiatrist." Never discount the power of one true soul healer whatever his or her heritage. In other words, Peter shows us the potential power of one true human being, and what better tribute is there? Thank you Peter!

David Oaks

David directs MindFreedom International, a non-profit coalition that unites 100 grassroots groups to win human rights and alternatives for people affected by the mental health system. David was a working class student attending Harvard University in the 1970's when he experienced psychiatric institutionalization five times. He was diagnosed schizophrenic, and underwent forced psychiatric drugging and solitary confinement. He wrote his senior paper about community organizing with psychiatric survivors, and graduated with honors in 1977. This is David's 31st year as a psychiatric survivor human rights activist. David lives with his wife in Oregon and loves camping and gardening. For more information see www.MindFreedom.org.

Chapter Eleven

World-Wide Influence

Introduction

Dr. Breggin's work has influenced people across the globe. Many have read his books, especially the English edition of *Toxic Psychiatry* with an introduction by noted British psychologist Dorothy Rowe. He has met many professionals while speaking in Canada and Europe and a number have come to the United States to visit with him and to attend the annual meeting of the International Center for the Study of Psychiatry and Psychology (ICSPP). He has worked on special overseas projects, such as psychiatrist Michael Corry's current efforts to prohibit electroshock treatment in Ireland, psychiatrist Bob Johnson's promotion of healing alternatives in England, and educator Brian Kean's continuing efforts to stop the psychiatric diagnosis and drugging of children in Australia.

In addition to the contributors in this chapter, several other international professionals have made contributions to this biography. British psychiatrist Joanna Moncrieff, MD published a scientific paper in appreciation of Dr. Breggin's work in a special issue of the journal *Ethical Human Psychiatry and Psychology* (excerpt in chapter 13). In the same journal volume, author and former psychoanalyst Jeffrey Masson, who now lives in New Zealand, described his trip with Dr. Breggin to Germany to talk about the role of psychiatry in Nazi Germany (excerpt in chapter 13). Physician, lawyer and international drug regulatory expert M. N. G. Dukes, MD, who is now a professor in Norway, described Dr. Breggin acting as an expert in the courtroom (chapter 8). Brian

Kean, an Australian professor and close friend, documented their personal relationship and their work together (chapters 1 and 9). Steve Baldwin, PhD, who taught in Australia and Great Britain, died at the height of his career. His contribution appears in chapter 12.

Unforgettable Scenes From the Life of Peter Breggin, MD
by Bob Johnson, MD

One inspiring scene from Peter's life, I shall never forget. Though he is well renowned for being a remarkable man, I doubt very much that what follows can be bettered for capturing that certain central essence which makes him so exceptional—so much so, that I feel this little glimpse deserves a wider audience.

Picture it—we are seated in a diner in Ithaca, New York. We have just placed our order and are awaiting delivery. We are re-commencing our on-going seminar which a conversation with Peter always elicits, when across the aisle from us, a commotion begins which not only grates on the nerves, but also actively impedes further intelligent exchange. A little girl, sitting at the end of her table, is weeping and caterwauling fit to bust. She has her elder sisters on either side, and further down her little table is her mother, who is at a loss as to what to do next. She tries all she knows, but the noise abates not. What would you do?

In England, to our shame, we would tend to talk politely amongst ourselves. Peter, of course, does not hesitate. I don't even recall him saying, "excuse me a minute!" In a flash, he is across the few yards that separates our table from theirs—and he has put his arm around the little girl, and is talking softly into her ear.

In a trice he is back—the noise has ceased, the little girl is all smiles, her sisters are looking sheepish, and, on their way out, they each make a grateful nod to Peter as they pass, the mother especially so.

Doesn't this just typify the man? If only he could work this magic on a wider sphere—read his books, look at his campaigns—it's all there. On this occasion he explained to our eager ears that the little girl had not got what she ordered, and her elder sisters were being unhelpful. I'm not sure how Peter pulled it off, or what he actually said—but he smoothed the ruffled emotions of all three parties, and the result was a win-win situation. What better description of therapy in its widest sense? What a parable for our troubled times.

There is another scene I must describe. We were so delighted when Peter agreed to come to London to talk at our James Nayler Foundation Annual Conference 2006 that I could not resist the splendid temptation of attempting to launch a public debate with Peter on one side, and the psychiatric establishment on the other. After much turmoil, we managed it. The motion to be debated was "this house believes that psychiatric drugs do more harm than good." I had hoped to get something a mite stronger, such as "unsafe at any dose," but those psychiatrists representing the Royal College of Psychiatry balked at that, so I wrote a book with that title instead.

Before describing the climax of that debate, I must emphasize just how big a debt I owe to Peter. I would never even have begun such a hazardous endeavour, had I not had his sterling presence and support. I know from bitter personal experience just how sharp orthodox psychiatric teeth can be—so without a solid, utterly reliable stalwart by my side, I would never have remotely considered venturing into their den.

During the debate, I showed a brief video clip from a recent session with a patient in psychosis—deluded, thought blocked, emotionally paralysed—and then in the same session, half an hour later, smiling at me, cracking jokes, and thoroughly "with it." Psychologist Dorothy Rowe was in the audience, and she later described these two clips, the first as showing "terror of annihilation," and the second the realization that "she was capable of pulling herself back together again."

Our two establishment psychiatrists however were not so benign. Firstly they tried to stop me showing the clips altogether by interrupting my 5 minute presentation by loudly doubting that

I had legal consent to show the video. Next they hammered me personally in the closing speech for being so outrageous. How can it be "outrageous" to show video evidence demonstrating that psychosis is curable? Let me assure you, that without the guarantee of Peter being there, holding the fort, there is simply no way I would have dreamt of setting up such a contest.

But the scene I want to close with is Peter's closing speech. Wow! The points made by the two established psychiatrists were abysmal. (You can read the entire transcript on our website, www.TruthTrustConsent.com.) They were quite disgraceful, showing pictures of lunatics in chains from the 19th century, and assuring us all, that this is where we would all be without the drugs. They were cut to the quick when Peter pointed out that these drugs inflicted "chemical lobotomies." One was heard muttering this challenging phrase in stunned disbelief, even as he left. He kept asserting he was 'enlightened'—but his failure to grasp what was obvious to the vast majority of the audience was painful to behold.

In response to a particularly outrageous and self-serving claim by one of the establishment psychiatrists, as Peter was summing up his side of the debate, he leans across the table, and cries "Shame. Shame. Shame." What a wonderful moment. It is captured on video, and I hope to have it out on a DVD shortly. Electric is the word! The precise point that had evoked this drama was the consistent contention by the established psychiatrists that the grievous neurological damage associated with drug treatments (the permanent drug-induced twitches and spasms called tardive dyskinesia) came not from the doctor-prescribed drugs but from the "mental disorder" itself. What a calumny. What a distortion. How can these doctors hold up their heads?

"For shame" is so entirely appropriate. I write with pesky words but these are nothing compared to Peter in full flood. He roundly condemned them, citing hundreds of papers in the literature showing that this dire toxic neurological damage comes from the drugs, not from the so-called mental disorder. One of the psychiatrists had protested that just as diabetes with time, caused arterial deterioration, so schizophrenia caused neurological decay. What an outrage! What gross medical ignorance! How can trained medical men persist in such gross self-deception?

So the scene which lives on is Peter standing up for the abused, holding forth in a calm incisive manner, propounding from his enormous knowledge of the literature just how drastically wrong these two psychiatrists, and their many colleagues, are. It was a wonderful picture.

At the conclusion of the debate, the packed room voted for who had presented the most convincing case, Dr. Breggin for the proposition, "Psychiatric drugs do more harm than good," or the British establishment psychiatrist who claimed that the drug treatments did more good than harm, and indeed were lifesaving. The vote was 85-3 in favor of my proposition, advocated by Dr. Breggin, that psychiatric drugs do more harm than good. There were eight abstentions as some folks apparently lacked the courage or conviction to show their hands one way or another.

So the scene which lives on, both in my memory, and happily on video, is Peter standing up for the abused, holding forth in a calm incisive manner, propounding from his enormous knowledge of the literature just how drastically wrong these two psychiatrists, and their many colleagues, are. It was a wonderful picture. It was so RIGHT.

Someday soon, the pendulum will swing back, and we'll have an accurate assessment of just how toxic these so-called "antipsychotics" are. I call them "pro-psychotics" since 50 years of evidence show they prolong the patient's condition. And when this glorious day does eventually arrive, we can look back with enormous gratitude to Peter Breggin MD, who never shrank from asserting it, and who so gloriously held up a lantern in a dangerously dark psychiatric world.

Thank you Peter, from the bottom of my medical heart!

Bob Johnson, MD

Bob is a Consultant Psychiatrist and member of the Royal College of Psychiatrists. He trained at Cambridge University with a degree in psychology; at the London Hospital; at Claybury Hospital, Essex learning the art of the Therapeutic Community Approach; and at the Columbia-Presbyterian Psychiatric Institute, New York City where he was awarded the Diploma in Psychotherapy, Neurology and Psychiatry. His work as a Consultant Psychiatrist in the Special Unit in Parkhurst Prison, Isle of Wight, UK, from 1991 to 1996 formed the basis of a documentary investigation by the BBC's flagship programme Panorama on 3 March 1997. His latest project is organizing Emotion Support Centres, where recoverers help others recover. He is the author of Emotional Health: What Emotions Are & How They Cause Social & Mental Diseases *(2002) and* Unsafe at Any Dose: Exposing Psychiatric Dogmas So Minds Can Heal (2006). *His website is www.TruthTrustConsent.com*

"Be The Change You Want to See"

by Michael Corry, MD

Dr. Peter Breggin stands as a giant in the world of psychiatry, unique in his stance of championing its true purpose, soul healing—psyche meaning "soul" and iatreia meaning "healing." As the profession becomes increasingly drug-dependant, more fundamentalist and harmful, departing radically from the Hippocratic Oath, enshrining the ethic of "First do no harm," Dr. Breggin continues to hold firm. He speaks from the heart, and empathizes with his patients in a deeply compassionate way, legitimizing their mental and emotional distress as inseparable from their individuality, race, color, creed, upbringing, belief systems, environments, relationships, socio-economic factors, life events and coping skills—the whole person. He calls to their spirit and imagination, helping them to find their place in the family of things.

He speaks from the heart, and empathizes with his patients in a deeply compassionate way, legitimizing their mental and emotional distress as inseparable from their individuality, race, color, creed, upbringing, belief systems, environments, relationships, socio-economic factors, life events and coping skills—the whole person.

Dr. Breggin's writings are benchmark works, refuting the inhumane practice of electric shock treatment, the indiscriminate use of stimulant medication in the young, and the irresponsible and blatant denial of the adverse effects of psychiatric medication. Because of what he represents, Dr Breggin was my automatic choice as a keynote speaker at our conference in Dublin, Ireland in October 2006, the title of which was Healing Depression Without Drugs and Electric Shocks, which was attended by over 700 delegates. His presence was electrifying on that day, and his impact on the media and public was such that it triggered a mental health debate, which is still running.

Dr. Breggin's influence is initiating efforts to ensure that Ireland stems the tidal wave of stimulant medication in the young.

As a consequence, the momentum to ban electric shock treatment in Ireland accelerated, and influenced the outcome of a parliamentary subcommittee on The Adverse Side Effects of Pharmaceuticals, castigating the disease-mongering of the pharmaceutical industry, their influence on the world of academia, and their corrupting effect on medical practitioners and the Irish Medicines Board (our FDA).

Ireland is a small soulful country of some 4 million people, located on the edge of Europe, the first to introduce a ban on smoking. Our objective is to achieve the same with electric shock treatment and in doing so to influence the rest of the European Community. In a similar vein, Dr. Breggin's influence is initiating efforts to ensure that Ireland stems the tidal wave of stimulant medication in the young, preventing us from taking the same path as the United States.

Dr. Breggin is an important link in the world-wide human consciousness movement, seeking to deepen our awareness of our individual and collective human potential, and the pressing need to move towards open-hearted practices in a climate of reductionism and violence. Dr. Breggin admirably walks the talk, at great personal and professional risk, truly embodying the spirit of the words of Mahatma Gandhi, another gentle warrior, "Be the change you want to see."

Michael Corry, MD

Michael is a Consultant Psychiatrist and Psychotherapist in Ireland. He qualified in medicine from University College Dublin, Ireland in 1973. He achieved higher qualifications in obstetrics, paediatrics, and worked as a volunteer doctor in Africa. He commenced his psychiatric studies in 1978 and trained as a constructivist psychotherapist. His interest in psychosis and altered states of consciousness developed from his work in St. Brendan's Psychiatric Hospital, Dublin. He developed and directed the demonstration re-socialisation pilot project of Europe which focused on the rehabilitation of long-stay institutionalised patients, teaching them the required social and living skills to function in the community. In 1988 he co-founded the Institute of Psychosocial Medicine whose ethos embodies a mind-body-spirit approach to psychological distress. He endeavours to give psychiatry it's true meaning (psyche meaning soul and iatriea meaning healing) by seeing each individual as a subjective spiritual being on a personal journey. The book Going Mad? – Understanding Mental Illness *which he coauthored with Dr. Aine Tubridy, is a product of his ongoing passion to see psychological distress explored in new ways.*

The Amazing Contribution

by Alberto Fergusson, MD

It will take some time before the history of psychiatry recognizes in full the amazing contribution of Peter Breggin. For all those who in one way or another have been dedicated to trying to improve the quality of life of so-called mentally ill people, Breggin's contribution has been crucial. Whenever we try to find good arguments to support the basic human rights of those diagnosed with mental illness, we find in Breggin's writings and teachings the precise scientific data and analysis that we need. In fact, the main characteristic of Breggin's work is that it combines rigorous scientific research with the best humanistic approach. Being a great scientist and a wonderful human being, together with the permanent presence of his marvelous wife Ginger, is what in my opinion has allowed Peter to build his enormous contribution to psychiatry. Amongst other things he is a great example of what I call the "natural therapist." By that I mean those privileged human beings that have a spontaneous capacity to heal. A simple email from Peter can sometimes be enough to bring relief and a very peculiar sense of peace. His friends and patients know exactly what I am talking about.

The fact that a great scientist like Peter has had the courage to speak the truth about psychiatric medication, changed the life of those imprisoned in what I call the new Chemical Asylum.

It is true that science and psychiatry have benefited enormously from Peter Breggin's work. Nevertheless so-called mentally ill people are undoubtedly the greatest beneficiaries of his work. In fact Peter has greatly improved the quality of life of those "diagnosed" or labeled as mentally ill. The fact that a great scientist like Peter has had the courage to speak the truth about psychiatric medication changed the life of those imprisoned in what I call the new Chemical Asylum.

I am pro-choice in that I believe that the individual must decide whether or not to use medication after studying available scientific evidence, including Breggin's writings of course. I believe that this choice is real thanks only to Peter's brave contributions.

Alberto Fergusson, MD

A psychiatrist in Columbia, South America, Alberto has developed the practice of Accompanied Autoanalysis in which deeply disturbed patients are provided the information to study and to learn independently about their own life story and how to live an individual, unique lifestyle that suits their inner world and diminishes their risk of entering a psychotic state. Alberto focuses on individuals diagnosed with schizophrenia and living in poverty. He has introduced his work to the United States and is Founder and President of the Foundation for the Advancement of Accompanied Self Rehabilitation in Washington, DC.

Peter Breggin and the Hegemony of American Psychiatry

by Pat Bracken, MD

In the final decades of the 20th century, the influence of American psychiatry on how mental health problems are understood across the globe became profound. The American Psychiatric Association (1994) *Diagnostic and Statistical Manual of Mental Disorders, Fourth Edition (DSM-IV)* came to be used throughout the world to order and classify states of madness and distress, regardless of location, culture or history. In some poor countries, the *DSM* came to be the only book available in many psychiatric clinics.

While the authors of the *DSM* have recently begun to pay some attention to the issue of culture, there is still no real questioning of the idea that some universal truth exists within the way that American psychiatry has come to understand the world. The research, the ideas, the priorities and the opinion leaders of psychiatry as a worldwide profession are located in the US.

Academic psychiatrists in particular have worked actively with the pharmaceutical industry to promote this international authority. With incredible resources at its disposal, this coalition has effectively shaped the professional response to mental distress and madness around the planet. Medical education has become an important part of drug company marketing strategy. In more recent years, it has also effectively worked to shape how lay people, consumers of services and their families have thought about mental health problems and what interventions might be appropriate. In the Western world, it is now commonplace for people to talk about the origins of states of sadness, not in the trials and tribulations of life, but in terms of brain levels of neurotransmitters such as serotonin and dopamine. This simplistic understanding of mental health problems underscores the huge profits of the pharmaceutical industry. In turn, these profits fund what now amounts to a form of cultural imperialism in the field of mental health.

When I had completed all my training as a psychiatrist in the early 1990s in the UK, I was aware of the growing influence of the pharmaceutical companies but felt that there was little to be done. The power of the biopsychiatry/Big Pharma coalition was such that resistance seemed impossible. The 1980s and 1990s were not times to be optimistic about alternatives. However, throughout this period Peter Breggin kept writing his books, taking on what he calls the Psychopharmaceutical Complex. He stood out amongst a handful of dissidents who were prepared to challenge the legitimacy of this powerful coalition. As such, he was an inspiration to a younger group of psychiatrists in different parts of the world who were, in various ways, beginning to question and challenge the global dominance of the American Psychiatric Association.

> We will look to Peter Breggin as one of the real heroes of the struggle against falsehood and deceit in the field of mental health.

I can recall reading Breggin's *Toxic Psychiatry* (1991) towards the end of my training and thinking that his analysis of the links between psychiatry and Big Pharma were in the true spirit of scientific inquiry. For real science is about questioning and doubt, not about arrogance and dogma.

The early years of the 21st century present a more optimistic terrain. I am a member of the Critical Psychiatry Network (http://www.critpsynet.freeuk.com/), an association of psychiatrists who came together in Bradford in 1999. The Network has campaigned against the British government's plans to extend compulsory treatment into the community and, more recently, has worked to expose the influence of the pharmaceutical industry on the profession. More importantly, an active and articulate service user movement has also emerged in the past twenty years. People who have used mental health services have started to come together to share experiences and demand change. This movement is international and increasingly organised and influential. While some service users are happy to use the vocabulary of psychiatry and to look to medical science for answers, a growing number of users argue for a very different agenda. They reject the psychiatric framing of their problems and campaign against the global alliance of biopsychiatry/Big Pharma. In addition, there is a growing body of medical journal editors who are prepared to critique the abuse of science, and an increasing number of journalists who are beginning to examine the evidence about psychiatric interventions from a critical angle.

I hope that as this century moves forward, we will see a stronger alliance between service users, critical professionals and those in the wider community who are interested in challenging corporate control of health care, and in particular, mental health care. I look forward to a time when our thinking about, and experience of, mental health problems is no longer dominated by models that are disempowering and mystifying. If we reach this goal, I anticipate that we will look to Peter Breggin as one of the real heroes of the struggle against falsehood and deceit in the field of mental health. For those of us from outside the USA who are struggling against the hegemony of the APA, his critique has not only been important but vital.

Pat Bracken, MD

Pat is a professor at the Institute for Philosophy, Diversity and Mental Health at the University of Central Lancashire, Preston, UK and Clinical Director and Consultant Psychiatrist, West Cork Mental Health Service, Bantry, County Cork, Ireland.

Long May You Run

by Craig Newnes, MSc

I first met Peter in 1992. He shared a platform with David Cohen at a London conference organized by the great Pam Jenkinson before her split with MIND (a British mental health organization). Both men were remarkable in their capacity to tell the truth about psychiatry, in a way both intellectually satisfying and, somehow, gentle. I asked them to join the board of *Changes,* now the *Journal of Critical Psychology, Counselling and Psychotherapy,* and they agreed—just like that. It was a sign of a spirit of generosity and collaboration I now recognise as absolutely typical. That same generosity has led Peter to contribute to *This is Madness Too* and take the time to write for the journal several times.

With audiences made up of those used and abused by Big Pharma Peter can be almost docile, like someone reading your favorite bedtime story, a teddy bear. With fellow psychiatrists he shows a fearsome intelligence and an understanding of research that leaves floundering anyone who dares take him on.

At that first public event I also witnessed something of a theme easily discerned on repeated exposure to Peter's style. With audiences made up of those used and abused by Big Pharma he can be almost docile, like someone reading your favorite bedtime story, a teddy bear. With fellow psychiatrists he shows a fearsome intelligence and an understanding of research that leaves floundering anyone who dares take him on.

Peter visited Shropshire a couple of times. The first time he took pains to talk with patients at our psychiatric hospital (little changed from its establishment in 1843). He discussed their diagnoses, their medication and their horrible drug-induced adverse reactions, eventually presenting an informal seminar on tardive dyskinesia to a spontaneously gathered group of patients and nurses.

Later, he demolished the then President of The Royal College of Psychiatrists in a debate on the use of neuroleptics. He cited example after example of tardive dyskinesia he had seen that very afternoon on the local psychiatric ward and had the local medics in an uproar of self-justification. A few years on he talked to another Shropshire audience about ADHD. The psychiatrists were conspicuous by their absence.

You can see teddy bear Peter in Happy Valley, a TV documentary about a clinical psychologist who diagnoses all his patients with depression before recommending Prozac. There he sits, gently poking fun at America's fix-it-quick mentality while explaining the effects of SSRIs on the brain. I last saw the all too reasonable academic Peter a year ago, this time in London, debating, yet again the use of neuroleptics. A psychiatrist in the audience, no doubt imagining his livelihood to be threatened, tried to dismiss Peter's raft of evidence by claiming Peter was "angry"—if you can't bear the message, shoot the messenger.

Peter looked surprised. His delivery had some passion, but not what you would call anger—unless you happened to be a furious medical colleague in the group. What the psychiatrist did was, of course, typical and all too human. He reacted out of anger and fear and labelled the object (Peter) with his own anger. Had we been in a case conference the label might well have been in Greek or Latin and rapidly followed by a prescription.

Telling it like it is wins you few friends in the world of Big Pharma. I have tried to tell it like it is many times but it was Peter whom I first saw publicly describe the commonplace inhumanity of psychiatric institutions in the 1950s; the vacuity of the symptom check list for ADHD; the extraordinary high risk of tardive dyskinesia; even the way to help people driven to distraction by voices or driving their families to distraction by their conduct: You sit quietly with all concerned for as long as it takes.

The last is an example of that most precious of commodities—the simple approach. Simple is best. The best theories are simple. Take those about hearing voices; there are many, from the economic (you can get state benefits if you say you hear voices and earn money by running workshops about your experience) to the biochemical (there are specific neurotransmitters for each voice—untestable rubbish of course) to the so-called cognitive (voice hearers make a coding error such that thoughts are coded as external voices—again untestable but it pays the salaries of a few psychologists) to the religious (the voices are real).

You sit quietly with all concerned for as long as it takes.

Try a simpler theory. Do this: Sit quietly after you have texted someone. You will hear an echo of the sound of the text keys. This may go on for a few minutes. It sounds like it is outside your head. The noises are just part of a naturally occurring tendency to retain sound for a while. Now imagine being shouted at, threatened, whatever, every day as a child. The voices echo for a very long time. And we have NO IDEA how many children live lives like this, but even the most noble-looking parents secretly explode with rage at their kids regularly.

The theory of threatening echoing voices from the past is as good as the others—but much scarier for adults to acknowledge. Worse, we have no way of remembering who did the shouting or when, as it may have gone on while we were too young to give names to our tormentors, and in any case it was a normal part of growing up so not worth commenting on.

Of course, those tormentors may have just been on autopilot; parents shouting threats were all part of parenthood. This theory will make me few friends and no money, so it's probably right. It also has the major advantage of making sense. To grasp it requires no understanding of brain biochemistry and no history of grappling with the intricacies of cognitive psychology. It's the kind of theory Peter would like.

To respond calmly to attacks by your supposed colleagues requires a particular kind spirit, one that takes self-sacrifice as a given and isn't that interested in being liked. Peter must be disliked by many. He is loved by many more.

Peter, long may you run.

Craig Newnes, MSc

Craig is a dad, gardener and writer. He is the former editor of the Clinical Psychology Forum *and the current editor of the* Journal of Critical Psychology, Counselling and Psychotherapy. *He is the commissioning editor for the critical psychology book series from PCCS Books. His latest book is* Making and Breaking Children's Lives. *He recently retired as the Director of Psychological Therapies for Shropshire County PCT, a department of over 80 people doing their best to enable people to emerge from the oppression we call modern society. Craig's latest works are* Tearagh't, *a novel about the Armada; Finnledoo, an illustrated saga and* The Malaysian Emergency, *a book co-written with Doug Newnes about the Malaysian Campaign, 1948-1953.*

An Island of Sanity
by Sami Timimi, MD

Peter Breggin wasn't mentioned once during my years of training to become first a psychiatrist and then a child psychiatrist. Like most psychiatric training schemes, the ones I was on (during the early and mid 1990s) airbrushed out of existence critics of mainstream ideology by simply refusing to mention that there was and is controversy, difference, and dissent within both the ranks of the profession and outside of it.

By the time of my child psychiatry training I had already become suspicious of the constructs, diagnoses, and medications used, having failed to see what scientific basis held up their validity or usefulness. Having already trained as a doctor and with many friends in other branches of medicine, it was easy for me to see that the system psychiatry used had little in common with the rest of medicine.

Having decided to pursue a career in child psychiatry to try and avoid becoming what I saw as a glorified pharmacist in adult psychiatry—where the system seemed hell bent on constructing viciously pathological interpretations of patients' complaints, wilfully ignoring their own interpretations and meanings—I was soon confronted with 'new' thinking and practice that saddened and angered me. In the UK of the mid 1990s, Attention Deficit Hyperactivity Disorder (ADHD) had become the new 'in thing' for child psychiatry. Child psychiatrists and pediatricians seemed to be buzzing around ADHD like bees around honey (or flies to something worse!) eager to embrace this American model of childhood, perceiving it as vital in helping child psychiatrists bolster their fragile sense of identity as a doctor.

In the spring of 1996 I agreed to join a small research project that my then supervising consultant wanted to start, a decision that set me on a path to writing books, actively critiquing the new ideological mantras of my chosen profession and discovering the work of Peter Breggin. My consultant wanted to research the prevalence of ADHD in children with "learning difficulties." I was asked to do a literature search and start the theoretical groundwork for this project. Whilst I did my supervising consultant no favors, the research never getting beyond this initial stage, unbeknown to him, giving me this task did me a huge one. I started to examine the ADHD research literature.

The more I delved into the scientific literature, the more I realized how shockingly lacking was the scientific basis. I simply couldn't get past first base on this one. How on earth did something as non-specific and ordinary as children's level of attention and activity become the basis on which to define a "neuro-developmental" disorder for which "speed" is prescribed? I looked and looked in vain for something tangible in the literature that gave the ADHD construct some validity at the neuro-physiological, psychological, or socio-cultural levels and found nothing but superficial theories and circular laboratory experiments that already assumed face validity for the construct.

As the years moved on I found that I was not alone in having these doubts. Indeed the majority of my non-medical colleagues shared these doubts, encouraging me to take my search wider. Now I entered the territory of critical perspectives and soon discovered the writing and campaigning of Peter Breggin. Reading his books was like coming home. I had found someone who had been through similar doubts, and had put down a challenge to the rest of psychiatry with his carefully argued and properly evidenced critiques; a challenge that psychiatry has tried to address in the same way we child psychiatrists are taught to handle "unruly" behavior—by ignoring him. It takes great courage, resilience and strength of mind to withstand such treatment without losing your integrity. Peter had dared to take on the psychiatric establishment, and in terms of strength of evidence, ethics and basic humanity, had won. No wonder knowledge of his work had been kept away from trainees like me all those years ago (as it continues to today). Although I don't agree with all of Peter's views, his importance to my personal journey and I'm sure countless others, through the murky, corrupted and oppressive world of mental "health" stands like an Island of Sanity in a sea full of ships of fools (mainstream psychiatry and all that supports it).

It's hard work to find yourself on board one of these ships every day you go to work. The messages that constantly surround you are "join us or we'll throw you overboard." Peter helped me realize that it was possible to challenge these ships and their crew without losing your bearings. As the old saying goes "You can fool a lot of people some of the time and some people a lot of the time, but you can't fool all the people all of the time." Peter's writing, campaigning and his relentless desire to uncover the truth, to help people and not to give in to those who would like to silence him, is testament to this wisdom.

Sami Timimi, MD

Sami is a Consultant Child and Adolescent Psychiatrist in the National Health Service in Lincolnshire, UK and a visiting Professor of Child and Adolescent Psychiatry at Lincoln University, UK. He writes from a critical psychiatry perspective and has published many articles on many topics including eating disorders, psychotherapy, behavioural disorders and cross-cultural psychiatry. He has authored three books including Pathological Child Psychiatry and the Medicalization of Childhood, *(2002), and* Misunderstanding ADHD: A Complete Guide for Parents to Alternatives to Drugs *(2007). He co-edited with Begum Maitra* Critical Voices in Child and Adolescent Mental Health *(2006),* Rethinking ADHD *with Jonathan Leo currently in press, and* Liberatory Psychiatry *with Carl Cohen currently in press.*

For Peter Breggin, in Admiration

by Benno Müller-Hill, PhD

When I received the invitation to write about the scientific work of Peter Breggin I felt honored but uneasy. I am neither a psychiatrist nor a psychologist. I am not even an MD. I am a molecular biologist interested in gene regulation. In the beginning of the seventies I discovered accidentally that almost nothing had been published about the activities of the geneticists and psychiatrists involved in the genocides by the Nazis. I investigated and in 1984 I published a book about it. It was translated into English and six other languages. In 1987 I invited all the people I knew who had interest in the question for a three-day conference on "Medical Science without Compassion," paid by the DFG, the central public funding organization for academic research. Peter Breggin was one of the invited speakers. The title of his talk was: "How and Why Psychiatry Became a Death Machine."

He discussed in detail how psychiatrists and other mental health professionals who were active in the US accepted and even promoted the eugenics of Nazi Germany.

I had not seen Peter before. I had been told that he was one of the very few American MDs interested in the question. So I saw him the first time when the conference began in Cologne. He discussed in detail how psychiatrists and other mental health professionals who were active in the US accepted and even promoted the eugenics of Nazi Germany. He mentioned the names of those who were for it and he cited what they had published. This had so far not been investigated by German or US historians of medicine or science.

Some of the German psychiatrists and anthropologists present at the conference were furious about what he said about human psychiatric genetics. They claimed that there was no evidence for what Peter Breggin was talking about. In contrast, I was positively impressed by his courage to say such things.

The moment of truth came when I tried to find a publisher for the speeches of the conference. Then I was informed that the publishing houses were interested in publishing what had been said about psychiatry in Nazi Germany. Everything else should be deleted. I was against such an expurgation. So the book was never published. It just exists as a preprint. However, Peter was able to publish his paper in a scientific journal.

> When it was possible I tried to see Peter. Then I asked him what he was doing and thinking. I recall our meetings vividly. I agreed in general with his positions. I found it so important that at least one person should defend truth and justice.

After the conference I went back again into molecular biology. Peter Breggin went back into present day psychiatry. So he criticized what he considered as being wrong treatments: electroshock, treatment of hyperactive children with amphetamine and amphetamine-like stimulant drugs. He never came back to Cologne. I came a few times to Washington. When it was possible I tried to see him. Then I asked him what he was doing and thinking. I recall our meetings vividly. I agreed in general with his positions. I found it so important that at least one person should defend truth and justice. Yet I could not help him. My activities were elsewhere.

So I come to the bottom line. I am for this type of professional connection, where one is informed by another about the present state of the world. I only wished I could have spent some more time with Peter.

Benno Müller-Hill, PhD

Benno is a full professor in the Genetics Institute of Cologne University, Germany. His main area of research is protein-DNA interaction and gene control. He recently published a book entitled The lac Operon: A Short History of a Genetic Paradigm. *In 1984 he published a book* "Tödliche Wissenschaft" *on the history of human genetics in Nazi Germany. The book has been translated into English* Murderous Science, *Oxford University Press, 1988 and six other languages including Japanese and Hebrew. A paperback edition with an afterword by James Watson was recently published by Cold Spring Harbor Press. He is an elected member of the European Molecular Biology Organisation [EMBO], the Human Genome Organisation [HUGO], the Academia Europaea and Honorary Fellow of the Hebrew University of Jerusalem.*

The Breggin Influence

by Terry Lynch, MD

I qualified as a medical doctor in Cork, Ireland in 1982. I trained to become a family doctor and worked as a family doctor in Limerick, Ireland from 1987. At that time, I expected to have a pretty typical medical career, building up my practice, working hard to be the best family doctor I could be. Twenty years later, my working life has turned out quite differently from that picture I used to have in my mind. Peter Breggin has played a significant role in the changes I initiated in my working life, changes which of course have spilled over into my life in general.

I first encountered Peter Breggin in the early 1990's. He was being interviewed on television, an Irish channel I think, expressing his concerns about psychiatric treatments. At that time, I was still quite accepting of the medical approach to mental health problems. Nevertheless, I was struck by this man's integrity. That interview had an effect on me and I filed it away somewhere in my mind for future reference.

By the mid-1990s, I was having major doubts about the rightness of the medical approach to health and health problems. My doubts extended from mental health to physical health issues such as cardiac, respiratory, the immune system, and many other aspects of health. In a nutshell, I became increasingly aghast at the mind-body split—how doctors could treat people as bodies only, when it was patently obvious that the individual's mind, experiences, world-view, patterns of living, sense of self, relationships, and other emotional/psychological/social aspects of the person frequently were live issues, highly relevant to the person's health problems, and therefore highly relevant also to the amelioration and prevention of their health problems. But such issues didn't (and generally still don't) come within the medical radar system.

I just knew I could not keep working within this narrow

and misguided medical model, but I wasn't sure exactly in what direction to turn. Around that time, I was browsing around a bookshop in Dublin, Ireland. I remember that mid-1990s day as if it were yesterday, because it was to have quite a transformative effect on my life. There, on a bookshelf looking out at me, was Peter Breggin's *Toxic Psychiatry*. The penny suddenly dropped within me that this was the man I had seen on that TV interview a few years earlier. I bought *Toxic Psychiatry* and read it over the coming weeks. Actually I read it in about two days. As I came to the end of this extraordinary book, I knew I could not continue working as a typical medical practitioner for the rest of my life. I was struck by Peter's adherence to true scientific principles, in marked contrast to the often-flawed science and logic that dominates mental health.

I was struck by Peter's adherence to true scientific principles, in marked contrast to the often-flawed science and logic that dominates mental health.

I found myself agreeing with so much of the book, nodding my head repeatedly, and feeling a sense of outrage that the profession I used to believe in totally could be so limited in its vision, so institutionalised in its methods, and so dependent on a group with a major vested interest, the pharmaceutical industry, and so unwilling to engage in serious debate with those expressing genuine concerns about the direction of mental health care.

Toxic Psychiatry was one of the main catalysts behind my changing the direction of my work. I undertook and completed an MA in psychotherapy. For the past seven years or so, I have operated my own recovery-focused, person-centered mental health service.

In 2001, my book *Beyond Prozac* was published. Among the themes I explored in this book were my concerns regarding the narrow vision of psychiatry, the lack of true scientific thinking in psychiatry, and the consequent limitations in the services provided for people experiencing mental health problems. In my book, I referred to the work of Peter Breggin many times, a testament to the regard in which I hold Peter and his work.

My favorite is *The Heart of Being Helpful.* I read this book in one sitting, such was the impact of Peter's humanness, warmth and compassion on me.

Over the years, I have read many of Peter's books, and learned a great deal from each of them. Perhaps my favorite is *The Heart of Being Helpful.* I read this book in one sitting, such was the impact of Peter's humanness, warmth and compassion on me. I've not met Peter yet, though I have spoken to him on the phone. During that conversation, a few years ago now, I was struck by his person, his humility, and gentleness, nicely balanced with steely determination.

For me, and I imagine for many others, Peter has been a beacon of light. For me, he is a person who is prepared to stand up for what he believes in, for what he knows to be true, irrespective of the consequences, professional and personal. This really impressed me, and helped me to also speak out in a similar fashion in Ireland over the past six years.

Peter's work has been an important inspiration for me over the years, encouraging me that the path I was on was a path of truth. Whilst at times mine was a rather lonely journey, over the years, I have experienced many benefits as a result of the work changes I have made in my life. These include many quality of life themes, such as enjoying my work to a far greater extent; far more meaningful relationships, both at a personal level and with the people who attend me; an inner calm and contentment I had not previously experienced; greater fulfilment; clarity about my work and about what really matters. I have been lucky enough to work at something that feels like a hobby, it is so in keeping with what I want to do. Working with people towards recovery is a privilege that still gives me goose pimples. Peter's writing played a significant part in the emergence of the life I now live. The pursuit of truth, and the integrity of truth are certainly worth the effort.

Peter's writing played a significant part in the emergence of the life I now live. The pursuit of truth, and the integrity of truth are certainly worth the effort.

I have often been struck by Peter's practical wisdom. For example, his recent commentary on the Virginia Tech shooting tragedy was the most incisive and accurate commentary on that tragedy I have read or seen anywhere (see Dr. Breggin's blog on www.breggin.com).

A final word about Ginger Breggin. Again, I have not yet met Ginger but we have spoken on the phone on a number of occasions. Ginger has impressed me greatly, from her general enthusiasm for life, her wonderful love and support for Peter and his work, extending to her work relating to the International Center for the Study of Psychiatry and Psychology over the years.

In a world where at times there appears to be a deficit of integrity and true courage, Peter Breggin is one of a limited number of people I truly admire to a very high degree. I am grateful for having encountered Peter and his work in my life.

What a fabulous legacy you have created, Peter!

Terry Lynch, MD

Terry is a family doctor and psychotherapist living and working in Limerick, Ireland. He qualified as a medical doctor at University College Cork in 1982. He then trained to become a GP, a role in which he worked in Limerick, Ireland until 1997. By the mid-1990s, Terry Lynch had become concerned about certain aspects of health and health care. In particular, he became very concerned about how people experiencing mental health problems were dealt with. Years of questioning and searching for understanding of mental health and mental health problems, and for better ways to work with people experiencing mental health problems, culminated in the publication of his book Beyond Prozac *in Ireland in 2001, and in Britain in 2004. This book was short-listed for the UK Mind Book of the Year award in 2002, and reached number 3 in the Irish non-fiction best-selling charts in 2001.*

Terry now works exclusively in the field of mental health. He runs his own recovery-oriented, person-centred mental health service. He was a member of the Irish Department of Health-appointed Expert Group on Mental Health Policy (2003-6). This Expert Group's Report, A Vision for Change *(2006), forms the basis of mental health policy for the next 7-10 years in Ireland. He is also a member of the Independent Monitoring Group for A Vision for Change (2006-8) and the Irish Health Service Executive's Expert Advisory Group on Mental Health (2006-8).*

Terry Lynch is fully registered with the Irish Medical Council. He is also a fully accredited member of the Irish Association of Humanistic and Integrative Psychotherapy.

My Friend Peter Breggin

by Dorothy Rowe, PhD

When HarperCollins UK became my publisher in 1986 I would often call in to see my editor Michael Fishwick in his office in London. Occasionally Michael would ask me to give an opinion of a manuscript that he had to assess with a view to publication. The ones he asked me to read had some connection to psychology, psychiatry or psychotherapy.

In those days manuscripts came only as hard copy—a pile of typed pages. Reading them was rarely a joyous task, mainly because psychologists, psychiatrists and psychotherapists tend not to be inspired or even skilled writers; but there were two manuscripts where the words seemed to leap off the page with the sheer vigour with which the writer discussed a topic of great importance. One of these manuscripts was Jeffrey Masson's *Against Therapy (*1988) and the other was Peter Breggin's *Toxic Psychiatry* (1991). The two books were very different in content and style but they were concerned with the abuse of power by those who purported to be honorable professionals.

I explained to Michael why each of these books was so important, but I pointed out that British psychiatrists would dismiss each of them as being not relevant to Britain. They would say that American psychiatrists were not properly trained and had some very peculiar ideas and practices, whereas in Britain the practice of psychiatry was impeccable. It was clear to me that each book needed an introduction by someone who knew the psychiatric scene in Britain extremely well and who could set each book in a British context. Michael had no difficulty in seeing that he needed to publish each book, and that the obvious person to write the introductions was myself.

Thus each book was published in Britain by HarperCollins and, when the respective authors came to the UK to publicize their books, I met each of them and began a long friendship. However, the paths of each writer's life were very different. Jeffrey Masson eventually grew weary of the whole psychotherapy debate, and now rarely lectures on the themes in his book; but Peter Breggin has gone on from strength to strength with a most extraordinary enthusiasm and courage.

After 18 years working as a clinical psychologist in the National Health Service I had left in order to devote myself to writing and teaching. I returned to live in Sheffield where I had a close connection to the Department of Psychiatry where I had obtained my PhD fifteen years earlier. When I had arrived in England from Australia in 1968 I went to work in the Department of Psychiatry when Alec Jenner had accepted the Chair of Psychiatry just two months earlier. Alec was already established as a very distinguished scientist and so he arrived at Sheffield University with a large grant to study the biological basis of mood change. He had gathered an extensive team of researchers from different scientific disciplines. He did not see me as someone who would be able to contribute to his research but he thought it might be interesting if I took as my research subject "Psychological aspects of people with regular mood change." (There aren't such people, but my research was devoted to the study of how people change.)

I had obtained my first degree at the University of Sydney where the major part of the psychology course was the theory of scientific method. My professor, William O'Neill, would tell his students that the task of science was not to discover facts but to ask a better question. I arrived in Sheffield thinking that this was what my work would be in the Department of Psychiatry. I couldn't have been more wrong, but incorrigibly naïve, I persisted in case conferences and informal discussions offering alternative formulations to the traditional psychiatric diagnoses created by my psychiatrist colleagues. They saw their diagnoses, not as hypotheses, but absolute truths. I rapidly became markedly unpopular with these psychiatrists.

Alec Jenner was not always pleased with what I was doing but he was, and is, a man for whom truth is more important than power and position. He loved ideas, and so he created the tradition of Tuesday evening lectures where the speakers came from a great variety of backgrounds and disciplines. The only requirement was that they had something interesting and thought-provoking to say. Hence, once I knew that Peter was coming to England, I asked Alec to invite him to one of the Tuesday evening lectures.

For all of us there who were familiar with the Tuesday evening lectures, it was an evening like most others. Peter presented ideas that challenged members of the audience, there was a lively discussion, and then we went to dinner. Afterwards Peter told me that this was one of the few times he had lectured to psychiatrists about tardive dyskinesia. His colleagues in the USA were loathe to give him a hearing. He knew from some of the questions he had been asked that many in his audience could not accept his views, but the whole discussion was conducted with courtesy. No one stormed out of the meeting; no one threatened Peter.

We do not like having to undertake the hard work of changing our ideas, and British psychiatrists are no exception. However, Peter played a major role in forcing British psychiatrists to change their ideas. They have not changed their ideas about schizophrenia as markedly as they have about depression (they no longer see chemical imbalance as the cause of depression); but, in the years after 1991, they ceased to think of schizophrenia as being an incurable illness. They still see schizophrenia as a mental illness with a physical (genetic) cause, but they can no longer exclude psychological and social factors in either the causation or the cure. Most of all, they cannot do what their predecessors did, claim absolute authority.

Last year in a debate with two consultant psychiatrists, Peter was subjected to great criticism by them, but it was personal criticism. Personal criticism always shows that the person inflicting the criticism has already lost the argument. Moreover, both these two psychiatrists wanted people to see them as being warm and caring human beings, something that the consultants I worked with in the 1970s would never have even considered doing, any more than Louis XIV of France would have pretended to be a mere plebeian.

I have shared many platforms with Peter where our hosts and our audience have been totally on our side. In such a setting Peter is able to show that wonderful warmth which makes him such a superlative friend. I suspect that this warmth has marvellous curative properties, as many of his patients must have found.

When he is under attack, Peter's warmth becomes a geniality that irks his critics, but even they, if they are honest, must be in awe of his courage. It is this courage which has changed, even saved, the lives of thousands of people, and for which we will always be in his debt.

Dorothy Rowe, PhD

Dorothy is a clinical psychologist, winner of the Mind Book of the Year Award in 1984, and a writer renowned for her work on how we create meaning, and how the meanings we create determine what we do. She writes regularly for newspapers and magazines, appears frequently in the media, and is the author of 15 books, the most popular of which are Depression: The Way Out of Your Prison *which is in its third edition, and* Beyond Fear *which is in its second edition. Her latest book is* My Dearest Enemy, My Dangerous Friend *(2007) and her forthcoming book,* What Should I Believe?, *considers why our beliefs about the nature of death and the purpose of life dominate our lives (October 2008).*

Chapter Twelve

Departed Friends and Colleagues

Introduction

Four of Dr. Breggin's closest professional colleagues and friends died much too early in their lives and are missed by the entire ICSPP community as well as by their families and many others around the world. Psychiatrist Marvin Skolnick, MD in his private practice specialized in the drug-free treatment of patients who would ordinarily be numbed with antipsychotic drugs. He also consulted to a clinic for seriously disturbed patients where he implemented these principles.

Psychiatrist Loren Mosher, MD and psychologist Kevin McCready, PhD were leaders in demonstrating that very disturbed patients, including those labeled "schizophrenic" and "bipolar," can be treated without medications in residential treatment centers or day clinics. Dr. Breggin and Dr. McCready were close friends and Dr. Breggin helped to promote his clinic as well as Dr. Mosher's reform efforts.

Psychologist Steven Baldwin, PhD wrote critically about ECT, especially in regard to children, and was developing a drug-free university clinic for the treatment of children labeled ADHD. He too was a close friend who worked hard to establish the journal *Ethical Human Psychology and Psychiatry* in the early years. All four were active in the International Center for the Study of Psychiatry and Psychology (ICSPP).

Fortunately, all four friends had occasion to write "testimonials" for Dr. Breggin in 1998 when he asked a number of his colleagues to write affidavits on his behalf supporting his standing and expertise within the profession. The project was the idea of an attorney who wanted to use the affidavits if lawyers tried to challenge Dr. Breggin's credentials in court.

The affidavits were never needed or used; but they preserved testimonials, in this case under oath, from four treasured colleagues who are no longer with us.

Providing Much Needed Balance

By Loren R. Mosher, MD. Loren was Clinical Professor of Psychiatry, Former Chief of the Center for Studies of Schizophrenia at NIMH, and Founder of Soteria House and Board Member of ICSPP. He lived in San Diego, California.

Dr. Peter Breggin is a very well trained, thoughtful, scholarly, and vocal critic of some current treatment methods used in psychiatry, especially the overuse and misuse of psychotropic drugs. His criticism is based on careful review and assessment of the evidence pertaining to the efficacy, side effects and toxicities of these drugs. His training, background and interests make him well qualified to review and comment on these issues.

Dr. Breggin's views are formulated on careful review of the relevant scientific literature, hence, in keeping with standard practice in the field. Because his conclusions are sometimes at variance with those of numerous proponents of extensive psychotropic drug use, they are invaluable. They provide much needed balance to an otherwise biased set of views.

By bringing important neglected information to light, Dr. Breggin is providing consumers and providers (MD's) the information needed to follow the physician's most important ethical dictum—above all, do no harm.

Not Radical But on the Mark

By Marvin R. Skolnick, MD. Marvin was Clinical Professor of Psychiatry, George Washington University; Board Member of ICSPP, Alexandria, Virginia.

I have known Dr. Peter Breggin for almost twenty years as both a trusted friend and valued colleague. While I was immediately impressed with his penetrating intelligence, integrity, dedication to pursue the truth, and his courage to speak up about what he considers serious abuses in the practice of psychiatry, I was initially reserved about what seemed to be a rather radical indictment of what I considered to be more gray areas in psychiatry. However, after twenty years of experience as a psychiatrist in various roles which have included director of a therapeutic community for formerly hospitalized patients, private practice, senior faculty member of the Washington School of Psychiatry, Clinical Professor at George Washington University, and Fellow of the A.K. Rice Institute, I have come to appreciate more fully the validity and importance of Dr. Breggin's contributions.

Particularly in my work with chronic mental patients whose chronicity has been exacerbated by damaging toxic effects of medication, ECT and insufficient understanding, I have come to see the full importance of Dr. Breggin's work, which I no longer feel is radical but rather is on the mark. The first duty of the physician is to do no harm. Dr. Breggin's scrupulous attention to the iatrogenic impact of ECT, lobotomy and now the epidemic proportions of indiscriminate dissemination of psychotropic drugs is in my view in the best traditions of Hippocrates.

Dr. Breggin comes to his position through what I consider unusual clinical wisdom and a very careful scholarship. As a reviewer of some of his publications, I can attest to his grasp of the psychiatric literature that is not exceeded by anyone I know.

Beyond Even the Slightest Reproach

By Kevin F. McCready, PhD. Kevin was a psychologist, Director of the San Joaquin Psychotherapy Center and Board Member of ICSPP, Clovis, California.

I am a practicing clinical psychologist, teacher, and author. I have been committee chairman or member on over a dozen doctoral dissertations and have supervised the training of mental health professionals for over ten years. I hold appointments as adjunct faculty at both California School of Professional Psychology in Fresno and at American Commonwealth University in San Diego.

I have been President of California Association of Psychology Providers as well as San Joaquin Psychological Association. I have been a board member of the California Psychological Association. Currently, I hold positions as an executive board member of the National Coalition of Mental Health Consumers and Professionals as well as a member of the executive board of the International Center for the Study of Psychiatry and Psychology.

Dr. Breggin's scholarship, ethics and credentials are far beyond even the slightest reproach. His work is painstakingly researched and thoroughly documented almost to the point of obsession. The foundations of his views are firmly grounded in the best traditions of science, philosophy and critical analysis. He is internationally acknowledged as an expert, albeit a critical one, on the fields of psychiatry and psychopharmacology. The scientific and clinical nature of his work is profoundly relevant, even crucial, not only to the field of psychotherapy but also to our society.

Dr. Breggin's moral and ethical character is more than laudatory. Unlike many researchers and authors, he has structured both his life and his work to assure that he is uncompromised by financial, social or political considerations.

Throughout North America, Europe and Australia

By Steve Baldwin, PhD. Steve was Professor of Psychology, Edith Cowan University, Western Australia and then Professor of Psychology, Teeside University, England and Board Member of ICSPP. Steve coauthored *Electroshock and Minors: A Fifty-Year Review*, with Melissa Oxlad.

I confirm my endorsement of the academic and professional qualifications of Dr. Peter Breggin. It is well recognized internationally that Dr. Breggin is a leading authority in the area of mental health human rights. His academic and professional qualifications in the area are without parallel, and in the last few years he has written some of the leading texts in the area.

Dr. Breggin is a leading international authority in the area of mental health human rights.

These publications include the landmark publication *Toxic Psychiatry – Drugs and Electroconvulsive Therapy: The Truth and the Better Alternatives* (1991). *Toxic Psychiatry* is recognized as one of the seminal texts internationally in the psychiatric literature. More recently, Dr. Breggin has published *Brain-disabling Treatments in Psychiatry: Drugs, Electroshock and the Role of the FDA* (1997). This text will stand the test of time as one of the most significant contributions to the world literature on human rights and a commentary on treatments in psychiatry. Most recently, Dr. Breggin has published *Talking Back to Ritalin* (1998). The book is sure to become an internationally-acclaimed text for researchers and practitioners.

Each of these texts has made a major contribution to the analysis and commentary of the role of physical treatments in psychiatry. Dr. Breggin is also the author of numerous articles and other key texts in the area of critical analysis of physical treatments in psychiatry and also in the more general area of human rights and mental health.

Dr. Breggin is also director of the International Center for the Study of Psychiatry and Psychology in Maryland. This pioneering organization is recognized as one of the key organizations in bringing together a collective of mental health professionals worldwide. The upcoming 1998 conference in Bethesda, Maryland will be a major event in the world of psychiatry, psychology and human rights.

> Dr. Breggin's ethical stance in the area of psychiatric treatment and human rights is virtually without peer in contemporary psychiatry.

The scientific foundation of Dr. Breggin's views in these key areas of psychiatric treatment, evaluation and human rights is virtually without rival in the 1990s. His in-depth views as a scientific investigator, clinical practitioner and researcher are held in high regard both in the USA and here in Australia.

Dr. Breggin is on the faculty of the Johns Hopkins University Department of Counseling and Human Services. He also has an appointment as Honorary Visiting Fellow, Regents College School of Psychotherapy and Counseling, in London.

The value and scientific work of Dr. Breggin's publications have been highly influential throughout North America, here in Australia and also in Europe. He has been invited to make scientific presentations at many professional meetings in the United States, Canada, and Europe.

Dr. Breggin's ethical stance in the area of psychiatric treatment and human rights is virtually without peer in contemporary psychiatry. At some personal cost and risk, he has made definitive statements about the use of psychiatric drug treatments and electroshock, which have provided foundational bedrock for students-in-training and for already qualified staff, both in psychiatry and psychology. I value his contribution to the contemporary debate both in psychology and psychiatry as a key world authority in the area of ethics and psychiatric drug treatments.

Chapter Thirteen

The Journal Honors Peter Breggin

Introduction

When Jonathan Leo, PhD was co-editor of *Ethical Human Psychology and Psychiatry,* he suggested doing a celebration or appreciation honoring Dr. Breggin's scientific work. Eight scientific papers were eventually published as a "Festschrift for Peter Breggin" (Volume 9, Number 3, 2007).

As mentioned earlier, the original call for papers resulted in many dozens of spontaneous tributes to Dr. Breggin, most of them too personal and informal for a scientific journal. They became the inspiration for this book.

With the permission of Springer Publishing Company, this chapter presents excerpts of the articles from the journal festschrift for Dr. Breggin. In addition, Professor of Psychology Bertram Karon, PhD also contributed a scientific article to the special issue of the journal, but he is represented in this book by an original contribution (chapter 1) and selected quotes.

Jeffrey Masson's article mentions a visit that he and Dr. Breggin took to West Germany in 1988 where they were invited to address the first-ever conference on medical abuses under the Third Reich. In his presentation, Dr. Breggin documented the role of the psychiatric "euthanasia" program as an entering wedge into the Holocaust (see Breggin, 1993a, in the bibliography). Dr. Masson described Carl Jung's support for the Nazis. Dr. Breggin was enormously grateful for the opportunity to cross into East Berlin with his friend Jeffrey who was fluent in German. East Berlin, drab and economically depressed, its desperate citizens confined behind walls like involuntary inmates, reminded him of a giant state mental hospital.

The First Document About the Killing of Mental Patients

By Jeffrey Moussaieff Masson, PhD. Jeffrey is the former Director of the Freud Archives and author of many books including *The Assault on Truth, Final Analysis* and *The Emperor's Embrace.*

Many years ago, Peter Breggin and I visited Germany together and spent time talking to each other and to other scholars about the killing of mental patients during the Second World War. We both spoke in 1988 in Cologne at a conference, "Medicine Without Compassion," the first ever devoted to the history of medicine in Nazi Germany. Peter addressed psychiatry's role in the holocaust (Breggin, 1993a) and I spoke about Carl Jung's Nazi sympathies and affiliations (Masson, 1988). We were invited by Benno Muller-Hill (1991), a German professor of genetics who wrote one of the first books describing how psychiatry's "euthanasia" program developed the theory and practice that led to the holocaust.

It was one of the most stimulating intellectual times I ever had. Peter had a knack for putting his finger on central issues ignored by others. Nobody was as intuitively right about some of the deepest issues facing psychiatry. Living in New Zealand, I sorely miss Peter's company. We were hoping to do a book, *Psychiatry and the Holocaust,* about the collusion between psychiatry and the Third Reich in the murder of possibly 300,000 so-called mentally ill people.

References

Masson, J. M. (1988). *Against therapy: Emotional tyranny and the myth of psychological healing.* New York: Antheneum.

Muller-Hill, B. (1988). *Murderous science: Elimination by scientific selection of Jews, gypsies and others.* Germany 1933–1945. London: Oxford University Press.

Norm Reference as it Applies to Ability and Disabilities; Reflections of a Former State-Government Official

By James A. Tucker, PhD. Jim holds the McKee Chair of Excellence in Dyslexia and Associated Learning Exceptionalities, University of Tennessee at Chattanooga and is co-editor of *Ethical Human Psychology and Psychiatry.*

During the first years of this period, I served as an administrator at the Texas Education Agency, where I helped to develop the state's legislation and programming in response to Public Law 94-142. Subsequently, I spent a number of years consulting with local, state, and federal education agencies. That phase of my career culminated in serving as the director of the Bureau of Special Education for the Commonwealth of Pennsylvania. It was during that period that I first met Dr. Peter Breggin. Several of my colleagues had told me about this psychiatrist, who thought outside the box of traditional service delivery. Imagine: An MD who didn't follow the prescriptions of the medical model! I first met Dr. Breggin in his home, and from that visit his influence has represented a form of leadership that I have grown to appreciate more and more as the years go by.

As the 1980s were ending and the 1990s were beginning, those of us in state government who were responsible for the statewide policy regarding the education of students with disabilities were faced with an insidious new category of reported disability: attention deficit disorder (ADD). Try as I might, I could not make sense of the published diagnosis for ADD. With little advance warning, I found myself being heavily lobbied by parents of students who were reported to be "suffering" from the effects of ADD and from the lack of concern being expressed by the schools. As the national organization Children With Attention Deficit Disorder (CHADD)—the national lobby organization supporting ADD—grew in prominence, we found ourselves aligned against a formidable foe. I remember, for example, the parent who met me as I was getting on an elevator in the office building of the Pennsylvania Department of Education. To this mother, the addition of ADD to the list of eligible diagnosed disabilities was a foregone conclusion. My responses had all been learned from my encounters with Dr. Breggin—his written material as well as our several conversations. As I talked with this well-meaning but ill-advised mother and presented the arguments that I had synthesized from Dr. Breggin, the woman became irrational, and, with tears streaming down her face, she berated me in the very public setting. Without the data that my conversations with Dr. Breggin provided, I would have been unprepared to cope with her onslaught.

> The difficult-to-control male child is certainly not a new phenomenon, but attempts to give him a medical diagnosis are the product of modern psychology and psychiatry.

It was from him that I learned of the connection between the drug- manufacturing company and CHADD. As a result, when an official of Pennsylvania's chapter of CHADD approached me requesting the state's support for students who were being diagnosed with ADD, I indicated that I would discuss the state's role only after CHADD disclosed the amount of support that the manufacturer of the medication being prescribed for students diagnosed with the "disorder" contributed to the organization. She never provided the information—and no one from the organization contacted me again.

In Pennsylvania, the pressure continued to build, as it did nationally... Our resolve, however, was equal to the opposition's—thanks to a small group of supporters, at the center of which was Peter Breggin. His book *Toxic Psychiatry* (1992) was in preparation at the time, but although it was not yet in print, those of us who were developing and administering state policy were well aware of the information that it would contain:

> Hyperactivity (HA) is the most frequent justification for drugging children. The difficult-to-control male child is certainly not a new phenomenon, but attempts to give him a medical diagnosis are the product of modern psychology and psychiatry. At first psychiatrists called hyperactivity a brain disease. When no brain disease could be found, they changed it to "minimal brain disease" (MBI). When no minimal brain disease could be found, the profession transformed the concept into "minimal brain dysfunction." When no minimal brain dysfunction could be demonstrated, the label became attention deficit disorder. Now it's just assumed to be a real disease, regardless of the failure to prove it so. Biochemical imbalance is the code word, but there's no more evidence for that than there is for actual brain disease. (Breggin, 1992, p. 278)

Dr. Breggin's work and his personal encouragement became a mainstay in the development of Pennsylvania's response to both federal legislation and the needs of individuals with and without so-called disabilities.

Dr. Breggin's work and his personal encouragement became a mainstay in the development of Pennsylvania's response to both federal legislation and the needs of individuals with and without so-called disabilities. In the face of what was by all reckoning an Insurmountable Force, his work gave those of us in the Pennsylvania Department of Education the courage—as well as the ammunition—to stand against the pressure to add ADD as a defined category of disability. For example, the state's Western Instructional Support Center in Pittsburgh produced a video presentation by Dr. Breggin on the subject of ADD. That video was circulated statewide as a tool in the campaign to present children as deserving recipients of individualized support as normal students rather than as medically diagnosed, defective children in need of medication to resolve their learning needs. …

Every individual can represent the power of one to affect the lives of all. Perhaps in our attempt to laud the individuals who have championed the causes that improve the world, we have allowed ourselves to slip into a form of elitism that puts back into place the very hierarchy of values that our inclusive rhetoric decries. William Penn, John Dewey, and Peter Breggin represent models who exemplify the ideological yet practical belief that the values of all matter.

Creating an Onion: Alternatives to Biopsychiatry

By T. J. Scheff, PhD. Tom is Professor, Department of Sociology, University of California-Santa Barbara and the author of many books including *Emotion and Violence, Emotions: the Social Bond and Human Reality*, and *Goeffman Unbound: Toward a New Paradigm in Social Science.*

Breggin's books on the damage caused by electroshock and psychiatric drugs were decidedly different from those of Szasz, Goffman, and Laing in their much greater specificity and concreteness. Where the other three writers tended to remain abstract and general, Breggin was specific in naming the types and effects of shock and names of the drugs, dose sizes, effects, and side effects. For this reason, his work probably has had much more direct impact on the understanding and behavior of practitioners and patients, perhaps more than all the other theorists combined.

> Peter Breggin's work probably has had much more direct impact on the understanding and behavior of practitioners and patients, perhaps more than all the other theorists combined.

Peter Breggin

By Jay Joseph, PsyD. Jay is a psychologist and researcher in private practice in the San Francisco Bay area.

In 1994–1995 I had a year off between the end of my clinical psychology master's program and the beginning of my doctoral program. I took this opportunity to read the works of several critics of mainstream theories in psychiatry and psychology. Among these authors were Thomas Szasz, R. D. Laing, Leon Kamin, and Mary Boyle. As I read their works, I began to question the mainstream psychiatric position that discrete mental disorders exist, as opposed to the idea that differing manifestations of human distress fall on a continuum. Moreover, in some cases psychiatric labels are used to stigmatize people who merely think and act in socially disapproved ways.

During this period I became acquainted with Peter Breggin's classic work, *Toxic Psychiatry* (1991). Previously, I had read many claims that the evidence overwhelmingly supported a biological and genetic basis for most mental disorders. Given that I was skeptical of such claims, I took great pleasure in reading this book very carefully. In particular, the chapter titled "The Biology and Genetics of 'Schizophrenic' Overwhelm" provided a welcomed response to the ubiquitous "schizophrenia is a brain disorder with a strong genetic basis" claim, which, unfortunately, remains standard fare in contemporary psychology and psychiatry textbooks. One reason for this, as Breggin pointed out in *Toxic Psychiatry,* is that "in psychiatry, biological research is guided, indeed driven, by the profession's need to justify its existence as a medical specialty" (1991, p. 101).

Inspired by *Toxic Psychiatry* and subsequent books and articles by Breggin and other critics, I began an in-depth investigation into the claim that "schizophrenia" has an important genetic basis. This became the topic of my doctoral dissertation (Joseph, 1998).

Subsequently, I published two books challenging genetic theories in psychiatry and psychology (Joseph, 2004, 2006). As it turns out, there exists little if any scientifically acceptable evidence that schizophrenia, depression, bipolar disorder, autism, ADHD, and other major psychiatric orders have any basis in genetics.

In *Toxic Psychiatry*, Breggin highlighted several important flaws in psychiatric twin and adoption studies. At the time, he was one of only a handful of authors to do so. And even then, nearly two decades ago, he cogently analyzed and refuted several subsequently unfounded "gene finding" claims in psychiatry....

I also appreciate Peter Breggin's opposition to genetic theories of criminal and antisocial behavior, which can be found in his book *The War Against Children of Color*, co-written with his wife, Ginger Breggin (1998). He took a courageous stand against the federal government–backed "violence initiative," which targeted inner-city youths as the alleged carriers of genetic defects leading them to commit a disproportionate share of violent crime. As Breggin showed, biological theories of criminal behavior have a long history in racism and eugenics....

Peter Breggin has been a tireless and courageous champion in the clinical, social, and literary arenas of the victims of psychiatric and governmental abuse. It has been my privilege to have known him and to have learned from him.

References

Joseph, J. (2004). *The gene illusion: Genetic research in psychiatry and psychology under the microscope.* New York: Algora.

Joseph, J. (2006). *The missing gene: Psychiatry, heredity, and the fruitless search for genes.* New York: Algora.

Confronting Risk About Antidepressants for Children

By David Antonuccio, PhD. David is Professor, Department of Psychiatry and Behavioral Sciences, University of Nevada School of Medicine, Reno, Nevada.

I first met Dr. Peter Breggin in 1992 when he gave a workshop in Reno, Nevada, on the toxicities of psychotropic medications. The workshop was cosponsored by the Reno V.A. Medical Center and the Department of Psychiatry and Behavioral Sciences at the University of Nevada School of Medicine. The events leading up to this workshop suggested that Dr. Breggin was a unique figure in psychiatry.

A couple of weeks before the workshop, someone from the American Psychiatric Association contacted the director of the hospital to tell him that it was unwise to allow Dr. Breggin to present his workshop because his views were dangerous and outside of mainstream psychiatry. The director arranged a conference call with the APA representative and the organizers of the workshop. Though I was not in the room, I was later told by someone who was, that during the course of the conference call, the director told the caller that the risks of medication treatment were a timely and

Someone from the American Psychiatric Association contacted the director of the hospital to tell him that it was unwise to allow Dr. Breggin to present his workshop because his views were dangerous and outside of mainstream psychiatry.

important topic. He also told the caller that the hospital and the medical school supported academic freedom and would not cancel the workshop. The only concession the director made was to agree to a debate at the end of the workshop on the balance of risk and benefit for psychotropic drugs.

Dr. Breggin's workshop went on as scheduled and resulted in the largest turnout of any workshop ever sponsored by the Reno V.A. Medical Center. Over 300 professionals (nurses, psychologists, counselors, and psychiatrists) attended, and many others were turned away at the door because the conference exceeded capacity. Dr. Breggin's presentation was passionate and data-based. The postworkshop debate with a prominent local psychiatrist was spirited and energized the crowd in attendance. The consensus was that Dr. Breggin handily won the debate.

What I learned from watching these events unfold was that there was a hunger among professionals for information about the risks of psychotropic medications. Although information was widely available on efficacy, the scientific literature had important gaps on the hazards of such treatment.

What I learned from watching these events unfold was that there was a hunger among professionals for information about the risks of psychotropic medications. Although information was widely available on efficacy, the scientific literature had important gaps on the hazards of such treatment. Dr. Breggin's book *Toxic*

Psychiatry (1991) helped to fill this gap in a way that no publication before it had done. In fact, the Department of Psychiatry and Behavioral Sciences chairman at the time encouraged the entire faculty to read the book. I remember reading the book cover to cover prior to the Reno workshop and feeling I had been exposed for the first time to an exhaustive accounting of the risks of commonly used psychotropic medications. I realized that it was impossible to conduct a true risk-benefit analysis of any intervention with adequate information only about benefit and inadequate information about risk. I had been trained in a "first do no harm" model of treatment, and this concerned me. I also learned that powerful forces could intervene to try to disrupt the flow of such information if it threatened corporate interests.

> I learned from reading Dr. Breggin's work that it is just as important to study risk as it is to study benefit of psychotropic medication. I learned that there are powerful corporate interests that might endeavor to keep such information under wraps if it threatens billions of dollars in generated revenue.

This experience contributed to a shift in my interests away from benefit alone to the balance of risk and benefit of treatments for depression (e.g., Antonuccio, Burns, & Danton, 2002; Antonuccio, Danton & DeNelsky, 1995; Antonuccio, Danton, DeNelsky, Greenberg, & Gordon, 1999;

Antonuccio, Danton, & McClanahan, 2003). I learned the importance of standing up for the data no matter whose ox is gored. I learned to appreciate my colleagues at the Reno V.A. Medical Center and at the Department of Psychiatry and Behavioral Sciences at the University of Nevada School of Medicine for their integrity and their support of academic freedom. In addition to finding him a warm and thoughtful individual, I came to respect Dr. Breggin's courage and stamina as a pioneer in the important and politically charged area of psychotropic medication risk. He was willing to answer any questions, and he would not shy away from a debate with anyone on the topic of psychotropic medications. His position was that the risks of these medications almost always outweighed the benefits.

I have vivid memories of reading the passage in his book about the original controlled studies on alprazolam (Ballenger et al., 1988; Pecknold, Swinson, Kuch, & Lewis, 1988), the first drug approved by the FDA to treat panic disorder. I was surprised to read that only the first 4 weeks of treatment showed benefit for alprazolam, and when the medication was tapered, the alprazolam group had 3.5 times more panic attacks than those randomly assigned to placebo (Marks et al., 1989). I was so surprised to read this information that I went to the original articles to verify its accuracy....

I learned from reading Dr. Breggin's work that it is just as important to study risk as it is to study benefit of psychotropic medication. I learned that there are powerful corporate interests that might endeavor to keep such information under wraps if it threatens billions of dollars in generated revenue. I also learned that the health of our children demands that we have access to information about these risks so we can balance them against the benefits and achieve truly informed consent. Anything short of that could appropriately be called misinformed consent.

References

Antonuccio, D. O., Burns, D., & Danton, W. G. (2002). Antidepressants: A triumph of marketing over science? *Prevention and Treatment,* 5. Retrieved July 1, 2007, from http://www.journals.apa.org/prevention/volume5/pre0050025c.html

Antonuccio, D. O., Burns, D., Danton, W. G., & O'Donohue, W. (2000). The rumble in Reno: The psychosocial perspective on depression. *Psychiatric Times,* 17, 10–13. http://www.psychiatrictimes.com/p000824.html

Antonuccio, D. O., Danton, W. G., & DeNelsky, G. (1995). Psychotherapy vs. medication for depression: Challenging the conventional wisdom with data. *Professional Psychology: Research and Practice,*26(6), 574–585.

Antonuccio, D. O., Danton, W. G., DeNelsky, G. Y., Greenberg, R. P., & Gordon, J. S. (1999). Raising questions about antidepressants. *Psychotherapy and Psychosomatics,* 68, 3–14.

Antonuccio, D. O., Danton, W. O., & McClanahan, T. M. (2003). Psychology in the prescription era: Building a firewall between marketing and science. *American Psychologist,* 58, 1028–1043.

Ballenger, J. C., Burrows, G. D., DuPont, R. L., Lesser, I. M., Noyes, R., Pecknold, J. C., et al. (1988). Alprazolam in panic disorder and agoraphobia: Results from a multi center trial. *Archives of General Psychiatry,* 45, 413-421.

Marks, I. M., De Albuquerque, A., Cottraux, J., Gentil, V., Greist, J., Hand, I., et al. (1989). The "efficacy" of alprazolam in panic disorder and agoraphobia: A critique of recent reports. *Archives of General Psychiatry,* 46, 668–669.

The Breggin Impact

By Clemmont E. Vontress, PhD. Clemmont is Professor Emeritus of Counseling, George Washington University, Washington, DC.

As we move through life, many people knowingly and unknowingly influence our journey. Peter R. Breggin impacted my life in a significant way. In 1995 he came to George Washington University to speak to a graduate student seminar in counseling. At the time, I was professor and director of the counseling program. In sharing his story with the group, Peter discussed several interesting events in his professional career. However, I am sure that he was unaware that he ignited in me a burning desire to explore two of the ideas that he touched on that day—love and depression. Although I had always considered these two concepts in the development of my existential approach to counseling, after hearing Peter's presentation, I understood them in a different light.

I am sure that he was unaware that he ignited in me a burning desire to explore two of the ideas that he touched on that day—love and depression.

In their book, *The War Against Children of Color*, Breggin and Breggin (1998) argue that love is basic to the healthy development of human beings. In a recent chapter on existential therapy, I (Vontress, 2008) followed up on this idea in making the case that love is essential to human existence. Starting early in life, it presupposes an individual's self-awareness and ability to empathize with others. The most important person to the fetus is the mother, in whose womb it resides. Feeling oneness with her, it develops a neurological network in which love is basic....

Binswanger (1975) coined the German word Mitwelt to communicate the existential and imperative connection that we have with our fellows. Love is an important ingredient of that linkage. It is the glue that ensures human togetherness that is indispensable to life. The neonate would not survive long without the love, care, and support of the mother. Her hugs release good-feeling chemicals in the child's brain. These are the biochemicals of love. As adults, individuals who have experienced love from their parents are apt to transfer it to others. They are inclined to continue to seek love and intimacy throughout their existence. For people, love and intimacy are liberating and healing. Instruments for connecting with others, love and intimacy provide a sense of self (Gallagher, 1975). They also add meaning to life.

For people, love and intimacy are liberating and healing. Instruments for connecting with others, love and intimacy provide a sense of self. They also add meaning to life.

Love is so basic to human existence that being able to exchange it with another person has implications for mental health. According to Ornish (1999), the child's perception of parental love and caring is a powerful predictor of future psychological well-being. Children reared without being hugged and touched early in life are likely to reveal high stress levels as adults. They also may grow up feeling that indeed they are unlovable. The impression can lead to depression and a lifelong search for palliatives, such as drugs and alcohol, to relieve the pain often associated with the absence of love....

Children reared without being hugged and touched early in life are likely to reveal high stress levels as adults. They also may grow up feeling that indeed they are unlovable.

Breggin's (1991) discussion of culture, ethnicity, and psychiatric diagnosis spurred my scholarship. I have devoted several years to studying cultural influences on psychological intervention. When I heard Peter discuss the often cavalier attitude of psychiatrists who diagnose and treat African Americans, I was motivated to pursue his lead and tease out some of the most devastating cultural factors that cause black clients to present as dysthymic or depressed.

References

Binswanger, L. (1975). *Being-in-the world: Selected papers of Ludwig Binswanger* (J. Needleman, Trans.). London: Souvenir Press, Ltd.

Gallagher, K. T. (1975). *The philosophy of Gabriel Marcel.* New York: Fordham University Press.

Ornish, D. (1999). *Love & survival: The scientific basis for the healing power of intimacy.* New York: Harper Paperbacks.

Vontress, C. E. (2008). Existential therapy. In J. Few & M. D. Spiegler (Eds.), *Contemporary psychotherapies for a diverse world* (pp. 141–176). Boston: Lahaska Press/Houghton Mifflin.

Understanding Psychotropic Drug Action: The Contribution of the Brain-Disabling Theory

By Joanna Moncrieff, MD. Joanna is Senior Lecturer in Social and Community Psychiatry, Department of Mental Sciences, the University College London (UCL) She is both an academic and a practicing psychiatrist who has published many scientific articles. She was founding member and is the co-chair person of the Critical Psychiatry Network in Great Britian. Her latest book is *The Myth of the Chemical Cure: A Critique of Psychiatric Drug Treatment* (2008).

The brain-disabling theory of psychiatric drug action is one of Peter Breggin's main contributions to our understanding of the nature of psychiatric drugs. It provides a clear and readily accessible explanation for the action of psychiatric drugs, both the effects that may appear to be useful and the effects that are unwanted or damaging. It has informed many subsequent critiques of drug treatment including my own work, in which I have characterized the different models by which psychiatric drugs may be said to work.

In Breggin's key books *Toxic Psychiatry* (Breggin, 1991) and *Brain Disabling Treatments in Psychiatry* (1997), he formulated the theory that psychiatric drugs, like other physical interventions in psychiatry such as electroconvulsive therapy (ECT) and lobotomy, work by disabling normal brain function. The latter book lays out the key principles of this idea clearly in 11 points, which are summarized below:

1. Physical psychiatric treatments act by disabling normal brain function.

2. They all cause generalized brain dysfunction.

3. Physical treatments achieve their therapeutic effects by impairing higher mental functions such as emotional responsiveness, self-awareness, and autonomy. They may cause typical signs

of severe brain dysfunction such as euphoria, apathy, and indifference.

4. Each treatment produces its brain-disabling effects in all people, including volunteers and people with all variety of psychiatric disorders.

5. There is individual variation in how people respond to drugs both physically and psychologically.

6. There are no known biological causes to most cases of psychological suffering for which people are prescribed drugs and other physical treatments.

7. Physical treatments may create their own psychiatric as well as physical problems.

8. Psychiatric drugs (and other physical treatments) are not specific for particular mental disorders.

9. The brain attempts to compensate for the effects of a foreign substance, and these adaptations cause withdrawal symptoms and other adverse effects. They are likely to be the cause of tardive dyskinesia (TD), for example.

10. While people are taking psychiatric drugs, or having other physical procedures, they may display poor judgment about how the treatment impacts their functioning.

11. Physicians who prescribe these drugs and treatments "often have an unrealistic appraisal of their risks and benefits" (Breggin, 1997, p. 10).

The brain-disabling thesis emphasizes that psychiatric drugs alter normal brain functioning. They are psychoactive drugs that induce abnormal brain states that give rise to characteristic drug-induced experiences or states of intoxication. We have no trouble recognizing this fact for recreational drugs, but somehow have a blind spot in the case of the drugs that are prescribed for psychiatric problems. However, the only difference between recreational drugs and drugs used in psychiatry is that many people enjoy the effects of the former, whereas the latter are usually experienced as unpleasant, at least by volunteers.

Recently, Breggin has coined the idea of "medication spellbinding" or medication-induced anosognosia to explore the implications of point 10 a bit further. Medication spellbinding is the phenomena whereby use of psychoactive drugs leads people to "underestimate the degree of his (or her) drug induced mental impairment," deny the harmful impact of drugs, and mistakenly believe that they are functioning better (2006, p. 214). Again, we are well aware of this phenomena in relation to alcohol, and we have legislation to prevent drunk driving because we know that people overestimate their capabilities when under the influence of alcohol. In chronic alcoholism and other substance dependencies, it is also recognized that people deny the degree to which their substance use is adversely affecting their functioning and their relationships. However, these effects are not generally recognized for psychiatric drugs, but once it is acknowledged that they are psychoactive drugs it becomes apparent that medication spellbinding is as likely to occur with them as with other substances. In fact, it may be more problematic in the case of psychiatric drugs because of the lack of recognition that may occur. An important implication of medication spellbinding is that people cannot truly evaluate the effects of taking a drug until after those effects have completely worn off....

> Peter Breggin has been at the forefront of presenting an alternative account of what psychiatric drugs do that helps to explode the myth that they act as disease-specific treatments.

Although the idea of drugs as having brain-disabling effects applies to all psychoactive drugs, including all drugs used in psychiatry, its implications are perhaps clearest with respect to the neuroleptics. Breggin was the first of a number of recent critics of psychiatric drug treatments who pointed out how the brain-disabling effects of neuroleptics were well recognized in the period after their introduction in the 1950s....

Breggin coined the phrase "deactivation" to summarize the effects of typical neuroleptic drugs. This phrase is useful because it vividly describes the Parkinsonian-like state that neuroleptics produce, with its reduced mental and physical activity....

The other important feature of the brain-disabling hypothesis, or the drug-centered model of drug action, is that it helps to explain how long-term drug use may result in neurological impairment. Breggin's work brings out the full nature of the damage that long-term use of neuroleptics can sometimes inflict....

The standard disease-centered account of drug action is so hegemonic that few doctors and psychiatrists are able to give a realistic appraisal of the risks and benefits of the drugs they prescribe, often for years on end. Peter Breggin has been at the forefront of presenting an alternative account of what psychiatric drugs do that helps to explode the myth that they act as disease-specific treatments and indicates the potential for harm that is an integral part of their action. He has helped many thousands of people with psychiatric problems to make a more informed choice about the treatment they are offered.

Chapter Fourteen

Thanking the Breggins

Introduction

There are at least two lessons from Dr. Breggin's career. First, one person can make a difference. Second, many people can make a bigger difference. Dr. Breggin's work should be an inspiration to all those who wish to stand up for higher ideals in the mental health professions or in any other arena that provides services to human beings. Fortunately, in the mental health field this no longer has to be done alone or in isolation.

The International Center for the Study of Psychiatry and Psychology (ICSPP.org) brings together professionals from around the world who want to stand up against abusive and scientifically untenable psychiatric practices and who want to promote more rational, ethical and caring psychosocial and educational approaches to helping children and adults in distress. *The Conscience of Psychiatry* is about Dr. Breggin and also about ICSPP. Professionals and non-professionals can find like-minded friends and colleagues, and help the reform work continue by joining ICSPP and participating in its activities, conferences, newsletter and journal.

Dr. Breggin formed ICSPP in 1972 as a support group for his ultimately successful efforts to stop the return of lobotomy and psychosurgery. As Dr. Breggin grew stronger and more effective as a reformer, the need arose for a mutual support group for professionals who want to improve the theory and practice of psychotherapeutic approaches while taking scientific and ethical stands against oppressive biopsychiatric practices, including psychiatric diagnosing, psychiatric drugs, electroshock, lobotomy and involuntary treatment.

In the early 1980s, Ginger joined Peter Breggin and soon decided to help him in his reform efforts. Almost single-handedly, she grew ICSPP from an annual meeting in their home to an active national organization with a large board of directors of esteemed professionals, annual conferences, a newsletter, and a listserv for advisory council members. Finally, she inspired the idea of a peer-reviewed journal and became the first Managing Editor of *Ethical Human Psychology and Psychiatry,* sponsored by ICSPP and published by Springer Publishing Company.

Non-professionals, including survivors of psychiatric abuse, their families, and other interested persons, are welcome to join ICSPP and to attend the annual conferences, and they often participate and give presentations. However, ICSPP's primary emphasis is upon bringing together reformed-minded professionals to criticize the dominant biological influence in psychiatry and mental health, and to support psychotherapeutic and educational approaches.

In 2002, prior to moving from Bethesda to the countryside in the Finger Lakes region of New York State, Ginger and Peter handed leadership of ICSPP and the journal to younger professionals, including the former director, Dominick Riccio, PhD and the new director, Toby Tylor Watson, PsyD. The organization continues to thrive. Information about the organization can be found at www.ICSPP.org.

Some of the many contributors to this biography who mention the importance of ICSPP in their personal and professional lives follow in this chapter.

My Round Table

by Al Galves, PhD

Funny how when you need something in your life, it shows up. Or is it that our minds have this wonderful capacity to know what's important, fix on it and store it somewhere to be found when we need it. Peter Breggin was that for me.

I knew I was going to retire from practicing psychotherapy and I was casting about for something to devote myself to. I knew I cared about the damage that was being done by biopsychiatry, not only to individuals but also to our conception of what human beings are all about, our fundamental understanding of human nature.

I had a vague notion that there was a guy named Peter Breggin who had written books that challenged biopsychiatry. Was he a psychiatrist or psychologist?

I googled him and found a phone number. Ginger answered. "I'd like to learn more about what you're doing," I said. "There's a conference this October in Newark that you can attend. Call either Dominick Riccio or Larry Simon in New York and they'll tell you about it." Sounded like the Mafia to me.

Dominick and Larry filled me in and I attended the 2003 ICSPP Conference in Newark. I was enthralled. These are my people. These are my fellow travelers, my comrades in arms. They understand. They care. They're doing something about it. And not only that, they are scientists. They aren't just blowing smoke. They have data, evidence. And they even have women who do hula dances (Sue Parry), and court jesters and priests and knights. This is my roundtable. These are people I can carry some water for.

I listened to Peter Breggin talk and I saw that this was a man who was living a life of purpose, who was walking the talk, not because he wanted to show everyone how smart he was (Oh, there may be a little bit of that going on), not because he wanted to be a big shot, not because he wanted to be oppositional, but because that was who he was, that was the muse he was following.

Since then I have learned how true that was. Peter Breggin through some kind of primordial wisdom has allowed himself to be driven by his awareness, his perception, his insight about the true, essential nature of human beings, what is really happening when they get scared, upset, enraged and confused and how they can be helped to move beyond those states of being into more healthy and enjoyable ones. And then he used his time, energy, enthusiasm and intelligence to DO SOMETHING ABOUT IT. How wonderful is that?

Through some kind of primordial wisdom he has allowed himself to be driven by his awareness, his perception, his insight about the true, essential nature of human beings.

I am forever grateful to Peter, Ginger and the others who founded ICSPP. You all have given me a group of colleagues with whom I can join in doing something to enhance the lives of human beings, not the least of which is my own.

Thank you, thank you, thank you.

Al Galves, PhD

Al received a PhD in clinical psychology from the Union Institute in Cincinnati, Ohio. He practiced psychotherapy in community mental health clinics, community health clinics and schools. He is the author of Lighten Up: Dance With Your Dark Side *and lives in Las Cruces, New Mexico with his wife Nancy.*

Peter Breggin, John Brown and Henry David Thoreau
by Bruce E. Levine, PhD

I was late in discovering *Toxic Psychiatry* because I had taken a sabbatical from browsing the "mental illness" sections in bookstores so as to regain my mental health. But in 1994, I received a telephone call from David Oaks, director of Support Coalition International (now MindFreedom International). He had spotted a letter-to-the-editor of mine debunking an article about adult attention deficit disorder, and David, being David, attempted to enlist me in the "dissident professional resistance movement." I responded, "What resistance? I don't know any shrink who's worth anything. I'm so embarrassed by what's going on that I am about ready to leave the profession." Then David asked me if I'd heard of a psychiatrist named Peter Breggin.

I remember being both amazed and energized by *Toxic Psychiatry*. Today, sixteen years after *Toxic Psychiatry's* publication, it has become much safer to criticize psychiatric drugs. As the blockbuster SSRI's lose their patent protection (and their multi-billion dollars in sales), drug companies have become less crazed about smearing critics. But in many of the current articles and books criticizing antidepressants, credit due Peter Breggin is conspicuously absent. While it has become easy to co-opt Breggin's drug critiques, Peter's co-opters back off from what is most important about Breggin: his exposure of psychiatry as an institution that people should be wary of placing their confidence in. Here is an example from *Toxic Psychiatry* that continues to separate Breggin from his co-opters: "By contrast, the typical modern psychiatrist—by disposition, training, and experience—is wholly unprepared to understand anyone's psychospiritual crisis. With drugs and shock treatment, the psychiatrist instead attacks the subjective experience of the person and blunts or destroys the very capacity to be sensitive and aware. No wonder the treatment of mental patients often looks more like a war against them. It often is." (p. 26)

There is a difference between reporting what is merely correct, e.g., abruptly discontinuing antidepressants can result in painful withdrawal; versus stating what is true, e.g., psychiatrists who have not rebelled against their socialization are the last people on the planet that you want to take seriously if you become depressed. Truth disturbs the status quo, and truth tellers are almost always labeled as extremists by those benefiting from the status quo.

One day I believe it will not take courage to assert the dehumanizing nature of biopsychiatric explanations and treatments offered up by the psycho-pharmaceutical industrial complex.

In the 1850s in the United States, the "reasonable" criticism of slavery was not about abolishing it but about restricting its spread. The relatively few Americans who actually demanded the abolition of slavery—the abolitionists—were called "radicals" and "extremists." Abolitionists such as Henry David Thoreau and John Brown were, in their day, labeled not only as radicals and extremists, but as "crazy." Thoreau and Brown were not without faults—who isn't?—but today nobody remotely humane would call them radical, extremist, or crazy when it comes to their loathing of slavery.

Just as it once took courage for a national figure to oppose the institution of slavery, it now takes courage for a psychiatrist to oppose "mental health" institutions that were first corrupted by drug companies and then virtually annexed by them. One day I believe it will not take courage to assert the dehumanizing nature of biopsychiatric explanations and treatments offered up by the psycho-pharmaceutical industrial complex. And when that complex is abolished, it will be merely correct to credit Peter Breggin for speaking out when it took courage to do so.

I contacted the Breggins after reading *Toxic Psychiatry,* and in 1998 Ginger Breggin invited me to the first International Center for the Study of Psychiatry and Psychology (ICSPP) conference in Bethesda. That conference was a unique experience for me. For the first time, I was at a gathering of many mental health professionals for whom I actually had respect. Afterward, Peter and Ginger invited my wife Bonnie and me to their home (a short walk from the conference). With us was Kevin McCready, who became a good friend, and over the years I would come to find other friends through ICSPP.

In 2001, Peter wrote a great blurb for my book *Commonsense Rebellion,* and in 2002 with the help of friends from both ICSPP and MindFreedom, Bonnie and I enjoyed touring North America promoting the book. I am grateful not only for *Toxic Psychiatry* and for Peter's endorsement but mostly for Peter and Ginger's creation of ICSPP and organizing its earlier conferences. Their efforts provided me and other alienated mental health professionals with—for the first time—a community of colleagues we could respect.

Bruce E. Levine, PhD

Bruce is a clinical psychologist in private practice in Cincinnati, Ohio. He is the author of Surviving America's Depression Epidemic: How to Find Morale, Energy, and Community in a World Gone Crazy, *and* Commonsense Rebellion.

Talking Back to Peter Breggin

by Andrew Crosby, MA

Story time, ladies and gentlemen. Sit back and get comfortable. It was my junior year in college and I'd accidentally gotten a full-time job. I wasn't looking or anything. Someone I knew said she'd just gotten this job, they were hiring, I should check it out. What? Me work? I interviewed for the practice. Never had a real job before.

The place was a community mental health center. The time was the mid-1980s. The job was as a counselor in the center's residence department. I walked through the interview, thanked them for the "practice," and eased on back to my dorm. Glad that was over.

A couple days later they called and offered me the job.

What? Me work?

I was in psychotherapy at the time with somebody who knew his stuff. He may have had something to do with the whole interview, job thing. He was always encouraging me. He was like that.

Most of the clients at the center were diagnosed with chronic schizophrenia and had been hospitalized more times than anyone could remember. My schoolbooks hadn't prepared me for much, and the supervision I received was little help. I had my psychotherapist, though, and as I said, he knew his stuff. He demystified a great deal about my encounters at work. He even discussed the necessity for the drugs the center's patients were taking. (Side note: I learned a lot about tardive dyskinesia at that place, too.)

A few years and a couple of jobs later I was back in psychotherapy with the same guy. He was still encouraging me, this time about graduate school. I finally got to it. I told him about some of the people I was working with at my latest job, and he was still my surrogate supervisor.

But something was different. I'd mention some drug a client was taking and my therapist would trash the stuff. I'd mention a diagnosis, and he'd say there was no such thing, it was a product of marketing. Actually his language was more colorful—we're from Jersey.

He was being inconsistent, which bothered me. As my therapist he was omnipotent, and omnipotent people shouldn't mess with you like that. I called him on it; told him he'd been saying drugs are good all along and now this.

He told me he'd been wrong.

He told me about the junk science behind the chemical imbalance and genetic theories. He said that all psychiatric drugs do is tranquilize or stimulate by impairing brain function and by damaging the brain. He said that psychiatry and the pharmaceutical companies had joined forces to create and promote the biopsychiatric hoax and that almost everybody on the planet had bought into it.

"Wait a minute," I said. "If that's true, then everything my professors have been saying about this is wrong."

"Yep."

"And my textbooks and those articles they make me read—that's all wrong?"

"Yep."

"And what newspapers and magazines print about this—that's all wrong?"

"Yep."

He was omnipotent, so I didn't want to insult him. But I had to ask: "Where you getting this stuff?"

He told me about a book he'd just read. It explained everything, debunked everything. He went on and on about it. Some book, I thought, and asked him what it was.

And he told me about Peter Breggin's *Toxic Psychiatry*. I asked for the author's name, scribbled it somewhere, and made for the nearest bookstore. I grabbed a copy and got to reading. Quite an education, ladies and gentlemen.

A few years, and several books, later I joined a group for an interesting three-day gathering in Bethesda, Maryland. The year was 1999, and the event was the first major conference of the International Center for the Study of Psychiatry and Psychology (ICSPP).

I'll say it again—quite an education. Fun too; I was like a kid in a candy store. More books and articles followed, from Peter and many others. There were more conferences and more speakers. Eventually, there was a newsletter, but I get ahead of myself. This is about Peter, and about some concepts I've picked up thanks to him and my association with ICSPP.

Lessons Learned Along the Way

Everything I Knew was Wrong. O.K. Not everything. But much of what I had been taught about psychiatric drugs, neurotransmitters, genetic theories, family studies, diagnostic reliability and validity, and research methodology as it was actually practiced was flawed, distorted, or, yes, just plain wrong. Peter revealed the evidence, and described the sound conclusions to which this evidence pointed.

I learned that the material that made it into my textbooks was often selective rather than definitive. Peter explained how this had happened. The conventional news media were also wrong about these matters, and this, too, was explored.

How could such bias be so widely disseminated and accepted? It was no hidden conspiracy, Peter explained, as business and political interests were more than sufficient and quite open about doing the job.

Peter was certainly not the first to spell out all of this. He gets credit, however, for being among the first to do so broadly—to connect the dots in so public a fashion.

Consider the Background. While reading *Toxic Psychiatry* I believed at first that Peter, like my therapist, was omnipotent. Soon I realized my error. Much of what Peter discussed in *Toxic Psychiatry*, and his other writings, was the work of his predecessors and contemporaries. It occurred to me that Peter was better than omnipotent—he was human. He shared the work and wisdom of others, giving credit where credit was due. There was a rich context and history to Peter's work and beliefs, and he has shared it with us.

Peter was better than omnipotent—he was human. He shared the work and wisdom of others giving credit where credit was due.

This historical background was so important to me that I set about obtaining and reading most of the work to which Peter referred in *Toxic Psychiatry*. There were books such as *Not in Our Genes* (Lewontin et al.,1984) and *The Limits of Biological Treatments for Psychological Distress* (Fisher and Greenberg, 1989). There were the oft-cited Amish and Danish studies (Egeland, et al., 1987; Kety et al., 1975), and the early reports on the first major psychiatric drug of the modern era, Thorazine (e.g. Lehmann and Hanrahan, 1954). There were articles and letters from professionals criticizing the conventional research and conclusions, and objecting to what psychiatry had become – a partner with the pharmaceutical industry.

I scoped out new and used bookstores. I haunted the library at the University of Medicine and Dentistry of New Jersey, because therein lay the best selection of journals in the region, some with volumes going back a century. Dime after dime I copied page after page, all the while thinking things like, "so, that's where Peter got that."

Why did I go through all that trouble? Partly because I wanted to absorb the history, and partly because of the next lesson I learned.

Don't Blindly Trust Authority. My undergraduate research methods professor taught that good researchers and practitioners don't trust authoritative sources in matters where sound evidence is lacking or contradictory. A prototypical example was that authorities once held that the sun revolved around the Earth. The evidence said otherwise, but what did it know, it was just the evidence.

Not all of us have been duped. Some of us think critically and logically, and read broadly, even going back over decades to explore thoughts and findings long ago committed to posterity. It's important to do so, because that is how we learn how ideas, right and wrong, form and evolve.

The truth is only revealed when sound evidence is allowed to trump authority. With truth, we move forward. Without it, it only looks like we do. I learned from Peter that as a society we are largely faking it. While believing that we are learning and hearing the truth about psychological distress we are in reality trusting the authorities. Even my undergraduate research methods professor was guilty. And probably still is.

We picture researchers, scientists, and FDA officials wearing white lab coats and glasses as they objectively seek the truth. We nod as they assure us that depression, schizophrenia, and everything else, are biological diseases and that science is homing in on the causes and cures.

As you know, of course, not all of us have been duped. Some of us think critically and logically, and read broadly, even going back over decades to explore thoughts and findings long ago committed to posterity. It's important to do so, because that is how we learn how ideas, right and wrong, form and evolve.

So I bought all those books and copied all those articles because I didn't want to blindly trust authority. Not even Peter. I read what Peter read, so I could consider the evidence and make up my own mind.

It Takes Courage. Like many of you, I learned the hard way that almost nobody accepts a non-biopsychiatric view. Some are downright scared of the prospect. I speak, of course, not only of the general public, but also of those who have joined us in the helping professions. I don't know how they get along, but get along they do.

Tough thing, being part of a group that's got so much wrong and doesn't know it. It raises difficult choices every day. Should I correct my peers and colleagues? How about my supervisors and administrators? If so, how and how often should I speak up? When I do speak up, it seems like I go over and over the same old thing. I wonder if anybody is listening.

Like you, I've come up with ways of handling these choices. I pick my battles. I've thought about how I've managed thus far, and here's my answer: I believe what the evidence suggests is the truth. I don't let myself be frightened by the truth, as so many others seem to be. I stick with it. I get pessimistic sometimes. You probably do, too.

Big deal. Pessimism is fleeting, but the truth is there no matter what happens. I ask myself where my loyalties are—with the common belief system or with the truth?

When I'm disheartened, I recall the tribulations (I could say, attacks) that Peter and so many others we've met through ICSPP have withstood. They've struggled, all right. Their determination to stand by the truth inspires courage.

So does another concept I picked up along the way. Which brings us to …

The Final Lesson

I Am Not Alone. And neither are you. There are many times, of course, when we are the only ones in the room who think as we do. But then, October rolls around and we find ourselves in a different room—the annual ICSPP conference. Our sense of community is strengthened and we find ourselves refreshed. We don't have to wait until October, though. The journal offers refreshment a few times a year, and I hope the ICSPP newsletter does as well.

All of the above, by the way, is Peter's doing. He (he would add, and his wife Ginger) is responsible for the ICSPP community that we so dearly value. He didn't do it alone. Nobody exists in, and nothing of import was ever created within, a vacuum. But the spark, the inspiration … that was Peter.

So, I take this opportunity to talk back to Peter Breggin. What I have to say, put simply, is thank you. Thank you for the ICSPP community. Thank you for the inspiration, the concepts, and the conferences. Thank you for the *Ethical Human Psychology and Psychiatry* journal.

Thank you for letting me and so many others know that we are not alone.

While I'm at it, thank you for the newsletter. I'm having a good time with it, and I'm told others are not displeased. And if you'd like to contribute, Peter, I'm sure we can work something out. You know where to reach us.

Bibliography

Egeland, J.A., Gerhard, D.S., Pauls, D.L., Sussex, J.N., Kidd, K. K., Allen, C.R., Hostetter, A.M., & Housman, D.E. (1987). Bipolar affective disorders linked to DNA markers on chromosome 11. *Nature*, 325, 783-787.

Fisher, S. & Greenberg, R.P. (1989). *The limits of biological treatments for psychological distress.* Hillsdale, New Jersey: Lawrence Erlbaum Associates, Inc.

Kety, S.S., Rosenthal, D., Wender, P.H., Shulsinger, F. & Jacobson, B. (1975). Mental illness in the biological and adoptive families of adopted individuals who became schizophrenic: A preliminary report based on psychiatric interviews. In R. Fieve, D. Rosenthal, and H. Brill (Eds.), *Genetic research in psychiatry* (pp. 147-165). Baltimore: The Johns Hopkins Press.

Lehmann. H.E., & Hanrahan, G.E. (1954). Chlorpromazine: New inhibiting agent for psychomotor excitement and manic states. *Archives of Neurology and Psychiatry,* 71, 227-237.

Lewontin, R.C., Rose, S., & Kamin, L.J. (1984). *Not in our genes.* New York: Pantheon.

Andrew Crosby, MA

Andrew is a social worker who lives and works in northern New Jersey. He writes for and edits the ICSPP Newsletter, *and is an amateur writer. Andrew, who is a Board Member of ICSPP, has another contribution in chapter 1.*

How I Met Peter Breggin (& How Thankful I Am That I Did!)

by Adina Lambert, MA

It was spring 1991 and I was about to graduate with my masters in counseling from The College of New Jersey (formerly Trenton State College). How fortunate I was to come down with a rather bad cold that sent me to bed for a day or two!

Lying in bed, feeling sorry for myself, I was watching an early morning talk show on our local ABC affiliate. The host introduced his guest as Peter Breggin, a practicing psychiatrist of national repute. The announcer stated that his distinguished guest had been called the "Conscience of Psychiatry" and had recently written a book entitled *Toxic Psychiatry.*

Here was a psychiatrist who was debunking the chemical imbalance theory of "mental illness." Instead, Dr. Breggin was speaking about soul pain and about psycho-spiritual/emotional overwhelm as the source of human suffering.

At this point I sat bolt upright in bed and paid very close attention to what Dr. Breggin had to say. I couldn't believe what I was hearing. Here was an M.D. psychiatrist, speaking out vehemently and eloquently against psychiatric drugs.

Here was a psychiatrist who was debunking the chemical imbalance theory of "mental illness." Instead, Dr. Breggin was speaking about soul pain and about psycho-spiritual/emotional overwhelm as the source of human suffering. Here was a psychiatrist verbalizing my own position on psychotropic drugs. Here was a psychiatrist speaking with great clarity, quiet dignity and authority against the cult of psychoactive drugs.

I was amazed and frankly thrilled. Finally, I thought, a voice of reason in a world gone mad! I was at the very beginning of my career as a therapist and yet, after a 10 month internship at a local mental health facility, I was already aware of the irreversible damage these drugs could cause. And there was Dr. Breggin speaking out with passion and conviction against the pervasive use of these toxic medications!

> Peter has had a tremendous influence on how I practice, and his deep conviction has given me the courage to discourage drug use and to help my patients find other solutions to their pain and angst.

I knew at that moment that I would buy Dr. Breggin's book and that I would do everything in my power to contact him. I needed to let him know how thankful I was to find a psychiatrist who not only didn't believe in psychiatric drugs but who was openly opposed to them.

I wrote Peter a long letter; then I called him on the phone. He was responsive and kind. To my delight, I learned that there was an entire organization based on his position against mainstream drug-dependent psychiatry. I joined ICSPP and attended one of the earliest national conferences.

Now, many years later, Peter has become much more than a colleague and mentor. As his book became my Bible, he and Ginger became my friends.

I also must thank him for his continued work and his many other books. *Your Drug May Be Your Problem* (co-authored with David Cohen) has become my second most important book—one that I routinely "prescribe" to my patients and their families.

As a practicing licensed psychologist over the past 16 years, I feel truly blessed that I came down with that cold so many years ago. Peter has had a tremendous influence on how I practice, and his deep conviction has given me the courage to discourage drug use and to help my patients find other solutions to their pain and angst.

Peter taught me—by example—what it means to be truly present with another human being; this above all has served me and my patients well over the years.

I attended 10 of the next 12 conferences and have been privileged to serve on the Board of Directors of ICSPP. I will be forever grateful to Peter for giving me the courage to stand my ground against the false promise of psychiatric drugs and the lucrative fraud of bio-psychiatry.

Peter is a warm, caring and compassionate person and I feel honored to be able to call him my friend.

Adina Lambert, MA

Adina is a Licensed Psychologist in private practice in Bucks County, PA outside of Philadelphia. She has been a member of ICSPP since 1992. She uses a drug-free approach to treat depression and anxiety; she does individual therapy, and family and marriage counseling. Adina lives with her husband of 40 years, Dr. Michael Pliskin, and a cat named "Miracle."

How Peter Breggin Has Influenced my Life

by Rick Winking, MMHC

It was sometime in the early spring of 1994. I was a graduate student at the time and I had been struggling with the idea of "chemical imbalances" and its influence on the counseling profession. At the time Prozac was starting to be seen as the cure all for everything—depression, obsessive-compulsive disorder, eating disorders, etc.—and it just was not sitting right with me. I would be in class and the professor would be talking about "endogenous vs. exogenous" depression and how the "endogenous variety" could be diagnosed when there was no external reason for this person to be depressed.

> Here was a man who was intelligently articulating my feelings on the chemical imbalance theory and biopsychiatry, and doing it as a psychiatrist.

I would then ask something like "How many people do you know will actually tell you what is going on in their lives in just a few short hours?" The reply would always be something like "You can usually get a sense of whether a person has been happy most of their life and then suddenly for no apparent reason becomes depressed. This would be an example of 'endogenous' depression or a chemical imbalance causing the depression and requiring medication."

I felt like someone in the classic Solomon Asch experiment on conformity, with all of my classmates nodding their heads and buying into this model and me not quite knowing what to do.

Around this time I was at home and sick with the flu. I was watching television and lying on the couch seemingly near death, when Oprah came on. Being a poor graduate student, I could not afford a TV with a remote and I was too sick to get up and change the channel, so I decided to suffer through whatever silly guest Oprah had to offer. I was then introduced to a book, *Toxic Psychiatry*, and its author, Peter Breggin. I came out of the sixties and this term is much overused, but my mind was blown. Here was a man who was intelligently articulating my feelings on the chemical imbalance theory and biopsychiatry, and doing it as a psychiatrist. Oprah then brought out the head of the American Psychiatric Association to debate Peter on this. Needless to say, Peter made mincemeat out of the guy's arguments. I decided that I needed to know more about this man and his book.

I do believe that if you give people a nurturing, caring environment, most people will heal on their own. This is what I believe Peter was trying to get across.

A couple of days later, I bought the book at the university bookstore and read it nonstop cover to cover. I could not understand why a book like this is not required reading in counseling psychology programs. Peter spoke eloquently about his experiment at Harvard where he went into the back wards of a mental institution and just hung out with and cared about the patients and how this had positive results and how psychiatry had not only ignored this but put a stop to it. I am not a "Rogerian," but I do believe that if you give people a nurturing, caring environment, most people will heal on their own. This is what I believe Peter was trying to get across, along with the fact that modern psychiatric methods actually do exactly the opposite and instead thwart the healing process.

I then wrote a letter to Peter. In the letter I said how I felt like I was the only person out here in Montana who was asking these questions and how much it meant to me to have someone of his stature speaking out on this. Within a couple of weeks, Peter and Ginger Breggin called me and, after chatting at length, they invited me to join the advisory council of the International Center for the Study of Psychiatry and Psychology (ICSPP). How could I not accept?

From there I bought Peter's other books, most notably *Brain-Disabling Treatments in Psychiatry* (1997 and 2008). Because of Peter and ICSPP, I have had the honor of being introduced to and being able to communicate with such great thinkers and authors as the late Loren Mosher and Kevin McCready, Grace Jackson, Bruce Levine, William Glasser and countless others. I remember telling Peter that I felt all alone with my ideas out here in Montana and how much I appreciate that there are people like him out there.

Again, thank you Peter Breggin. I no longer feel alone. How could I be, with people like you around?

Rick Winking, MMHC

Rick is a retired musician who appeared on album or stage with a variety of artists from BB King, Stevie Ray Vaughn and Ray Charles to Willie Nelson and countless Grand Ol' Opry stars. He is currently the Director of The Alcohol and Drug Assistance Center at Montana State University-Bozeman and is in private practice.

My First Contact with Peter Breggin

by Robert Foltz, PhD

After several years in graduate school in the Chicago area, I was participating in an ongoing discussion group on the psychotherapeutic treatment of schizophrenia. Not only was this a controversial topic (and remains so), but challenging the medication treatment of schizophrenia was even more provocative. Graduate courses had educated me to believe that these major disorders were caused by disrupted neurochemicals, and the most effective treatment was medication. However, one of my most inspiring professors (D.D.) passed along a copy of Peter Breggin's book, *Toxic Psychiatry* (1991).

Toxic Psychiatry invigorated me by challenging most of what I had been taught about the causes and treatments of severe psychiatric disorders. Early in my career in psychology, this book made me hungry for more information, either to confirm—or to dispel—the information that Breggin provided in such a compelling way.

I found myself ambitiously attempting to contact Peter Breggin as a result of reading this book. Toxic Psychiatry was quickly changing the way I viewed the field of psychology and psychiatry, and was dramatically altering the way I understood the anguish of those we label "disordered." As an idealistic young graduate student, I was uncertain as to how my attempts to contact "the doctor" would be received.

After several days leaving messages expressing my hope of making contact, I received a voicemail telling me a good time to call. Excited and intimidated, I called. Peter took my call with an unexpected warmth and friendliness. In our conversation, I shared with him my hope that he could come to speak to the group of Chicago area clinicians on the treatment of schizophrenia. As we talked, he shared what the expense would be to have him speak to a group of professionals. Quickly deflated, I responded with, "we're just a group of graduate students, psychologists, and psychiatrists interested in schizophrenia...we wouldn't be able to reimburse you."

Without hesitation, Peter responded: "I'm going to be coming to Chicago in a few weeks for a book fair at McCormick Place" (It was 1997, and he was simultaneously releasing two books, *The Heart of Being Helpful* and *Brain-Disabling Treatments in Psychiatry*). He explained, "If you can take me to O'Hare afterwards, I'd be happy to speak to your group."

Peter provided several hours of discussion to a very informal group of students and clinicians where he took questions—and challenges—to his provocative ideas around the non-use of medications in the "treatment" of people labeled with schizophrenia. Equally compelling, he shared a very sensitive, thoughtful perspective on how caring, compassionate relationships can be so healing for those in the most severe forms of distress. These ideas, while familiar to me in my education, were somewhat unexpected, based on my years of experience working in psychiatric hospitals. As I've become more acquainted with Peter and Ginger over the years, compassion and sensitivity to others is shown clearly as a guiding force in their work.

> Peter shared a very sensitive, thoughtful perspective on how caring, compassionate relationships can be so healing for those in the most severe forms of distress.

One trend that stands out in my earliest experiences with Peter, as reflected in our trip to O'Hare airport, is his insight into where "science" is guiding the field. Amazingly, his analysis of the research around SSRI antidepressants proved to be true. His *Talking Back to Prozac,* co-authored by Ginger, highlighted the dangers of these drugs that are now at last officially confirmed by the FDA. This book was published in 1994. The field is now gaining momentum with revised ideas about mindfulness, and a renewed appreciation on the healing qualities of relationships.

> Now much too big to fit in the Breggin living room, the ICSPP conferences remain an annual refueling for me. Being able to visit with Peter, Ginger, and the other members of the organization is invaluable.

Many others have in recent years begun to frame these psychospiritual concepts around the biological concept of "neuroplasticity." On my drive to O'Hare with Peter, he shared his thoughts on these topics, pointing out that our brains are continually being modified by our experiences. This was not information I had received in my graduate training. He shared a range of day-to-day examples to illuminate the principles of neuroplasticity, and highlighted its relation to human connectedness. This drive to O'Hare occurred more than 10 years ago.

With a warm handshake, I dropped Peter off at the airport to catch his flight home. I was excited, with a renewed curiosity for the field, and a refreshed energy around critically scrutinizing the "science" of mental health treatments. Just a couple weeks later, Ginger contacted me. She was inviting me to be part of ICSPP, suggesting that I attend an upcoming gathering—to be held in their home—to discuss these exciting ideas, and more importantly, to connect with other professionals sharing this curiosity, ambition, and excitement over learning and challenging what we "think" we know.

Now much too big to fit in the Breggin living room, the ICSPP conferences remain an annual refueling for me. Being able to visit with Peter, Ginger, and the other members of the organization is invaluable. Since my earliest contact with the Breggin's, I'm now a Board Member of ICSPP and continue to pursue, and promote, the ideas and principles of the organization.

In writing this, I hope it's made clear: My contact with Peter and Ginger Breggin, and my subsequent involvement in ICSPP and the powerful members of that group, has been one of the most profound influences in my professional development as a clinical psychologist. I'm grateful for his generosity to a young graduate student, for his contributions to the field, for his compassion for those in distress, and for his courage to pursue the truth.

Robert Foltz, PhD

Bob is a clinical psychologist in private practice and the Assistant Executive Director at Camelot Residential Treatment Center, in the Chicago area. He is a Board Member of ICSPP, managing editor for the journal, Ethical Human Psychology and Psychiatry, and serves on the Advisory Board for the American Association of Children's Residential Centers. He has published, and presented nationally, on the use and misuse of psychotropic medications in youth, as well as the subjective experience of being medicated in those diagnosed with schizophrenia.

A Personal Tribute to Peter R. Breggin

by Lloyd Ross, PhD

For years, many of us have worked with people in pain and both for instinctive and theoretical reasons, did not see drugs as a therapeutic device. I am a psychotherapist, not a researcher. I started a private practice in 1977. I had been trained in psychoanalysis and ego-developmental psychotherapy and I have always truly believed that the emotionally based problems we develop as human beings have to do with aspects of our development or things that happen to us that we do not handle or negotiate properly. I have always rejected as unfounded and simplistically reductionistic, biochemical explanations of behavior and development. My experiences with people taught me that medication was unhelpful in psychotherapy in that it interfered with real psychotherapy by providing "magic" for the client and by turning the therapist into a powerful magician, like a surgeon, thereby interfering with the real work that needed to be done.

I also realized early on that I was virtually alone in my view. The vast majority of psychiatrists, psychologists, social workers, and counselors saw drugs as aiding the therapy and I often wondered what kind of therapy they were really doing. Although my own training analyst, most of the therapists I have supervised, and a few of my colleagues also held my view, the vast majority of therapists looked at me strangely.

Since I never incorporated drugs into my practice, I never really explored the issue of side effects of those drugs and, therefore, I was not really knowledgeable about drug effects. Basically, from 1977 to 1994, I avoided the issue of drugs in my practice as the rest of the world became increasingly drugged.

The Awakening

In the winter of 1995, I received a call from my daughter Holli, who was a freshman at Vassar College, and was taking her first psychology course. She was concerned that her professor, at the start of the course, asked the class to share their views and opinions about the field of psychology. She said that one girl in the class said that psychotherapy was not very important anymore because researchers found that all mental problems are biochemical and that we now have drugs that correct all of these chemical imbalances. Holli said that she responded to the girl by quoting 8 or 9 studies that contradicted what the girl said. The girl started to cry she was so upset and my daughter felt bad because she wasn't trying to hurt her feelings.

I asked Holli what happened next. She said that her professor asked her where she got that information from and she held up Peter Breggin's book, *Toxic Psychiatry.* The professor smiled and then told the class that he was scrapping the first of three books that were listed as required reading and replacing it with *Toxic Psychiatry.*

I asked Holli, "Who the hell is Peter Breggin?" She said "Dad, this guy is saying the same things about medications that you always say, but he has it all documented...He sounds like you." I asked Holli to spell his name and proceeded to get a copy of the book. After reading it voraciously, non-stop over one weekend and highlighting almost every paragraph, I proceeded to go out and buy all of Peter's books as of that date. I was amazed. A researcher-scientist-therapist had confirmed just about all of my gut instincts about drugs as well as the philosophical underpinnings of looking at people's problems totally outside of the medical model.

I noticed in one of Peter's books that he had started an organization called the International Center for the Study of Psychiatry and Psychology and that the group was going to have its second annual conference in Bethesda, Maryland. I called his number and spoke to Ginger Breggin, who filled me in and welcomed me. I promptly joined ICSPP and arranged to go to the conference. I also spoke to other colleagues, told my daughter about it, and the day before the conference, Robert Sliclen, Holli, and I set out for Bethesda.

More meaningful and significant than the material I had read, what I found at this Conference was that I WAS NOT ALONE. Here I was, in a large conference room full of people, very powerful and significant people, caring, concerned, and wonderful people, who all strongly supported the view that people who were in trouble emotionally did not have a disease that needed medicating, did not have some mysterious and evasive brain chemistry problem, and were not different in any way from me or anyone else. On that weekend, I spent a great deal of time talking with Peter and Ginger. I also met and befriended Clemmont Vontress, a formidable figure at the conference, as well as Tom Scheff, Ron Hopson, Nora Porter, Larry Epp, Keith Hoeller, Tom Greening, and Jake Johnson. I was also lucky enough to spend some time talking with Steve Baldwin before his tragic death, and was lucky enough to meet and become good friends with Kevin McCready and Loren Mosher before their untimely deaths.

On the Saturday night of the Conference, I listened through the wee hours of the morning to stories by the best story teller I've ever heard, Bert Karon, whose book, *The Psychotherapy of Schizophrenia,* I have always had on my office bookshelf. My daughter, Holli, was enthralled listening to the humor of Kevin McCready. I met David Stein there, who also became a good friend. I heard powerful presentations from Graham Dukes and David Cohen, and was impressed with the brilliance of David Oaks. The most powerful thing for me of the whole conference was ECT-survivor Leonard Roy Frank's presentation, which brought me to tears. I also met Doug Smith at the Conference, a quiet, soft-spoken young psychiatrist from Alaska whose knowledge of drug research was vast and reality bound. I have never met anyone who could take apart a piece of research like Doug. I also met Ty Colbert, bought his book, *Broken Brains or Wounded Hearts,* which is probably the best beginning read for any person just getting into this field.

While at the conference, I met some other people from the New York Metropolitan area, including Dominick Riccio, (It was his first introduction to ICSPP also), and Adina Lambert. Before the Conference was over, we all agreed to meet when we got back home and maybe form a regional section of ICSPP in order to provide some emotional support for each other.

What I came away from that conference with was different from any other conference I had ever attended. Before that conference, I felt alone in this field. At this conference, led by Peter and Ginger, I became part of a family of psychiatric survivors, educators, therapists, and medical practitioners. I was no longer alone in the trenches.

How I See Peter Breggin

Probably, the best way to accurately present the way I see Peter Breggin is to repeat what Ty Colbert said in his wonderful book *Broken Brains Or Wounded Hearts.* Ty describes the three people that both he and I consider to be heroes in this field.

The first, Philippe Pinel, in the early 17th Century, went into the horrible asylums in Paris, where he saw people in chains, forgotten by the world. He insisted that the "mentally ill" were ordinary people who had been deprived of their reason by horrific personal problems and that they needed to be treated humanely and that this would lead to their recovery. He drastically increased the recovery rate but the power of the establishment was brought down upon him. Pinel stood his ground.

The second hero in the field is Sigmund Freud. Freud developed theories about the development of psychopathology from a psychological developmental point of view, which clearly turned away from the biological model. He developed this by simply "listening to his patients." Although he must be given credit for a huge feat, he did, nevertheless, waver somewhat under political pressure.

The third hero in this field is clearly Peter Breggin, a 20th and 21st century ultra professional who, like Pinel, got his real education in a state mental hospital, in Peter's case as a Harvard undergraduate volunteer. Peter observed the effects of drugs and ECT on patients, which damaged them and made them obviously less reachable. Peter went on in his professional career to take on, head on, the American Psychiatric Association, the National Alliance For the Mentally Ill (NAMI), and the international pharmaceutical cartel (Big Pharma). Why not? After all, in high school he was a football player, as I found out when I attended an award ceremony for him as an honored alumni of the class of 1954.

To stand up and be counted when there is no one behind you, which Peter did in those early battles, is so awe inspiring that I cannot put it into accurate or sufficient words.

These groups attacked Peter openly, tried to get his license to practice medicine revoked, and tried to discredit him in other ways. In Maryland, where his medical license was attacked, not only was he exonerated—beyond that the licensing board apologized to him and thanked him for his contribution to mental health in Maryland. Peter successfully fought the potentially massive return of psychosurgery in the United States. He has also fought against the increasing use of ECT. He has highlighted in his books, in a well-documented manner, the dangers of neuroleptics, SSRI antidepressants, and stimulants for children.

The part of this that keeps me in awe, however, is that Peter Breggin fought all of these battles virtually all alone in the professional community. It is very different to stand up and fight for what is right when you have people behind you, and Peter certainly has that now. But to stand up and be counted when there is no one behind you, which he did in those early battles, is so awe inspiring that I cannot put it into accurate or sufficient words.

My final comment exposes where I grew up, in the slums of Hudson County, New Jersey. However, I find that I can't truly express the way I feel about this man accurately in any other way. Peter Breggin is a man who took on Goliath, Darth Vader, and all the evil people in Big Pharma and bio-psychiatry, kicked their ass, and continues to kick their ass. Thank God for this incredibly brave man who is my hero.

Lloyd Ross, PhD

Lloyd has been in full time private practice for the past 30 years with specialization in child, adolescent and family psychotherapy, therapist supervision, and forensics. He has been a consultant to several adolescent and child treatment centers and is currently the United States District Executive Director, the International Center for the Study of Psychiatry and Psychology. He is a Founding Fellow of the American College of Advanced Practice Psychologists.

Chapter 15

Empathic Therapy and Principled Living

Introduction

Dr. Breggin began his private practice in 1968 in the Washington, DC area, and for several decades he saw more than 30 hours of patients a week in individual, couples and family therapy, including children in the context of their family and school life.

Since moving his office to Ithaca, New York in November 2002, he has continued with a smaller practice with adults, including families with children, conducted on the basis of the same drug-free, voluntary principles, which are most recently and thoroughly summarized in the final chapter of *Brain-Disabling Treatments in Psychiatry* (2008).

From the start of Dr. Breggin's career as a Harvard College student leading a college volunteer program in a state mental hospital, caring and ethical human services have been the bedrock of his approach to helping children and adults across the spectrum of psychological distress and disturbance. "People need people, not pills," became a kind of motto. In later years he would refine his principles of therapy, including how to help people understand and overcome their helpless, self-defeating thoughts and behaviors patterns; but the caring relationship would remain the center of his psychotherapeutic work.

For Dr. Breggin, the contest is not between oppressive biological psychiatry and psychotherapy but between biological psychiatry and all the more positive opportunities that life has to offer, including a wide variety of psychosocial therapies and educational approaches, philosophy, religion, marriage, family and the joys and challenges of everyday life. Increasingly he would emphasize that life can only be lived effectively according to sound ethical principles including personal responsibility and the courage and the determination to love. To triumph over conflict and emotional distress, people need to feel and to express love for one another, for productive work, for nature, for music and art, for creativity, and for higher ideals including God.

Dr. Breggin continues to write and to lecture about how to live life with a drug-free or "unmedicated" mind. His most comprehensive discussion is found in *The Heart of Being Helpful* (1997). He has also written in *Beyond Conflict* (1992) about his overall approach to optimizing human life and relationships through the rejection of coercion and the promotion of liberty and love. In addition, he has written several articles and book chapters about therapy (for example, Breggin 1971, 1974, 1975a, 1988, 1988-9, 1991, 1998c, 1999d, and 2003b). Most of his books conclude with chapters about alternatives to psychiatric drugs, including how to raise children and to overcome emotional distress in adulthood through improved principles of living. He is fond of saying that "all of life" is the alternative to biological psychiatry with its diagnoses, drugs and electroshock.

As the following commentary confirms, Dr. Breggin is not in retirement:

A Lifelong Ambition. "The Breggins Move to Ithaca, New York" by Ginger Breggin, *ICSPP Newsletter*, Fall 2002.

In keeping with a lifelong ambition to live in the mountains and near the water, Peter and Ginger Breggin are moving to Ithaca, New York, the Finger Lakes region of the Empire State....

Peter is not retiring. As a psychiatrist he plans to continue a clinical and consultation practice in Ithaca, New York, and to work as a medical expert in the legal arena. Of course he'll also continue to write books….

The move is part of an overall lifestyle change. Recently Peter and Ginger selected new leadership for the International Center for the Study of Psychiatry and Psychology and for its journal, *Ethical Human Sciences and Services.* Peter remains as Director Emeritus of the center and both remain as Founding Editors and consultants to the journal, but have no direct responsibility for these activities. They expect to continue to be active at the national conferences and to offer inspiration to the reform movement.

Peter and Ginger believe that this can be a time of renewed, increased enthusiasm and action in the psychiatric reform movement. As they focus on other aspects of their personal and professional lives, they look forward to an inspired new leadership with many new faces and ideas.

Empathic Therapy. "Relationship as Healing" review by Arthur C. Bohart, *Contemporary Psychology*, APA Review of Books, **2004.**

Dimensions of Empathic Therapy [by Peter R. Breggin, Ginger Breggin, and Fred Bemak] is not primarily about empathy. Rather, its "metapurpose" is to present an alternative to the dominant medical model of current mental health practice. The book is generally against psychiatric diagnosis, pathologizing, use of medication, and psychotherapies that are primarily technological. It is also generally against hierarchical power relationships where mental health professionals, operating from a presumed posture of greater expertise, decide for clients what is good for them…. The book is "for" the primacy of empathic and authentic relationships as the core of healing….

Overcoming McDrug Culture. "Prozac's Reign Ends But Legacy Endures: Drug Has Altered Views of Mental Illness" by Shankar Vedantam, *the Washington Post,* August 4, 2001.

"People don't want to look deeply into their psyche, they don't want to see depression as a signal that we need to change the way we behave," said Bethesda psychiatrist Peter Breggin, author of *Talking Back To Prozac* and other books. "It's becoming a McDrug culture.... Psychiatry is dominated by pharmaceutical company interests, and the money that flows out of the pharmaceutical companies controls what the public hears."

The Key to Healing. "Out of the Blues" by Randi Henderson, *Common Boundary,* January/February 1998.

Ask someone the best way to treat depression and you're likely to get the answer "medication." But a host of alternative therapists tell a different story....

Many alternative treatments—particularly herbs, nutrition, acupuncture, and exercise—aim at biochemical modifications that are ultimately not that different from the goals of conventional psychopharmaceutical treatment. But others suggest a more intuitive, humanistic approach. "Depression is a feeling that you can't do life, and the opposite is learning how to live a good, empowered life," says Peter Breggin, a Bethesda, Maryland, psychiatrist and the author of *Talking Back to Prozac: What Doctors Aren't Telling You About Today's Most Controversial Drug* and *The Heart of Being Helpful: Empathy and the Role of a Healing Presence.*

"You have to learn that you're a lovable, competent human being, and many things can help—sports, nature, family. But no wise person has ever thought that drugs are the answer. In my experience, the person in the depths of despair is the one most in need of human contact. That must be your starting point.

"One of the big mistakes of the alternative movement is that it still takes a mechanistic approach to depression—a new herb, a new manipulative approach," Breggin continues. "This may have a palliative effect, but it won't help you live a more loving, principled life."

Breggin says that the key to healing depression is empathy. He admits that empathy can be in short supply in our modern culture, but he feels that the therapist can serve as an excellent source of this understanding and compassion for the depressed person. In what he calls " a classic psychotherapeutic approach," Breggin describes empathy as "the central process of helping people," adding that it can come not just from the therapist but also from a spiritual counselor, a coach, a parent, a friend.

A primary mission of this empathic approach is to help a depressed person understand himself or herself as a child. "The key to not being depressed is to be empathic to what we suffered as kids. If you can be in touch with your own suffering, then you can be caring to yourself as an adult and to others."

Gratitude. Book Review of *The Heart of Being Helpful* on Amazon.com by "A Customer," July 10, 1997.

There is a humility in Dr. Breggin's writing that is rare. We discover the reason for this in his chapter on gratitude. Being able to help others is a gift—whether it is one that is innate or one that we have learned—and we can only be grateful for such a gift. When a client can sense that we are grateful for having the opportunity to help them, it breaks down further the barrier created by our "professional" aura, leaving room for our empathetic, healing presence.

Is love enough? No, of course not. Therapists need training, information, skills and wisdom. But without empathy and love to underscore our other professional resources there will be no healing or spiritual growth.

Plunged into Self-Assessment. Book Review of *The Heart of Being Helpful (*1997) on Amazon.com by A. Chaney, based on his review in *Contemporary Psychology,* APA Review of Books, 2006.

Several of the book's essays–for that is what each chapter offers—plunged me into reassessment and a soul searching of my own practice. Am I creating and fostering a "healing presence" with each client? Am I respectful and sensitive to my own vulnerabilities so that I can sense and respect the vulnerabilities of my clients? Do I falsely allow my clients to think that I am adequate to every challenge I face and thus disempower them to become more adequate when facing their own challenges? Do I really understand the sine qua non of empathy? And, yes, am I too quick to discuss and recommend pharmacotherapy and leave it at that? Twenty-five years as a practitioner enhances rather than diminishes the need for periodic self-evaluation. The essays in this book are a fine catalyst for doing so.

I see two audiences benefiting from this brief but meaty book. One is salty, chronologically gifted practitioners like myself, with many years and clients behind us and hopefully many more ahead, who can profit from the periodic review of the basics and the frequent self-evaluation we were trained to conduct. The essays in this book facilitate that. The second audience is therapists-in-training, those who may not have read *On Becoming a Person* by Rogers (1961). For that reason, I've ordered a copy of this book and sent it to my daughter, a graduate student in clinical community counseling at Johns Hopkins, where Breggin once taught.

The "Breggin Principles"

by Douglas Smith, MD

Many aspects of Peter Breggin's work and thinking over the years have been courageous and independent, and worth describing. There are two that I want to highlight. The first is what I call the "Breggin Principle," namely, that "all biopsychiatric treatments have a common mode of action: the disruption of normal brain function." The second is what he calls the process of "empathic transformation." Dr. Breggin has published and spoken about many noteworthy ideas, but these are the two that stand out in my mind as having been most helpful and influential to me.

The Breggin Principle is actually the first principle listed in both the first and second editions of Breggin's book *Brain Disabling Treatments in Psychiatry* (2008, p. 2). It is as pithy as it is profound. And it is true. Or at least, I know of no data to contradict it. It is seen most obviously as true in the example of frontal lobotomy – the treatment that Breggin was a pioneer in opposing. No one would dispute that lobotomy "works" by disrupting normal brain functioning.

No one would ever claim that lobotomy corrects or normalizes or improves brain functioning. Breggin had the clarity of thinking and insight to see that the same is true of all biopsychiatric treatments, including medications – antidepressants, antipsychotics, anxiolytics, and mood stabilizers. This had never occurred to me until I read it from Breggin. But it makes perfect sense, and it makes all the otherwise confusing and contradictory data from psychiatric research make sense and fall into place.

Pharmaceutical marketing states that psychiatric drugs work by correcting something in the brain. Usually some sort of chemical imbalance is supposed, although I remember being taught in medical school that some medicines may work by stabilizing cell membranes, and more recently theories about axonal growth, or prevention of cell death, and many other theories have emerged. But pharmaceutical marketing is just that; marketing. It is not fact. Psychiatric researchers are actually much more honest in admitting that we really don't know how medications work. For that matter, we don't really know the causes of mental illnesses, at least not in biological terms. Therefore, it would be impossible at this point for us to identify any ways in which medications correct or normalize brain functioning.

The genius of the Breggin Principle is that it recognizes that there is no basis for distinguishing between an effect and a side effect. The only difference is whether the effect is considered desirable.

There is also plenty of evidence out there that medications disrupt normal brain functioning. This is referred to as "side effects." The genius of the Breggin Principle is that it recognizes that there is no basis for distinguishing between an effect and a side effect. The only difference is whether the effect is considered desirable. A lobotomy or a stiff drink of alcohol can cause many effects, some of which may be considered desirable. But all effects of biopsychiatric treatments, desirable or not, are brought about by the disruption of normal brain functioning.

This viewpoint fits the data perfectly, but it is not good for marketing. Therefore, with the psychiatric industry being dominated by pharmaceutical profits the way it is, there is little research into the actual mechanism of action of psychiatric drugs. Occasionally a researcher will dare to draw inferences along the line of the Breggin principle, but it is not frequent. It is startling, in fact, how little curiosity or research there is into what the actual effects of medications are. What do antidepressants actually do to relieve depression? Do they energize? Do they bring about more positive thinking (at the expense of reality)? Do they block empathy so that relational problems aren't as upsetting? It is well established in the literature that antidepressants can cause syndromes of apathy and indifference and frontal lobe-like syndromes, but little is said about how these effects differ, if at all, from the "antidepressant" effects. It is an alarming issue because it leads to questions about the price we pay as a society and as individuals for such "antidepressant" impairment.

> Breggin observes that patients often have severe functional impairments from antidepressant medications without being aware of it....This is a spellbinding in which patients have sometimes-gross impairments without any awareness of it, or even thinking they are functioning at an improved level.

In the second edition of *Brain-Disabling Treatments in Psychiatry* (2008), Breggin has recently expanded on his first brain disabling principle with the concept of "spellbinding"—a wonderful everyday term for "intoxication anosognosia." He observes that patients often have severe functional impairments from antidepressant medications without being aware of it. This is different from the "side effects" which patients are aware of and complain of. This is a spellbinding in which patients have sometimes gross impairments without any awareness of it, or even thinking they are functioning at an improved level. This concept also fits the clinical experience I have quite regularly in my office. Family members sometimes call me asking me to try to talk their loved one into reducing or stopping their medicines because they are "zonked out" by it, or have become a "different person" who is difficult to get along with, but that person is oblivious to what the family members observe. The cases I have seen where a full-blown frontal lobe syndrome developed from antidepressants all occurred without the patient having any awareness of a problem.

> Breggin takes the issue beyond the usual risk-benefit analyses, and looks at the fact that these drugs cause impairments in brain functioning, not improvement.

I think when we read the news today and see an epidemic of violence and suicide precipitated by people on antidepressants, we have to take seriously the concept of spellbinding. The FDA now is warning us about the risk of suicide in children and teenagers who take antidepressants. Not only is the risk present, but it arises without the patient being aware of what is going on, or having the presence of mind to think that the antidepressant might be causing the problem. That is why there is such an urgent need for us to warn our patients and their families.

I cannot overemphasize the uniqueness and importance of the Breggin Principle. Many researchers and authors have addressed the fact that psychiatric medications have low efficacy and high rates of "side effects." Those are important issues, but in a way they miss the point. Even if psychiatric drugs were 100% "effective" and had no side effects, we would still need to ask the question "what are these medications actually doing?" Breggin takes the issue beyond the usual risk-benefit analyses, and looks at the fact that these drugs cause impairments in brain functioning, not improvement.

By not being influenced by profit motives and pharmaceutical company manipulation, Breggin has been able to see larger issues and principles of drug action. In other words, the psychiatric industry may come to recognize adverse effects of medications, but for marketing purposes they portray them as isolated events related only to particular medications. Breggin is able to look across all the data and see general principles that psychiatric drugs follow in every person who takes them–differing only in degree and quality. Another example of this would be the issue of medication withdrawal as outlined in the book *Your Drug May Be Your Problem* (co-authored by David Cohen) (2007). Psychiatry recognizes withdrawal states but prefers to call them something else ("discontinuation syndromes") and to portray them as isolated events associated with only certain medications. Breggin recognizes that all psychoactive substances have their effects, at least in part, through neuroadaptation. Once the drug is removed, the brain has to "unadapt" back to normal. That creates a withdrawal state. This is true as a general principle and is evident in all psychoactive substances in varying degrees and qualities.

The second of Breggin's principles that I want to highlight is the principle of self-transformation. It is defined in his book *The Heart of Being Helpful: Empathy and the Creation of a Healing Presence* (1997, p. 5) as follows:

"To create healing presence, we fine-tune our inner experience to the inner state of the other person. We transform ourselves in response to the basic needs of the person we are trying to heal and to help. Ultimately, we find within ourselves the psychological and spiritual resources required to nourish and to empower the other human being."

I recently had an experience with a patient in which all our discussions quickly degenerated into arguments. I felt like my words were constantly distorted by the patient, and I found myself wanting to defend and explain my intentions. I felt annoyed with this patient and had an impulse to give up on treatment and send the patient away. But in a quieter moment of reflection, I took a different view of this patient. I became aware that her attacks on me were defensive in nature – she perceived herself to be attacked by me. She had a remarkable ability to hear my most benign comments as some sort of attack or criticism. I began to realize how terrified this patient was of being attacked, and how vulnerable she felt to it. She also had a profound fear that she was a total failure, and that therapy would not only be a process of pointing out her failures, but that she would fail at it. She thought my comments were aimed at revealing her as a failure. She defended against these thoughts and feelings by arguing with me and pointing out my failures.

> An aspect of Breggin's concept of empathic transformation that I think is extremely important is that it does not infantilize the patient.

Once I began to see what was happening, it was not too difficult for me to make an empathic transformation and begin responding to her differently and more helpfully. I believe this is an example of an empathic self-transformation where at least the initial change that needed to take place between me and the patient was a change inside of me – my way of looking at and understanding what was happening. Once I was able to make this transformation, growth and healing became possible for the patient. This is an important point that often gets lost in the practice of modern psychiatry. The psychiatric model sees the problem as taking place entirely within the patient, or rather the patient's brain, and the only change that needs to be made is in the patient's brain. The only change a psychiatrist is likely to make is in the medication or dose.

An aspect of Breggin's concept of empathic transformation that I think is extremely important is that it does not infantilize the patient. A year ago I retired from Public Health after 24 years of practicing psychiatry in various agency settings, and I am now in private practice. Reflecting on the way Mental Health care is delivered in various settings, I think the biggest impediment to care is the way patients get infantilized. This is not only an aspect of the medical model, but it is an aspect of agency work in general. It is sometimes hard to identify from within because each person in the agency believes he is acting benevolently in the only way possible. And disturbed patients often draw parental responses from us. Breggin outlines a different approach in *The Heart of Being Helpful.* He treats his patients with dignity and respect, as fellow adults. He is not coercive or manipulative. He even gives examples of dealing with crises and with severely disturbed patients. He does "love" his patients, but not with an infantilizing love. He defines love as "joyful awareness." He sees himself as being helpful to his patients as opposed to taking care of them, supervising them, or even necessarily curing them. I think these are critically important distinctions. It is no secret that mental health agencies have extremely poor outcomes, and the outcomes are declining despite all the newer pharmaceuticals. The parental medical model leaves patients disempowered and dependent. In order for that to ever change, agencies and providers would need to undergo a major "empathic transformation." They could learn from Peter Breggin how to become truly helpful.

Douglas Smith, MD
Doug is a psychiatrist in private practice in Juneau, Alaska.

A Moment in Time with Peter Breggin

by Fred Bemak, EdD

I had heard about this psychiatrist, Peter Breggin, who was becoming known in the psychology and counseling world as a bright and articulate advocate for children and a critic of psychiatry. He had been advocating against the psychiatric establishment's abuse of medications and the dehumanization of clients. I was interested to find out more, since Breggin's value system seemed to coincide with my values and professional history as a former Director of a federally funded Upward Bound Program that addressed poverty, race and ethnicity, families, and education; former Director of a national pilot community-based treatment program for highly disturbed adolescents; and former Clinical Director of a National Institute of Mental Health–funded consortium based at a medical school providing extensive consultation and training in community mental health. It was clear from my experience that not many psychiatrists were speaking out, and Breggin was certainly a refreshing anomaly. Who was this Harvard educated psychiatrist who had stepped out of the pack and was challenging the mental health field about their medical practices, degradation of people under the guise of mental health treatment, and the link between big business corporate monopolies and the promotion of psychotropic medication?

All of this was particularly interesting to me since I was then employed in one of the bastions of medicine and psychiatry, The Johns Hopkins University. At that point in my career I was the Chair of the Department of Counseling and Human Development at Johns Hopkins University, which was housed in Education. I had developed linkages with some of the more progressive and humanistic faculty in the Psychiatry Department in the School of Medicine and in the School of Public Health. My entire career, including the experiences mentioned above, had been devoted to working with youth and families identified as being at high levels of risk, with a focus on cross-cultural mental health and poverty. Added to my interest about Peter Breggin's work was my long-standing attention to Szasz's work, and the vacuum in leadership by anyone from psychiatry to carry the torch challenging the medical model establishment practices. So I was quite interested in finding out more about this guy, Peter Breggin.

Hearing about Breggin's work, I decided to contact him and determine whether or not he might be a viable adjunct faculty member to teach an elective class in my Department. I remember initially contacting Peter by phone to discuss his work and interests. That call did it! Peter and I hit it off by phone, had an incredibly vibrant and energetic conversation, and agreed to meet. Quite remarkably, it was an immediate profound connection.

As I grew to know Peter I realized that these were interesting times for him. As our friendship grew, I learned about Peter's struggles. The pharmaceutical companies were defending themselves by targeting Peter's personhood, his professional career, his medical license, his character, and his integrity. During those years Peter didn't have the standing or backing he has nowadays and hadn't cultivated a solid support base. Consequently he was vulnerable to losing everything. This was deeply affecting Peter, leaving him distrustful of others, skeptical of motivations and the deviousness of the drug companies, and highly anxious about what might happen. Through this maze of aggressive and vicious attacks on Peter we forged a close and vital friendship. Over time Peter shared with me his alienation, loneliness, and concern about what was happening to him personally and professionally.

It was during this time that I found a wonderful friend and person, deeply committed and passionate about his work. Peter was courageous, highly intelligent, and willing to take on the battles that needed to be fought. I began inviting Peter into my classes as a guest lecturer. The students loved him. So we expanded, and I asked Peter to teach courses. The result, Peter Breggin began teaching as an adjunct faculty member in the Department of Counseling and Human Services at Johns Hopkins University. This added to our relationship that now incorporated a deep friendship with professional ties.

Those years were turbulent—Peter was starting to build the International Center, allies were just beginning to more openly come out of the shadows in support of Peter, and an Advisory Board was loosely formed for the Center. The Board would gather in Peter's living room discussing hopes, dreams, and directions for the Center. Along with this excitement was Peter's realization that there was some light in the darkness that had surrounded him through the build up of relentless attacks from the drug companies and psychiatric field. His personal and professional social support network was expanding and it was wonderful to watch Peter begin to walk with more lightness.

> It was a wonderful time for developing a deep friendship and also watching Peter building a growing inertia of strength and energy around his work.

At the center of this whirlwind of professional experience was the increasing social time that Peter and Ginger Breggin and Rita Chi-Ying Chung (my wife) and I spent together. We had dinners, spent time at the beach on weekends, visited each other's homes, and talked about life, work, philosophy, values, relationships, and friendship. It was a wonderful time for developing a deep friendship and also watching Peter build a growing inertia of strength and energy around his work. He was winning some important battles about key issues in mental health and gaining tremendous recognition—his books were being widely distributed and acknowledged, and colleagues were gaining courage to be more outspoken and stand beside Peter. Simultaneously Peter was being invited to speak at well established professional forums about his work (we presented numerous times together on panels with other colleagues that highlighted our mutual ideas about the misuse of medications, culturally inappropriate diagnoses and treatment, challenges to the perpetuation of the medical model, mental health violations against people of color, etc.) and receiving increasingly positive coverage by the national media. All of these led to great successes in the national forum and Peter was on the upswing.

It was wonderful to watch the evolution from the darkest days to buoyancy, lightness, energy, and vibrancy for Peter. He came back to himself with renewed energy and commitment, he had many supporters and people who would help in carrying his work forward, and most importantly, he was no longer alone or as alienated on the journey. Peter is a great colleague and friend, and it is outstanding that the International Center for the Study of Psychiatry and Psychology is doing this wonderful book for him.

Fred Bemak, EdD

Fred holds a doctorate in Counseling from the University of Massachusetts. He is currently a Professor and Program Coordinator for the Counseling and Development Program in the Graduate School of Education at George Mason University. He has given seminars and lectures and conducted research in the areas of cross-cultural psychology and at-risk youth. He has worked in over 30 countries and throughout the United States and is a former Fulbright Scholar. He is the author of three books and numerous book chapters and professional journal articles.

In Praise of the Gifts of Dr. Peter Breggin

by Delores Jankovich, MA, MSW

One dismal Sunday morning in December 1999 I was filled with the grief of watching my loved one's mental, physical and spiritual well being literally disappear on his forced drug regimen. With my mind desperate with questions regarding what was happening and what I might do to help I headed for solace at one of the local Barnes & Noble Bookstores. As was my usual practice when I wanted to be distracted or find something of interest, I was wandering from floor to floor when I noted a book titled *Your Drug May Be Your Problem* (Breggin & Cohen, 1999). Curious to see if it might be something that would benefit me, I quickly thumbed through it. Indeed, it was a book I had to have.

Thus began my acquaintance with Dr. Breggin's prolific work that has transformed my life. I went home and read the book that Sunday and phoned Ginger Breggin the next day. Ginger informed me about the work of the International Center for the Study of Psychiatry and Psychology (ICSPP) and gave information regarding people who were helping troubled individuals without the use of damaging drugs.

Since discovering Dr. Breggin's work I have been influenced by many of his books and articles, and have been richly informed and inspired by his presentations at the annual ICSPP conference. I had worked 15 years in institutional settings as a master's level psychologist and decided in 2002 that I needed a terminal professional degree in order to further contribute in the area of social justice and psychosocial work. I had a brief conversation with Dr. Breggin at the 2002 ICSPP conference at Newark when he advised that an MSW might be most helpful. I was then inspired to pursue and complete a master's in social work.

My life has been radically changed by encountering writing that clarified many of the myths in mainstream psychiatry and mental health. I found Dr. Breggin's work to be the doorway to meeting compassionate professionals who are addressing human rights in mental health. These are people who are doing sensitive work that focuses on both the internal and external environment of the individual. I now have support and an arena for learning as I develop my work as someone who focuses on the whole person without the use of psychotropic drugs.

Dr. Breggin's critical mind is coupled with an empathic response when relating to both colleagues and patients. He is my hero. I could not have conceived of continuing work in my field of endeavor without support in addressing people's need for care that addresses their right to self-determination, and the strengths that are inherently present within them. It is not possible to assist people in making life changes when their problems have been reduced to the theoretical presence of a chemical imbalance. Such reductionistic thinking leads to drug-based treatment that renders it impossible for people to access their true thoughts and feelings, thus blurring their identities, and exposing them to the toxicity of dangerous substances.

Through Dr. Breggin's work I have found pride once again in my profession as I meet more people who are respectful of the unique qualities and needs of their patients and who understand the damage done when suffering is addressed with toxic chemicals. I have renewed faith in my own ability to grow in understanding and love, through relationship, and faith in the core of goodness with which I believe people come into this world. Faith to me implies more strength and sustenance than hope, for it gives me the courage to proceed even when the path is uncharted and the suffering may be great.

I will briefly mention a few of Dr. Breggin's books that have been of extensive help to me. *Toxic Psychiatry* (1991) is a resource from which all people who wish to be in charge of their health will benefit. Dr. Breggin shows great courage in exposing the practices of mainstream psychiatry, and the iatrogenic helplessness and brain damage caused in particular by neuroleptics and by antidepressants. It needs to be a standard reference in one's library as it provides the truth about psychiatry, drugs and other damaging treatment such as electroconvulsive shock therapy.

Peter Breggin and Ginger Breggin co-authored *Talking Back to Prozac* (1994), which gives comprehensive warnings about the dangers of taking Prozac, the first SSRI (selective serotonin reuptake inhibitor) that was marketed. This book addresses negative behavioral changes, including violent reactions, related to the use of Prozac. Dr. Breggin authored *The Antidepressant Fact Book* in 2001 in which he discusses SSRIs as well as other antidepressants. For individuals seeking to regain their well-being and freedom from depression, these books assist people in exploring a different attitude toward depression and allowing them informed choice regarding the risks and benefits of antidepressants.

If we are to become successful mentors and parents, we must allow and encourage children to teach us about what is needed in their young lives.

Dr. Breggin's knowledge of antidepressants, in particular the SSRIs, has led to his work as expert witness in trials where the defendant has been apparently influenced by the use of prescription drugs. His courage and resolve restores hope that there is someone willing to step forward to seek justice in dire circumstances. Dr. Breggin addresses the tragic outcome for people changed by these drugs and the people they victimize as a result of this harmful change. In Peter and Ginger Breggin's important book, *The War Against Children of Color (*1998), they make clear our society's attempt through psychiatry to promote social control through medicating those said to be predisposed to violence. Peter and Ginger emphasize the need to intervene to stop any damaging programs and to address the rights and needs of children.

Peter Breggin continues to express loving wisdom in his book, *Reclaiming our Children* (2000). He cites statements from a "think tank" on violence involving youngsters: "Feeling disconnected, unsupported and unloved led to poor communication skills and aggression" (p. 223). Dr. Breggin confronts the need for our young to be engaged with loving, concerned mentors, teachers and parents. I find his work with children to be equally helpful in thinking about the therapeutic needs of adults. Those adults who have been long disconnected from any childhood trauma are blind to childhood injuries that could very well be causing depression or other symptoms in the present.

Dr. Breggin points out that rather than be concerned about the behavior of our children, we need to be concerned about them. It is awareness, respect, empathy and engagement that reaches not only the less troubled but the severely disturbed. He comments that we need to treat our children with the same respect and consideration with which we might treat a revered elder. It is our task to listen to, be with and provide resources for our children. Ultimately if we are to become successful mentors and parents, we must allow and encourage children to teach us about what is needed in their young lives. Indeed, we must ask ourselves how we might best change in order to learn from our children, especially the most troubled.

Our culture has contempt for vulnerability and many of us will do most anything to avoid feeling deeply vulnerable. We must search our souls to ferret out any contempt in our hearts. For it is only then that we may honor others' vulnerability as well as our own. As we embrace our vulnerability we will more clearly know our strengths as well as the strengths of others. We can then pursue healing (change) through relationship.

I thought it timely, as I reread some of Dr. Breggin's writings, that my daily meditation reading contained the following scripture: I John 3:18 "Little children, let us love, not in word or speech, but in truth and action." For compassion without action soon loses its power to impact.

Compassion informs Peter Breggin's work. He asks us to step up to the task of caring for our most vulnerable. We cannot condone destructive or violent acts that are often blamed on mental illness, or in some cases, genetic tendencies. However, we must address the fact that those who cannot speak of what has happened to them sometimes tell their stories through their actions. Dr. Martin Luther King, Jr. noted that once someone has been injured he or she must be responsible for the healing of that injury. Taking responsibility for our own healing then allows us to be responsible for our interactions with others.

Dr. Breggin's work invites us to reclaim the context of our lives. It is through discovering our commonality with others and our mutual connection that we heal. That connection is made more possible through engaging one's mind and feelings with another while in a drug-free state.

I am deeply grateful to Dr. Peter Breggin for showing the way and for the mentoring provided through his work. His gifts continue to provide the critical expertise, learning and courage from which I and untold others benefit.

Though it seems much too simple, I can only offer my deepest thank you for all you do, and all you continue to do, Dr. Breggin!

Delores Jankovich, MA, MSW

Delores lives in Overland Park, Kansas where she is a mental health professional and mother of a son who was harmed by psychiatric diagnosis. She is coeditor of the ICSPP Newsletter *and an active member of the organization.*

Shared Values

by Thomas E. Bratter, PhD

Peter Breggin's work enunciates many principles I have implemented at the John Dewey Academy, a drug-free high school that works with disturbed and destructive teenagers (Bratter 1972, 1977, 2006; Bratter et al., 2006 & 2007; Glaser, 1990). Although we developed our basic theories and practices independently, Breggin's work has helped to clarify and to reinforce my own convictions and efforts.

Breggin was among the first to attack and reject the trend to medicate when he pronounced that taking pills under medical supervision communicates the anti-therapeutic message that "something is wrong with your brain, and you need a potent medication to function as 'normal'."

In *Toxic Psychiatry* (1991), Breggin wrote, "biopsychiatrists typically reject psychological approaches and instead make extraordinary claims for their efficacy" (p. 150). Quite understandably, he received a massive, hostile reaction motivated by economic concerns from the proponents of the "better living through chemistry" club, who viewed Breggin as an enemy who needed to be silenced.

A decade and a half before it became fashionable, again in *Toxic Psychiatry* (1991) Breggin attacked not only the biological theory of depression but also the use of the older antidepressants to treat this "biochemical disease":

> For years the dominant biological theory of depression, ...was derived from speculations on how and why medications sometimes seem to alleviate depression. One of the earlier groups of antidepressants, the monoamine oxidase inhibitors (MAOIs)...tends to increase the levels of available norepinephrine in the central nervous system. So it was hypothesized that depression might result from the opposite—too little norepinephrine. Later studies

> showed that some so-called antidepressants may cause an increase in the availability of another neurotransmitter, serotonin. So the theory was enlarged: some forms of depression may be due to too little serotonin as well....
>
> Eventually the theory was punched full of holes by contradictory evidence. For example, some drugs that mimicked these biochemical effects did not seem to alleviate depression, and others that are thought to sometimes relieve depression have a wholly different biochemical mechanism. Furthermore, the supposed efficacy of the antidepressants...is much in doubt (pp. 141-142).

Biological psychiatry assumes mental illness is caused by a chemical imbalance in the brain. Pharmacological solutions create the comforting illusion that deviance can be controlled easily and cheaply by pills.

Breggin excoriates pharmacologic researchers and the FDA for uncritically accepting self-serving and flawed studies financed by pharmaceutical corporations for their economic benefit. Breggin (1991) debunked assertions and justifications for medication with observations that have gained increasing validity in the past fifteen years:

> In...psychiatry, claims can become truth, hopes can become achievements, and propaganda is taken as science. Nowhere is this more obvious than in psychiatric pretensions concerning the genetics, biology, and physical treatment of depression and mania...biopsychiatric research is based too often on distortions, incomplete information, and sometimes outright fraud--at the expense of reason and science.
>
> There are no known biological causes of depression... There is no known genetic link in depression. There is no sound drug treatment for depression... The biomythology of depression denies the obvious causes of depression (pp. 182-183).

Breggin was among the first to contend the myth of a biochemical disorder is precisely that--a malicious myth. Frighteningly, his second contention—that the only chemical disorder is the ingestion of psychotropic poisons that cause imbalances—has been ignored until recently.

Refusing to be silenced and often in the forefront of the fray, Breggin (2005) continued to confront the FDA when he criticized the agency for refusing to heed warnings of the increased harm posed by the SSRI antidepressants. He had exposed these risks more than a decade earlier.

Breggin continued to confront the FDA when he criticized the agency for refusing to heed warnings of the increased harm posed by the SSRI antidepressants. He had exposed these risks more than a decade earlier.

Finally, confirming conclusions that Breggin had documented since 1991, in 2003 the British equivalent of the Food and Drug Administration, the Medicines and Healthcare Products Regulatory Agency, notified the medical community to cease prescribing most SSRI antidepressants for the treatment of depression in children due to a combination of lack of efficacy and an increased risk of suicidality.

A year earlier, Connor (2004) commented, "The FDA released a statement regarding...Paxil for pediatric depression...[There] is a statement...that three well-controlled trials in pediatric patients with major depressive disorder failed to show that... Paxil was more effective than placebo. As far as I know these studies never have been published"(p. 127). Brent (2004) observed that the "problem is exacerbated when studies are financed and directed by the pharmaceutical industry when there is a great disincentive to publish negative results...The FDA should require that these data be made public in a timely manner" (p. 127).

Whittington et al. (2004) warned that children and adolescents are at-risk to attempt suicide: "The possibility that a drug might increase that risk without clear evidence of benefit, should in our view discourage its use...A possible increased risk of suicidal ideation, serious adverse events, or both, although small, cannot be ignored (p. 1344).

As Breggin often has noted, a quid pro quo exists: If researchers want to receive funding, research needs to justify dispensing medication. Psychiatric journals, subsidized by advertising from Big Pharma, know survival depends on this money. An editorial in *The Lancet* (2004), a respected and trusted British medical journal, concluded that research regarding selective serotonin reuptake inhibitor use "in childhood depression is one of confusion, manipulation, and institutional failure. Although published evidence was inconsistent...use of SSRIs to treat childhood depression by pharmaceutical companies and clinicians world-wide continues" (p. 1335).

Breggin has concluded that, while causing suicidality, the drugs do nothing to prevent it. There can be no justification for the federal policy to pander to the corporations. Connor (2004) protested, "How can we practice in the best interests of child and adolescent patients if negative trial data are withheld from the scientific journals and only positive studies are published?" (p. 127).

The John Dewey Academy

The John Dewey Academy is based on the same guiding principles as Peter Breggin's critique of biological psychiatry, i.e. drugs do more harm than good, and individuals need to learn to determine the course of their lives in more ethical and self-fulfilling ways.

The mental health establishment has refused to support the John Dewey Academy but, significantly, psychiatrists often send their sons and daughters; at any time, more than ten percent of the Dewey population has at least one parent who is a psychotherapist.

William Glasser (1990) observed that one of my revolutionary passions for starting The John Dewey Academy was to demonstrate to mental health professionals that when adolescents with self-destructive behavior are treated in a setting that demands their best, they can transcend their previously nihilistic behavior and achieve greatness.

Adolescents who attend The John Dewey Academy have engaged in self-destructive, stupid, immature, irresponsible, and sadistic behavior. They have toxic attitudes of entitlement and reduce others to objects to satisfy narcissistic needs. Medication cannot change attitudes, which is why the recidivism rate of medicated teens remains high. The presenting psychological problem, reduced to its lowest common dominator, is that prior to attending John Dewey students developed negative, self-destructive, and often antisocial attitudes.

The John Dewey Academy is a voluntary, residential, college preparatory and therapeutic high school for gifted, angry, self-destructive adolescents. Bratter, Bratter, Coiner, Kaufman, & Steiner (2006) noted that many students were drug-dependent and arrived dually diagnosed, most with bipolar and/or depressive disorders. A third have been hospitalized for at least two months. More than three quarters have been treated by psychiatrists. Approximately two-thirds arrived addicted to, or unable to withdraw from, potent psychotropics such as stimulants, benzodiazepines, SSRI antidepressants,, monoamine oxidase inhibitors, and tricyclic antidepressants.

More than two thirds have medicated themselves to relieve painful feelings of failure, rejection, and fear. Sadly, at the beginning of the third millennium, experimentation with psychoactive substances remains the "rite" of initiation into adolescence.

Prior to attending John Dewey, many students were promiscuous to neutralize loneliness. One-fifth considered or made suicidal attempts. Some have stolen cars, computers, and credit cards. Several have eating and sleeping disorders. After creating constant crises by performing dangerous and self-destructive acts, these acting-out adolescents need a structured, safe, and supportive residential treatment environment to help them control and curtail dysfunctional behavior. By any objective criteria, students who attend John Dewey were psychiatric casualties plagued by poor and dangerous decision-making.

Compassionate Confrontation: Rebutting the Critics

Psychopharmacologic and biopsychiatric claims that intrapsychic problems are caused by metabolic disorders, genetic imbalances, and cellular deficiencies are refuted by The John Dewey Academy. Feelings of depression, pain, shame, inadequacy, and fear that overwhelm adolescents are caused by conscious dysfunctional, dishonest, destructive, and dangerous decisions, not by biological aberrations. When asked why they feel depressed or ashamed, students provide realistic explanations. The John Dewey Academy asserts that personality and affective disorders are rarely cured by medicinal approaches; no pill can teach self-respect or cure noxious narcissism, dishonesty, and anti-social attitudes. No psychotropic medication, therefore, is prescribed at John Dewey. Becoming free of psychiatric drugs is a viable treatment goal.

The goal of treatment at Dewey is to force students to become more rational and responsible. The intent is to penetrate barriers of self-absorption, denial and deceit. When viewed from a humanistic and realistic perspective, contrary to what critics contend is cruel, confrontation demands the best rather than conceding that the individual cannot change. Personal choice is stressed, which negates the anti-therapeutic concepts of mental illness and un/pre/subconscious etiology. The expectation that adolescents become responsible and honest is intense.

When the intent of confrontation is positive and sincere, I submit that "attack therapy" becomes tangible proof of love and concern—i.e., to demand that the person terminate self-destructive, sadistic acts and improve.

The treatment orientation is existential-humanistic and confrontational. Students are forced not only to accept accountability for dysfunctional attitudes and acts but also to improve in a stressful, unrelenting, and uncompromising environment that demands educational excellence and personal integrity. New students experience shock at being expected not only to take control of their lives but also to accept responsibility for personal acts and attitudes. Students remain persons and perpetrators, not patients and victims.

At Dewey, there is a concerted effort to nurture the psychological, moral, and spiritual growth of students by creating conditions conducive to gaining or rehabilitating self-respect and integrity. Students are encouraged to establish positive personal identities while concurrently learning how to form mature interpersonal relationships. Bratter (1972, 2003, 2006; Bratter et al., 1995, 2000, 2006, 2007) have described a group process in which peers confront each other's destructive attitudes and acts by relating to their experiences and providing advice on how to change, which provides catalytic conditions for self-exploration and growth. The group demands that members accept responsibility for failures and helps to resolve intrapsychic and interpersonal problems. Positive peer pressure is the primary psychotherapeutic approach, which stresses empowerment. Gifted, creative, alienated, and angry adolescents respond positively to a confrontational, cognitive, and existential therapeutic orientation with high expectations for improved behavior stressing self-respect, integrity, and human dignity that Bratter (1997) has described.

Defining a goal of treatment, Breggin (1997) wrote:

> Humanistic and existential psychologists have sought to find one...guiding impulse of...life. They have called it self-realization, self-actualization, and individualism. If there is such a...principle, we could...call it love--love for ourselves, for others, and for life...There are...ways to list...basic needs. There are needs for love and esteem; for emotional safety and security; for relief from...painful emotions such as guilt, shame, and anxiety; for autonomy and independence; for recognition of one's identity, individuality...for authenticity...sincerity or honesty in our relationships; for the exercise of... cognitive, creative, and spiritual capacities; for the performance of useful and worthwhile activities; for purpose in our lives; for knowledge of our place in the past, present, and...future of our family, culture, and planet; for meaning beyond ourselves...The need for esteem, love, or identity cannot be separated from the people who promote or injure our esteem, who share or reject our love, who enhance or threaten our identity (pp. 31-33).

Empowering Persons-in-Treatment

In many books and articles, Breggin has pointed out that the biopsychiatric approach reinforces the patient's worst feelings about himself that he is helpless and at the mercy of forces beyond his or her control. According to Breggin, the patient often feels "defective" before arriving in the psychiatrist's office. The psychiatrist reinforces the patient's helpless feelings and sense of being defective by insisting that he has a biochemical imbalance—and that he needs to be controlled by additionalforces beyond his control, psychiatric drugs.

In *The Heart of Being Helpful,* Breggin discusses the roles of empathy and love in the psychotherapeutic process. To love and be loved, Breggin (1997) contends, "is...to feel empowered—to feel in control of one's ...spiritual state" (p. 78). Breggin urged that psychotherapy attempt to empower those who seek help to become persons who "are active forces in their...lives." Rightfully, Breggin (1997) suggested that the sense of helplessness needs to be resolved:

> Behind emotional psychological helplessness lies a subjective judgment about our...capacity to handle ourselves and our lives...As a healing person, nothing is more crucial than encouraging people to overcome...feelings of helplessness. Helplessness reflects a judgment...that nothing can be done...The alternative to helplessness is a feeling of self determination and mastery, the sense of taking control over one's...feelings and thoughts, and giving direction to one's life (pp. 72-73).
>
> What makes "giving up" or quitting so debilitating is "when a feeling of helplessness... increases, because the individual may lose control in reaction to a seemingly slight frustration" (p. 73).
>
> In philosophical terms, they have autonomy and are capable of self-determination...Because human beings must exercise free will...to survive and to prosper, they need...personal freedom...Approaches to deeply disturbed human beings should...respect their autonomy, independence and freedom...Empowerment involves self-understanding, moral encouragement through a caring relationship, and guidance toward...autonomous and loving principles of life...Deeply disturbed people should be viewed as...struggling to survive and to grow--as persons in conflict with themselves and with [others]. Healing comes through a combination of self-development and beneficial relationships (pp. 2-3, 7).

Breggin (1991) correctly identified this therapeutic challenge when he proposed that each person needs to "choose whether or not to overcome any hardship or oppression inflicted by the family, society, or psychiatry. Human beings retain...free will...Indeed, without the exercise of that flickering will, there is no hope. That is the helper's role, to encourage every hint of self-determination" (p. 45).

Teenagers suffer from what Breggin (1991) has labeled a psychospiritual crisis, usually surrounding issues of basic identity, shame, and, typically, overwhelming feelings of outrage:

> By refusing to diagnose or to label people who...feel rejected and humiliated, we welcome them back to the human community and promote humane, respectful, and loving attitudes toward them" (pp. 45-46).

At The John Dewey Academy, a restoration of hope must occur before adolescents contemplate investing in themselves and in changing their behaviors. These teens know that their decisions have jeopardized, at the very least, future educational, professional, and social options; they feel demoralized and are mired in self-pity, so they lack the incentive to try to improve themselves.

Advocacy at The John Dewey Academy

Underneath students' thin layers of anger exists a profound depression--indeed, demoralization. Self-mutilators can wear long sleeves to conceal self-imposed scars, but those who have under-achieved academically or have been incarcerated are not so lucky. They have records which, if found, not only imprison them in mediocrity but also bar them from upward mobility. Stated simply, these individuals lack credibility, so they are powerless to plead their cases to convince anyone--including colleges of quality, which literally can fill classes with those who have all "As" and come close to having perfect SAT scores--to give them a chance they do not deserve. Dewey students, therefore, are not competitive academically or, for that matter, in any other area, so they need an aggressive advocate to help them leave the figurative sewer in which they have imprisoned themselves.

If so inclined, the psychotherapist possesses the credibility and expertise to know how to navigate the treacherous waters of immature, impulsive, illicit, and sadistic behavior. Unless the therapist becomes an advocate, there is little incentive for the individual to contemplate constructive and creative change; the odds against upward mobility are minuscule.

Agreeing to serve as an advocate transforms the treatment relationship from merely defining, setting, and enforcing limits, which the person-in-treatment sometimes experiences as intrusive and hostile, into a positive alliance.

Agreeing to serve as an advocate transforms the treatment relationship from merely defining, setting, and enforcing limits, which the person-in-treatment sometimes experiences as intrusive and hostile, into a positive alliance. The therapist is thrust into the role of a consultant who can advise the individual how to extricate him/herself from the negative self-fulfilling labyrinth where failure begets failure, rejection begets rejection, and dishonesty begets mistrust. Few psychotherapists and treatment programs either know how or agree to assume this advocate role, which explains the high rates of recidivism. In many publications, I have discussed the relationship between potent and positive therapeutic advocacy and the incentive to improve by working diligently.

Advocacy includes making phone calls, writing letters, visiting facilities, attending conferences, and contacting influential persons who can maximize the chances that the person-in-treatment will receive preferential consideration. It needs to be emphasized that, since this is a time-consuming activity, I refuse to make this investment until the person has convinced me that changes not only are real but also permanent. Before agreeing to play this instrumental role, I demand that the person agree to abstain from all psychoactive substances for the duration of college. I have rescinded recommendations when adolescents do not continue to improve or make reasonable commitments to maximize their chances of success.

When the intent is to demand respectful, responsible, and productive change, confrontation becomes the ultimate expression of what Breggin terms "empathetic love;" the confronted feels the confronter's concern that refuses to accept anything less than the best.

These young people exist in the existential present and do not contemplate the payoffs and consequences of attitudes and acts, so they need a more extreme treatment approach. I label this approach to be compassionate confrontation that shatters denial, distortion, and destructive attitudes. The John Dewey Academy refuses to apologize for being unrelenting and uncompromising by constantly escalating its expectations. Critics, who do not appreciate the extent of the destructive and dangerous behavior of Dewey students, view this treatment process to be punitive.

These critics are right, but for the wrong reasons: Unless students discontinue malignant attitudes and acts, they will be consumed by destructive behaviors that produce severe consequences such as hospitalization, incarceration, and/or premature death. Undeniably, confrontational psychotherapy is painful: It forces students to recognize masochistic and sadistic behavior. This prevents minimization, glorification of behavior, and passivity. When viewed from this humanistic perspective, confrontation becomes a caring act by the therapist, who intervenes to convince the adolescent to become more responsible, responsive, and respectful.

All treatment modalities can abuse power and trust. It would be dishonest, indeed, to suggest that confrontational psychotherapy, when the intent of the confronter is to humiliate, hurt, and intimidate, is not an abuse of power. When the intent is to demand respectful, responsible, and productive change, however, confrontation becomes the ultimate expression of what Breggin terms "empathetic love;" the confronted feels the confronter's concern that refuses to accept anything less than the best. While perhaps frustrating, the message, "You can do much better" is indeed therapeutic and is prima facie evidence of genuine care.

The Bottom Line

Before attending The John Dewey Academy, most students had mediocre grades and inconsistent academic records. Many function more than one grade level below their age, so they need intensive, individualized instruction to remedy educational deficits.

Compassionate confrontation both obliterates defenses and stimulates growth and improvement. Prior to stumbling into John Dewey, these adolescents were untreatable, uneducable, unreliable, unmanageable, unruly, uncivilized, untrustworthy, unlovable, unworthy, unwanted, undisciplined, unfaithful, unpredictable, unhappy, unlawful, unstable, and unsuccessful. They were not unmotivated, but rather unconvinced.

While controversial and, at times, painful, compassionate confrontation is effective. Traditional treatment and teaching techniques fail to penetrate defensive barriers, which renders these approaches ineffectual for troubled, talented, and troublesome teens who, until convinced that a decision makes sense, will not invest time or energy and remain alienated and resistant.

Since the first class graduated in 1987, all John Dewey graduates have attended college. Similar to elite prep schools, The John Dewey Academy wants to be judged by the reputations of the colleges that admit its graduates. Seventy percent attend the most selective fifty colleges. A third have made the Dean's List at top colleges.

The John Dewey Academy class of 2007 will send students to Brown University (2), Colby College, Columbia University, Mount Holyoke College (2), Skidmore College (2), St. John's College (MD), and Vassar College. One student was wait-listed by Harvard pending assurance he would attend if admitted. Dewey students were admitted but declined to attend Columbia College (2), Davidson College, Georgetown and Northwestern Universities, Duke, Johns Hopkins, Chicago, Edinburgh, Vassar (2) and Williams College (2).

The academic achievements of Dewey graduates make this Academy indistinguishable from the most elite and prestigious prep schools in America.

Breggin's Mission

Breggin has been called a "hero" by Masson (1984), the former director of the Sigmund Freud Archives who was excommunicated by the American Psychoanalytic Association when he committed heresy by repudiating Freud's sacrosanct Oedipal Complex. Masson opined that Freud, like the psychiatric establishment, had betrayed children. Freud withdrew from his initial discovery that adult psychological disturbances often resulted from child abuse. Instead, he defended the adult establishment by promulgating the myth that children lusted after adults and then imagined these abuses.

In many books and articles culminating in *Brain-Disabling Treatments in Psychiatry: Drugs, Electroshock and the Psychopharmaceutical Complex* (2008), Breggin continues his noble crusade by exposing another form of child abuse—the scandal of treating ADHD with stimulant drugs. He is a modern day David who slays Goliath with research as his weapon. Breggin no longer seems quixotic in his titanic struggle to educate the public; many organizations and research scientists have joined his crusade.

Peter Breggin is right! I know! We fought similar wars at different times to expose the conspiratorial fraud that medicine is the panacea for affective and behavior disorders.

If the American Psychiatric Association believes in the Hippocratic oath to "do no harm," then Breggin needs to be elevated at the very least to "hero" status—if not sainthood—for his efforts to protect the public from what he aptly calls "toxic psychiatry."

Peter Breggin is right! I know! We fought similar wars at different times to expose the conspiratorial fraud that medicine is the panacea for affective and behavior disorders. Breggin documented pharmaceutical frauds by using the mass media, attacking flaws in research design, exposing deliberate distortions of the data, and demystifying unproven assumptions by proving them contradictory or, in many cases, wrong. In so doing, he attacks from the front. Breggin has fought to protect innocent consumers who have been physically damaged by the prescription of psychotropic poison. Rather than receiving the Nobel Peace Prize for "courageous and significant work," he has been condemned by powerful pharmaceutical corporations. Fortunately, efforts to dismiss, discredit, and vilify Breggin have failed. In fact, much of what he has discovered is being validated. By changing the labels for a variety of drugs, including SSRIs, even the corrupt and ineffectual FDA begrudgingly concedes that Breggin is right in many of his conclusions and that the manufacturers of psychotropic poisons have been wrong; many of their self-serving conclusions are without merit.

> Breggin has fought to protect innocent consumers who have been physically damaged by the prescription of psychotropic poison.

Breggin and I agree that Big Pharma is an awesome adversary. My impact is more limited than Breggin's: For almost half a century, I have worked with talented, troubled, troublesome, and tortured teens and have challenged the FDA methadone maintenance program hoax where one narcotic is simply replaced with another. Breggin has attacked most psychotropics to be harmful and fought this meritorious war in his publications and in the court room.

My mission has been to justify my existence to myself. I had a choice: To play it safe and walk the path traveled by most, or to assert myself, to do it the way I believe to be right. Like Peter, I chose the latter.

This article has been fun to write because it has given me an incentive to reread Breggin's works. I admit I like being linked with him. He is my mentor and peer. I appreciate the opportunity to write about Breggin, especially since we share many beliefs and because I have had the privilege to successfully implement our shared ideas with a most difficult population that has remained immune to traditional therapeutic techniques.

References

Bratter, T.E. (1972). Group therapy with affluent, alienated, adolescent drug abusers. *Psychotherapy: Theory, Research, & Practice,* 9, 308-313.

Bratter, T.E. (1977). The psychotherapist as advocate: Extending the therapeutic relationship with adolescents. *Journal of Contemporary Psychotherapy,* 8, 119-127.

Bratter, T.E. (1983). Games mental institutions play: Iatrogenic disturbances caused by oppression and repression. *International Journal of Therapeutic Communities,* 4, 57-66.

Bratter, T.E. (2006). Advocacy: Its impact on the treatment alliance with gifted, angry, self-destructive, and drug-dependent adolescents. In Flathery, L.T. (Ed.) *Annals of Adolescent Psychiatry,* 30, 85-100.

Bratter, T.E., Bratter, C.J., Coiner, N.L., Kaufman, D.S., & Steiner, K.M. (2006). Motivating gifted, defiant, and un-convinced students to succeed at The John Dewey Academy. *Ethical Human Psychology and Psychiatry: An International Journal of Critical Inquiry,* 8, 7-16.

Bratter, T.E., Kaufman, D.S., Lubbock, F., & Sinsheimer, L. (2007). Confrontation—A potent psychotherapeutic approach with difficult adolescents. In Flathery, L.T. (Ed.) *Annals of Adolescent Psychiatry,* 30, 103-115.

Brent, D.A. (2004). Dr. Brent replies. *Journal of the American Academy of Child & Adolescent Psychiatry,* 43, 127-128.

Connor, D.E. (2004). Paroxetine and the FDA. *Journal of the American Academy of Child & Adolescent Psychiatry,* 43, 127.

Editorial (2004). Depressing research. *The Lancet,* 369, 1355.

Eli Lilly & Company (1971). Prozac Product Information Leaflet. Indianapolis. 1-4.

Glasser, W. (1990). The John Dewey Academy: A residential, college preparatory, therapeutic high school: A dialogue with Tom Bratter. *Journal of Counseling & Development,* 68, 582-585.

Masson, J.M. (1984). *The assault on truth: Freud's suppression of the seduction theory.* New York: Farrar, Strauss and Giroux.

Whittington, C.J., Kendall, T., Fonagy, P., Cottrell, D., Citgrove, A., & Boddington, E. (2004). Selective serotonin reuptake inhibitors in childhood depression: Systematic review of published versus unpublished data. *Lancet,* 369, 1341-1345.

Thomas Edward Bratter, PhD

Tom is President of The John Dewey Academy in Great Barrington, Massachusetts and the author of many studies of how to help gifted, rebellious youngsters with confrontational psychotherapy in a residential setting. He emphasizes the importance of community values within the school, and caring psychotherapy that demands responsibility and self-discipline on the client's part. The success of his school is demonstrated by its ability to turn self-defeating, failing students into socially and academically successful students.

Pre-Publication Endorsements for Peter Breggin's Next Book: *Wow, I'm an American!*

Most recently, Peter Breggin has been exploring the relationship between the traditional values of the American Founders and living a good life in the twenty-first century. With a fresh eye he has identified historical perspectives and skills that enable modern individuals to more fully and richly live well and prosper.

Psychological insights of individual behavior coupled with an examination of the core principles and beliefs of America's Founders and their families offer cogent guidance for individuals and families.

Early indorsements follow:

Admiration for Breggin's Insights. Barry Strauss, PhD, the author of *The Spartacus War* and Professor of History and Classics, Cornell University.

As a historian, I admire Peter Breggin's insight into the American past. As a parent, I am grateful for his wisdom about how to communicate with children. *Wow, I'm an American!* teaches a lesson that is as old as the Greeks and as astute as the Constitution: education in freedom and responsibility is the bedrock of a republic. If you want one book that explains for the whole family what America is all about, look no further.

A Fresh Approach to American History. William Glasser, MD, a psychiatrist and author of *Reality Therapy* and *Choice Theory*, Los Angeles, California.

Takes a fresh new approach to American history that will give you a deeper appreciation of the people who founded our nation and how to apply their beliefs to your everyday life.

An Inspiring Book for Families. Christopher Harper, Associate Professor of Journalism, Temple University, and a former Washington Correspondent for *Newsweek*.

When I teach the history of American journalism, my students often don't appreciate what the founders accomplished in creating a nation of principles and ideals. Peter Breggin's book describes the magic and majesty of what the founders did for us. An inspiring book that my family, including my 16-year-old daughter, enjoyed.

Teaching Us How to Live as Americans. Douglas C. Smith, MD, is a psychiatrist in private practice in Juneau, Alaska and Commander, U.S. Public Health Service, retired.

The man who taught us to be fully alive rather than deaden ourselves with psychiatric drugs, now goes a step further to teach us how to live as Americans. Breggin brings us to marvel at what our Founding Fathers accomplished and the guiding principles they followed. The principles of freedom, responsibility and love are not only the foundations of our great nation, but can become the foundations for each of our individual lives. How could we have forgotten that? Breggin reminds us and inspires us in a most timely way.

The principles of freedom, responsibility and love are not only the foundations of our great nation, but can become the foundations for each of our individual lives. How could we have forgotten that?

I read this book at a time when I was facing an important career decision. It was perfect timing, as if guided by the invisible hand of God, which our founding fathers believed in and experienced. I made the choice that led me to the most freedom and independence, which in turn allows me to become a grateful source of love – read this book and you'll know what I'm talking about. I want my children to read this and for it to be our dinnertime conversation for a long time to come.

This is a Great Primer. Brian Kean, PhD, Professor of Education, Southern Cross University, Australia.

Take it from an Australian who loves America: This is a great primer on how to live like an American. I often wish that my American friends had more appreciation for the basic values that make your country unique and great. This book fills that need. It's written so simply that a teenager with no background in history can grasp the principles of the Founding Fathers and it's written so originally that even an adult with more depth of historical knowledge should find it enlightening. Its principles of freedom, responsibility and love can guide us both in our political thinking and in how we live our everyday lives.

Principles of Life

by Peter R. Breggin, MD

The following principles of living are taken from the final chapter of Dr. Breggin's book, *Medication Madness: A Psychiatrist Exposes the Dangers of Mood-Altering Drugs* (2008):

1. **Love is joyful awareness.** Love life—people, animals, nature, gardening, art and music, sports and exercise, literature, God—anything and anyone that brings you a joyful awareness of the wonder of being a living creature in a world far greater than ourselves.

2. **Gratitude satisfies the spirit.** Be grateful for all that you love and if you cannot think of anyone or anything to love, then be grateful you still have a chance to love. Be especially grateful for the opportunity to help and to serve other people and good causes.

3. **Gratitude is the antidote to self-pity.** Feeling sorry for oneself is ruinous. Especially don't fall into believing that we live in the worst of times. It takes little imagination to know how much worse it has been for other people in previous ages and in other places. Be grateful for this life.

4. **Ethics guide the good life.** Put ethics and principles above pleasure, convenience, safety, income, career, your presumed place in the world, and the way others view you. Living a principled life is the key to a satisfying life.

5. **Everything good requires courage.** Find the courage to love, to be grateful, and to live by sound ethics. Especially be brave enough to speak honestly and to stand straight when you are afraid.

6. **Dare to seek romantic love.** Abiding love for a partner in life is the nearest we get to heaven this time around.

7. **Make a living at something you respect and love.** Many people find a way to do it. Your occupation should feel like a privilege, a pleasure, and an opportunity to serve. It should offer you the opportunity to improve the lives of others.

8. **Approach every single challenge in life with determination to master it.** Otherwise you won't handle it. Feeling helpless in the face of adversity is a prescription for failure. Deciding to take on the important challenges is a prescription for self-satisfaction and makes success more likely.

9. **Don't hide from your painful emotions.** While it's often destructive to voice or act upon our negative feelings, it's important to recognize them. Feeling pain signals that there is something wrong in our lives that needs immediate attention. Invite your painful emotions to tell you everything they can about what you really want out of life.

10. **Don't think of yourself as a survivor.** Intending to survive guarantees little more than getting by and ultimately leads to failure. Think of yourself as someone who intends to triumph in life.

11. **Forgiving other people liberates us from hate.** You won't get even by hating, you'll get miserable, bitter and spiritless. Take care of yourself by forgiving, and if necessary by avoiding hurtful people, but don't waste a minute hating.

12. **Seek a worthwhile life rather than happiness.** There are no shortcuts to happiness; no trick ideas or drugs that can make us happy. The search for happiness will lead you to false "cures," distract you from what matters, and even make you crazy. Much of happiness is often a matter of luck—the way we are shaped by childhood, where we happen to be born, health, and circumstance; but we increase the opportunity for happiness by remaining principled and loving in the face of adversity.

13. **No one knows the meaning of life but it's certain that life is best lived with love, gratitude, ethics, courage, and a determination to give it your best effort.** A sense of worth is guaranteed by principled living and happiness will often tag along as well.

14. **Let your spirit be touched, and touch the spirit of others, with love.** Nothing is more important than expanding our own capacity, and humanity's capacity, to love one another.

15. **You cannot solve your problems by taking psychoactive substances that impair your mind and the expression of your spirit.** From illegal drugs to psychiatric medications, all drugs suppress and distort our real emotions and should be avoided, especially in time of suffering and fear when we especially need to know what we are feeling and to control our actions.

16. **Reject being labeled with a psychiatric diagnosis.** Don't allow the sum total of your life to be reduced to phrases like clinical depression, bipolar disorder or anxiety disorder. There are no "psychiatric disorders;" only life disorders. Instead of being mangled by someone else's cookie cutter definition of your life, seek to know the unique story of your own development and evolution as a person. Remember that all of us have to struggle, to go through hard times, and to find a way of becoming more in control of our emotions and more honorable and successful in our actions.

17. **Choose your last resort wisely.** When you feel most desperate and alone, where will you go—toward psychiatry with its biological explanations and mind-altering drugs or toward improved principles of living, a more responsible and loving life, the fulfillment of your ideals, and oneness with a Meaning or Power beyond yourself? Your chosen last resort defines you as a person and gives direction to your life.

Appendices

I. Books by Peter R. Breggin, MD

Non-Fiction

College Students in a Mental Hospital: Contribution to the Social Rehabilitation of the Mentally Ill (jointly authored) (1962)

Electroshock: Its Brain-Disabling Effects (1979)

The Psychology of Freedom: Liberty and Love as a Way of Life (1980)

Psychiatric Drugs: Hazards to the Brain (1983)

Toxic Psychiatry: Why Therapy, Empathy and Love Must Replace the Drugs, Electroshock and Biochemical Theories of the "New Psychiatry" (1991)

Beyond Conflict: From Self-Help and Psychotherapy to Peacemaking (1992)

Talking Back to Prozac (coauthor Ginger Breggin) (1994)

Psychosocial Approaches to Deeply Disturbed Persons (coeditor E. Mark Stern) (1996)

The Heart of Being Helpful: Empathy and the Creation of a Healing Presence (1997)

The War Against Children of Color: Psychiatry Targets Inner City Children (coauthor Ginger Breggin) (updated) (1998)

Reclaiming Our Children: A Healing Solution to a Nation in Crisis (2000)

Talking Back to Ritalin, Revised Edition (2001)

The Antidepressant Fact book (2001)

Dimensions of Empathic Therapy (coeditors Ginger Breggin and Fred Bemak) (2002)

The Ritalin Fact Book (2002)

Your Drug May Be Your Problem: How and Why To Stop Taking Psychiatric Medications, Second Edition (coauthor David Cohen) (2007)

Brain-Disabling Treatments in Psychiatry: Drugs, Electroshock and the Psychopharmaceutical Complex, Second Edition (2008)

Medication Madness: The Role of Psychiatric Drugs in Cases of Violence, Suicide and Crime (2008)

Fiction

The Crazy from the Sane (1970)

After the Good War (1971)

II. Selected Articles by Peter R. Breggin, MD

A more extensive bibliography can be found on www.breggin.com, where most of Dr. Breggin's scientific papers can be read and retrieved.

Breggin, P. (1964a). The psychophysiology of anxiety. *Journal of Nervous Mental Diseases,* 139, 558-568.

Breggin, P. (1964b). Coercion of voluntary patients in an open hospital. *Archives of General Psychiatry,* 10, 173–181.

Breggin, P. (1965). The sedative-like effect of epinephrine. *Archives of General Psychiatry,* 12, 255-259.

Breggin, P. (1971). Psychotherapy as applied ethics. *Psychiatry,* 34, 59–75.

Breggin, P. (1972a). The return of lobotomy and psychosurgery. *Congressional Record,* 118, E1602-E1612. Republished with a new introduction in Breggin (1980a).

Breggin, P. (1972b). Psychosurgery for the control of violence–including a critical examination of the work of Vernon Mark and Frank Irvin. *Congressional Record* 118, E3350-E3386. Revised and republished in Breggin (1975b).

Breggin, P. (1972c). Lobotomy is still bad medicine. *Medical Opinion,* 8, 3236.

Breggin, P. (1972d). Lobotomies: an alert. *American Journal of Psychiatry,* 129, 98-99.

Breggin P. and Greenberg, D. (1972e, March 15). Lobotomy. *Science and Government Policy,* 2(2), 1.

Breggin, P. (1973a). Psychosurgery. *Journal of the American Medical Association,* 226, 1121.

Breggin, P. (1973b). The second wave of psychosurgery. *M/H (Mental Health),* 57, 10-13.

Breggin, P. (1974). Therapy as applied utopian politics. *Mental Health and Society,* 1, 129-146.

Breggin, P. (1975a). Psychiatry and psychotherapy as political processes. *American Journal of Psychotherapy,* 29, 369-382.

Breggin, P. (1975b). Psychosurgery for political purposes. *Duquesne Law Review,* 13, 841-862.

Breggin, P. (1975c). Psychosurgery for the control of violence: a critical review. Chapter IV in W. Fields W and W. Sweet (Eds.), *Neural Bases of Violence and Aggression.* St. Louis: Warren H. Green. Revised and reproduced from Breggin (1972b).

Breggin, P. (1980). Brain-disabling therapies. In E. Valenstein (Ed.), *The psychosurgery debate: Scientific, legal and ethical perspectives* (pp. 467–505). San Francisco: Freeman.

Breggin, P. (1981a). Disabling the brain with electroshock. In M. Dongier & D. Wittkower (Eds.), *Divergent views in psychiatry.* Hagerstown, MD: Harper & Row.

Breggin, P. (1981b). Psychosurgery as brain-disabling therapy. In M. Dongier and D. Wittkower (Eds.), *Divergent views in psychiatry.* Hagerstown, MD: Harper & Row.

Breggin, P. (1981c). Madness is a failure of free will; Therapy too often encourages it. *Psychiatric Quarterly,* 53, 61-68. Originally published (in French) in Verdiglione A (ed):La Folie Dans La Psychoanalyse. Paris, Payot, 1977.

Breggin, P. (1982). The return of lobotomy and psychosurgery. In R. Edwards (Ed.), *Psychiatry and Ethics,* pp. 350-352. Buffalo: Prometheus Books. Republication of Breggin (1972a) with a new introduction.

Breggin, P. (1983a). Iatrogenic helplessness in authoritarian psychiatry. In R. F. Morgan (Ed.), *The iatrogenics handbook.* Toronto: IPI.

Breggin, P. (1983b). What cost leucotomy? *American Journal of Psychiatry,* 140, 1101.

Breggin, P. (1984). Electroshock therapy and brain damage: The acute organic brain syndrome as treatment. *Behavior and Brain Sciences,* 7, 24-25.

Breggin, P. (1986). Neuropathology and cognitive dysfunction from ECT. *Psychopharmacology Bulletin,* 22, 476–479.

Breggin, P. and de Girolamo, G. (1987). Ellettroshock: Tra Rischioiatrogeno e Mito Terapeutico *Quaderni Italiani di Psychiatrica,* 6, 497-540.

Breggin, P. (1988). A hierarchy of values for evaluating human progress on an individual, institutional and societal basis. In K. Kollenda (Ed.): *Ethical Individualism and Organizations.* New York: Praeger.

Breggin, P. (1988-1999). The Three Dynamics of Human Progress: A Unified Theory Applicable to Individuals, Institutions and Society. *Review of Existential Psychology and Psychiatry,* 21, 97-123.

Breggin, P. (1989a). Addiction to neuroleptics? *American Journal of Psychiatry,* 146, 560.

Breggin, P. (1989b). Addiction to neuroleptics: Dr. Breggin replies. *American Journal of Psychiatry,* 146, 1240.

Breggin, P. (1990). Brain damage, dementia and persistent cognitive dysfunction associated with neuroleptic drugs: Evidence, etiology, and implications. *Journal of Mind and Behavior,* 11, 425–464.

Breggin, P. (1991). Psychotherapy in the shadow of the psychopharmaceutical complex. *Voices (journal of the American Academy of Psychotherapists),* 27, 5-21.

Breggin, P. (1992a). A case of fluoxetine-induced stimulant side effects with suicidal ideation associated with a possible withdrawal syndrome ("crashing"). *International Journal of Risk and Safety in Medicine,* 3, 325–328.

Breggin, P. (1992b, February 11). The president's sleeping pill and its makers. *The New York Times,* p. A24.

Breggin, P. (1993a). Psychiatry's role in the Holocaust. *International Journal of Risk and Safety in Medicine,* 4:133-148, 1993. Adapted from a paper delivered at "Medical Science Without Compassion" in Cologne, Germany and published in the conference proceedings.

Breggin, P. (1993b). Parallels between neuroleptic effects and lethargic encephalitis: The production of dyskinesias and cognitive disorders. *Brain and Cognition,* 23, 8–27.

Breggin, P. (1995, September). Prozac "hazardous" to children. *Clinical Psychiatry News,* p. 10.

Breggin, P. (1996a). Should the use of neuroleptics be severely limited? *Changes: An International Journal of Psychology and Psychotherapy,* 14, 62-66.

Breggin, P. (1996b, July 8). The FDA was agitated over Halcion. *Business Week,* p. 12.

Breggin, P. (1998a). Risks and mechanism of action of stimulants. In NIH consensus development conference program and abstracts: *Diagnosis and treatment of attention deficit hyperactivity disorder* (pp. 105–120). Rockville, MD: National Institutes of Health.

Breggin, P. (1998b). Analysis of adverse behavioral effects of benzodiazepines with a discussion of drawing scientific conclusions from the FDA's spontaneous reporting system. *Journal of Mind and Behavior,* 19, 21-50.

Breggin, P. (1998c). Psychotherapy in emotional crises without resort to psychiatric medication. *The Humanistic Psychologist,* 25, 2-14.

Breggin, P. (1998d). Electroshock: Scientific, ethical, and political issues. *International Journal of Risk & Safety In Medicine,* 11, 5-40.

Breggin, P. (1999a). Psychostimulants in the treatment of children diagnosed with ADHD, Part I: Acute risks and psychological effects. *Ethical Human Sciences and Services,* 1, 13–33.

Breggin, P. (1999b). Psychostimulants in the treatment of children diagnosed with ADHD, Part II: Adverse effects on brain and behavior. *Ethical Human Sciences and Services,* 1, 213–242.

Breggin, P. (1999c). Psychostimulants in the treatment of children diagnosed with ADHD: Risks and mechanism of action. *International Journal of Risk and Safety in Medicine,* 12, 3–35. (simultaneous publication of 1999a&b)

Breggin, P. (1999d). Empathic self-transformation and love in individual and family therapy. *Humanistic Psychologist,* 27, 267-282.

Breggin, P. (2000a). What psychologists and psychotherapists need to know about ADHD and stimulants. *Changes: An International Journal of Psychology and Psychotherapy, 18*, 13-23.

Breggin, P. (2000b). The NIMH multimodal study of treatment for attention-deficit/hyperactivity disorder: A critical analysis. *International Journal of Risk and Safety in Medicine,* 13, 15–22.

Breggin, P. (2001a). MTA study has flaws. *Archives of General Psychiatry,* 58, 1184.

Breggin, P. (2001b). Empowering social work in the era of biological psychiatry. (The Ephraim Lisansky lecture of the University of Maryland School of Social Work) *Ethical Human Sciences and Services,* 3, 197-206.

Breggin, P. (2002). Fluvoxamine as a cause of stimulation, mania, and aggression with a critical analysis of the FDA-approved label. *International Journal of Risk and Safety in Medicine,* 14, 71–86.

Breggin, P. (2003a). Suicidality, violence and mania caused by selective serotonin reuptake inhibitors (SSRIs): A review and analysis. *Ethical Human Sciences and Services,* 5, 225–246.

Breggin, P. (2003b). Psychopharmacology and human values. *Journal of Humanistic Psychology,* 43, 34-49.

Breggin, P. (2005). Recent U.S., Canadian and British regulatory agency actions concerning antidepressant-induced harm to self and others: A review and analysis." *Ethical Human Psychology and Psychiatry,* 7, 7-22. Simultaneously published in the *International Journal of Risk and Safety in Medicine,* 16, 247-259, 2005.

Breggin, P. (2006a). Court filing makes public my previously suppressed analysis of Paxil's effects. *Ethical Human Psychology and Psychiatry*, 8, 77–84.

Breggin, P. (2006b). Drug company suppressed data on paroxetine-induced stimulation: Implications for violence and suicide. *Ethical Human Psychology and Psychiatry*, 8, 255–263.

Breggin, P. (2006c). How GlaxoSmithKline suppressed data on Paxil-induced akathisia: Implications for suicide and violence. *Ethical Human Psychology and Psychiatry*, 8, 91–100.

Breggin, P. (2006d). Intoxication anosognosia: The spellbinding effect of psychiatric drugs. *Ethical Human Psychology and Psychiatry* 8, 201–215.

Breggin, P. (2006e). Recent regulatory changes in antidepressant labels: Implications for activation (stimulation) in clinical practice. *Primary Psychiatry*, 13, 57–60.

Breggin, P. (2008). Practical applications: 22 guidelines for counseling and psychotherapy. *Ethical Human Psychology and Psychiatry*, 10, 43-57.

Breggin P. and Breggin, G. (1993). A biomedical programme for urban violence control in the US: The dangers of psychiatric social control. *Changes: An International Journal of Psychology and Psychotherapy*, 11, 59-71.

Breggin, P. and Breggin, G. (1996). The hazards of treating "attention-Deficit/Hyperactivity Disorder" with methylphenidate (Ritalin). *Journal of College Student Psychotherapy*, 10, 55-72.

Breggin, P. and Breggin, G. (2008). Exposure to SSRI antidepressants in utero causes birth defects, neonatal withdrawal symptoms, and brain damage. *Ethical Human Psychology and Psychiatry*, 10, 5-9.

III. Brief Biography of Peter Breggin, MD

Peter R. Breggin, MD began in the full time private practice of psychiatry in 1968. For most of his career he practiced in the Washington, D.C. area. Then in late 2002 he moved his practice to Ithaca, New York, in order to enjoy the beauty of central New York.

For many decades, Dr. Breggin has been informing the professions, media and the public about the potential dangers of drugs, electroshock, psychosurgery, involuntary treatment, and the biological theories of psychiatry. His work has encouraged FDA-mandated label changes in many psychiatric drugs. He has been a consultant to the FAA on the effects of psychiatric drugs on airplane pilots.

Dr. Breggin serves as a medical expert in civil and criminal suits including individual malpractice cases and product liability suits against the manufacturers of psychiatric drugs. His consultations provided the scientific basis for the original combined Prozac suits. He also testifies for defendants in criminal cases when individuals have committed crimes while under the influence of psychiatric drugs.

Since 1964 Dr. Breggin has been publishing peer-reviewed articles and medical books in his subspecialty of clinical psychopharmacology. He is the author of dozens of scientific articles and nineteen professional books, many dealing with psychiatric medication, the FDA, negligence in drug development and marketing, the evaluation of clinical trials, and standards of care in psychiatry and related fields. Two of the most influential books are *Toxic Psychiatry* (1991) and *Talking Back to Prozac* (1994), written with his wife Ginger. His two most recent books are *Brain-Disabling Treatments in Psychiatry, Second Edition* (2008) and *Medication Madness* (2008).

In 1972 Dr. Breggin founded the International Center for the Study of Psychiatry and Psychology (ICSPP) as a nonprofit research and educational network. ICSPP is concerned with the impact of mental health theory and practices upon individual well-being, personal freedom, and family and community values. In the late 1980s, his wife Ginger Breggin joined him in his reform work and greatly expanded the ICSPP membership and activities. With his wife Ginger, Dr. Breggin founded the peer-review scientific journal, *Ethical Human Psychiatry and Psychology.* In 2002, Dr. Breggin and Ginger Breggin selected new and younger professionals to take over leadership of the journal and ICSPP (see ICSPP.org). Dr. Breggin continues to write for the journal and he remains active in the organization as a speaker at annual meetings and as Director Emeritus.

Dr. Breggin's background includes Harvard College, Case Western Reserve Medical School, four years of internship and psychiatric residency including a teaching fellowship at Harvard Medical School, and a two-year staff appointment to the National Institute of Mental Health (NIMH). He has had numerous faculty appointments, including the George Mason University Institute for Conflict Analysis and Resolution and the Johns Hopkins University Department of Counseling. Most recently he was Visiting Scholar in the Department of Counseling and Psychological Services at SUNY Oswego.

Dr. Breggin's newly redesigned website www.breggin.com contains much more biographical information, including descriptions of some of the major lawsuits in which he has been a medical expert, as well as many of his reform accomplishments.

IV. Glossary

ADHD—Attention Deficit Hyperactivity Disorder. A controversial psychiatric disorder characterized by hyperactivity, inattention, or impulsivity, usually diagnosed in childhood.

AMA—American Medical Association.

Anosognosia—Not knowing that one has symptoms of injury and illness.

APA—American Psychiatric Association or American Psychological Association.

CDC—Centers for Disease Control.

Center for the Study of Psychiatry (CSP)—Original name for ICSPP.

CHADD—Children and Adults with Attention Deficit Disorders. Advocacy group supported by drug companies.

DSM—*Diagnostic and Statistical Manual of Mental Disorders* published by American Psychiatric Association.

ECT—Electroconvulsive Treatment. Same as EST or Electroshock Treatment.

EHPP—*Ethical Human Psychology and Psychiatry*, scientific journal founded by Peter and Ginger Breggin, sponsored by ICSPP and published by Springer Publishing Company. Formerly named *Ethical Human Sciences and Services.*

FDA—U. S. Food and Drug Administration.

ICSPP—International Center for the Study of Psychiatry and Psychology, Inc, psychiatric reform organization founded by Peter R. Breggin, MD in early 1970s.

NAMI—National Alliance for the Mentally Ill. Advocacy group supported by drug companies.

Neuroleptic drugs—Antipsychotic drugs, FDA-approved for the treatment of psychoses.

NIH—National Institutes of Health.

NIMH—National Institute of Mental Health.

Psychiatry and psychiatrists—Psychiatry is a medical subspecialty concerned with "mental illnesses." Psychiatrists are physicians trained in the subspecialty.

Psychology and clinical psychologists—Psychology is a non-medical academic discipline. Clinical psychologists can treat clients with psychotherapy.

Psychopharmacology—The science of drugs that impact the brain and mind.

Psychopharmaceutical Complex—The combination of interest groups that promote the use of psychiatric drugs including the pharmaceutical industry, the FDA, both APAs and the AMA, NAMI, NIMH, NIH, and the health insurance industry.

Psychosurgery—Psychiatric surgery, mutilation of the highest centers of the brain for the control of emotions or behavior. Lobotomy is a form of psychosurgery that damages the frontal lobes of the brain.

Psychotherapy—"Talking therapy" conducted with individuals, families or groups.

SSRIs—Selective serotonin reuptake inhibitors, a class of newer antidepressants that includes Prozac, Paxil, Zoloft and other drugs.

Tardive dyskinesia—Also called TD, a medication-induced disorder that causes abnormal movements that are commonly irreversible and largely untreatable.

Violence Initiative—A planned inter-agency federal program that contained a psychiatric or biological component aimed a studying and treating violence in inner-city children. Successfully opposed by Peter and Ginger Breggin in the early 1990s.